Bed[ding] Her Boss

Working late beneath the sheets…

Three passionate novels!

By Request

In January 2007 Mills & Boon bring
back two of their classic collections,
each featuring three favourite
romances by our bestselling authors…

BEDDED BY HER BOSS

Back in the Boss's Bed
by Sharon Kendrick
Her Boss's Marriage Agenda
by Jessica Steele
His After-Hours Mistress
by Amanda Browning

WEDDING VOWS

In the Best Man's Bed
by Catherine Spencer
The Wedding Dare by Barbara Hannay
The Wedding Challenge by Jessica Hart

Bedded by
Her Boss

BACK IN THE BOSS'S BED
by
Sharon Kendrick

HER BOSS'S MARRIAGE AGENDA
by
Jessica Steele

HIS AFTER-HOURS MISTRESS
by
Amanda Browning

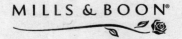

MILLS & BOON®

DID YOU PURCHASE THIS BOOK WITHOUT A COVER?

If you did, you should be aware it is **stolen property** as it was
reported *unsold and destroyed* by a retailer. Neither the author nor
the publisher has received any payment for this book.

*All the characters in this book have no existence outside the
imagination of the author, and have no relation whatsoever to anyone
bearing the same name or names. They are not even distantly inspired
by any individual known or unknown to the author, and all the
incidents are pure invention.*

*All Rights Reserved including the right of reproduction in whole or
in part in any form. This edition is published by arrangement with
Harlequin Enterprises II B.V. The text of this publication or any part
thereof may not be reproduced or transmitted in any form or by any
means, electronic or mechanical, including photocopying, recording,
storage in an information retrieval system, or otherwise, without the
written permission of the publisher.*

*This book is sold subject to the condition that it shall not, by way of
trade or otherwise, be lent, resold, hired out or otherwise circulated
without the prior consent of the publisher in any form of binding or
cover other than that in which it is published and without a similar
condition including this condition being imposed on the subsequent
purchaser.*

*MILLS & BOON and MILLS & BOON with the Rose Device
are registered trademarks of the publisher.*
Harlequin Mills & Boon Limited,
Eton House, 18-24 Paradise Road, Richmond, Surrey, TW9 1SR

BEDDED BY HER BOSS
© by Harlequin Enterprises II B.V. 2007

Back in the Boss's Bed, Her Boss's Marriage Agenda and
His After-Hours Mistress were first published in Great Britain by
Harlequin Mills & Boon Limited in separate, single volumes.

Back in the Boss's Bed © Sharon Kendrick 2003
Her Boss's Marriage Agenda © Jessica Steele 2004
His After-Hours Mistress © Amanda Browning 2003

ISBN 10: 0 263 85133 8
ISBN 13: 978 0 263 85133 5

05-0107

*Printed and bound in Spain
by Litografia Rosés S.A., Barcelona*

BACK IN THE BOSS'S BED

by

Sharon Kendrick

Sharon Kendrick started story-telling at the age of eleven and has never really stopped. She likes to write fast-paced, feel-good romances with heroes who are so sexy they'll make your toes curl!

Born in west London, she now lives in the beautiful city of Winchester – where she can see the cathedral from her window (but only if she stands on tiptoe). She has two children, Celia and Patrick, and her passions include music, books, cooking and eating – and drifting off into wonderful daydreams while she works out new plots!

Don't miss Sharon Kendrick's exciting new novel *The Sheikh's English Bride* out in March 2007 from Mills & Boon Modern Romance™

With thanks to Edward Heckels for all his
invaluable advice – this book is for him and
for all future Heckels. Vote for Edward!

CHAPTER ONE

ADAM BLACK'S grey eyes glittered like sunlight on a wintry sea. 'So, Vaughn?' he questioned softly.

From his wheelchair, the old man looked up at the tall, dark man who dominated the room. 'I hate asking anyone for favours!' he rasped. 'Even you.'

'And I hate granting them,' said Adam, his hard mouth relaxing by just a fraction as he acknowledged the old man's indomitable character, recognising in him something of himself. 'But in your case, I'll make an exception. What's up?'

There was a pause. 'You remember my granddaughter?' Vaughn demanded. 'Kiloran? She's been running the business—only she's come up against problems. Big problems.'

Kiloran? Adam let his memory stray back, then back further still, and a fleeting image of a green-eyed girl in pigtails flitted in and out of his mind. A little princess of a girl, despite the pigtails and the grubby jeans. But the Laceys had been rich, as rich as Adam had been poor—and the power of money had clung to her like a second skin.

'Yeah, I remember her. Vaguely.' He frowned. 'Though she would have just been a kid at the time. Nine—ten maybe.'

'That was a long time ago. She's not a kid anymore.

She's twenty-six, and a woman now. Kiloran is my daughter's child,' added Vaughn, his eyes half closed with reminiscence. 'You must remember her mother. Everyone remembers Eleanor.'

Adam stilled.

Oh, yes. This particular memory snapped into crystal-sharp focus. He had locked it away, as he'd locked so many things away over the years, but Vaughn's words were the key to the door, and now it swung open. 'Yes, I remember Eleanor,' he said slowly.

It had been every teenage boy's fantasy, except maybe his.

He had been eighteen, all long legs and muscle—strong as an ox and tanned as a berry. The summer had been hot—too hot to load boxes all day, but that had been his job, his way out of the dark tunnel his life had become. God, it seemed so long ago.

Eleanor must have been about…what? Forty? Maybe younger, maybe older—it was hard to tell with women of a certain age. All Adam had known was that she'd been a looker.

The men working in the warehouse had just stopped what they'd been doing, their breath hot with lust when Eleanor had walked by, as walk by she so often had—making excuses to visit the factory, wearing tiny denim shorts and a T-shirt which had been rucked tight across her breasts. The beautiful widow—she might have been called the Black Widow, if her hair hadn't been the colour of spun gold.

Adam had listened to them talk. A tease, they'd

called her. Look but don't touch. She was protected by the power of her position. The boss's daughter.

She'd known the power of her own sexuality, too—it had radiated off her like a shimmering heat and it had fuelled many fantasies those hot summer nights.

But not Adam's.

Something about her had made him recoil. Something about her hooded, predatory look had made him look away. Maybe it had reminded him too much of what he had left behind at home.

She'd noticed him, of course. He'd been different. He'd been bright and smart. Stronger and bigger and fitter and more ruggedly handsome than any of the permanent loaders. And she'd noticed the way he hadn't noticed her. Some women liked a challenge.

She'd waited until his last week there—presumably not to give herself time to get bored, or to risk angering her father. Vaughn had been a stickler for sticking to the rules and a penniless kid from a rough family on the wrong side of town had not been for his daughter, not in any way.

But Eleanor had had other ideas.

She'd brought him a beer one baking afternoon, when the ground had scorched your feet—the first taste of liquor he had ever had. On such a hot day, it had been too tempting to refuse and it had filled him with a kind of warm wildness. But he had stayed his distance, his eyes as wary as a cornered animal when she had patted the haystack where she'd lain sprawled.

'Come over here,' she purred.

'I'm fine where I am,' he said.

She didn't like being refused, nor did she take the hint. She knew what she wanted and she wanted him.

She was wearing a flowery little shirt that day—a teensy little thing with buttons all the way down the front, and when she began to brazenly pop them open, one by one, her green eyes meeting his, he froze.

Maybe there wasn't another man on the planet who would have refused what Adam was so freely being offered, but Adam wasn't most men. He had seen what weakness and excess could do. Wasn't his presence here doing a dead-end job the very result of it?

Nothing was said. He simply picked up his denim shirt and thanked her for the beer, and strolled out into the mercilessly hot sunshine. He didn't see her look of frustrated lust, but he felt it. It was the first time it had happened to him, but it wouldn't be the last.

He gave Vaughn a cool look. 'Yes, I remember your daughter. What happened to her?'

Vaughn gave a wheezy laugh. 'She did what she wanted to do—married a millionaire and moved to Australia.' He shrugged. 'Said she wanted a better life—and you know what women are like.'

There was a pause, while Adam remembered the woman he had taken for dinner on his last night in New York. A sloe-eyed beauty who had cooed into his ear that what he didn't know about women could be written on the back of a postage stamp and still leave room to spare! He hadn't made love to her—his body had been willing but his mind had not, for he had never been able to separate the intellectual from the physical. She had cried. Women always cried when they couldn't get what they wanted, and mostly they wanted him. It was not an arrogant assessment of his attributes as a man and as a lover, it was fact— plain and simple.

'Yes, I know what women are like,' he said shortly. 'So Kiloran stayed, did she?'

Vaughn nodded. 'She went away and then came back. She missed the house.' He gave a look of pride. 'She loves it just the same as I do. But loving a house is not the same as running a business. I was a fool to let myself think she was capable of taking charge. Yes, she had experience of company life—but it was too big a project to handle.' He shook his head. 'She twisted me round her little finger—the way she can twist any man around her little finger! And Kiloran always knows best!'

Adam didn't point out the glaringly obvious. That in this instance she had failed completely in her judgement.

'You said you weren't working at the moment,' growled Vaughn. 'So, in theory, you have a little time on your hands.'

Adam stared unseeingly out at the sunlit gardens beyond which seemed to stretch on and on as far as the eye could see. The Lacey mansion had always seemed like a different world when he had been young—like an unattainable mountain to climb—only now he was a part of that world. He hadn't been back here since the day he'd left—not to this house, nor the pitiful version of a house he had grown up in. And now his two worlds had merged in the way that fate so often decreed they did. It felt strange, he thought. Had it been a mistake to come?

'That's right,' he agreed. 'I don't start my new job until next month.'

Vaughn drew himself up, his stiff body moving awkwardly. 'I want you to make Lacey's what it was, Adam. If anyone can do it—you can. Before I die, I want my good name to stand and I want this firm to carry on. For Kiloran's sake. Will you do that?'

Adam's dark eyebrows knitted together. 'But how's Kiloran going to feel about it? If she's heading up your company, how's she going to adapt to taking her orders from me? Unless.' His eyes took on a watchful wariness. 'Unless you want her out of the way, of course. You're not planning to sack her, are you?'

Vaughn let out a wheezing laugh. 'Sack her? I'd sooner take on the devil himself than risk that!'

'But, you know—' Adam's grey eyes grew thoughtful and flinty '—if it's as bad as you seem to think it is, and you want results, then I'm going to have to be tough with her.'

The old man smiled. 'Be as tough as you like. Maybe I've been too soft with her in the past. Show her who's in the driving seat, Adam. She needs to know—she's a stubborn little thing.'

Adam digested this in silence, knowing that no one could match *him* for stubbornness. And he wondered whether perhaps it *was* Vaughn's intention to use him to oust his stubborn granddaughter from her position of power. Maybe that was one of his reasons for approaching him. Get someone else to do your dirty work for you.

But he put it out of his mind. Personalities didn't come into it and neither did other people's agendas.

There were facts and you acted on those facts. Didn't matter who said what, or to whom. Didn't matter if Kiloran Lacey was a clone of her mother and started fluttering her pretty eyelashes at him, trying to get her own way. She would soon find out, just as her mother had done, that he was *not* the kind of man she could twist around her little finger. From now on he was going to decide what was best, and if she didn't like it—well, that was just too bad.

Vaughn gave a satisfied nod and pressed the bell on the side of his wheelchair once more, and the door was opened to reveal a middle-aged woman, bearing a tray containing two glasses and a bottle of champagne, cooling in an ice bucket.

'Ah, Miriam,' said Vaughn. 'Pour Mr Black a drink, would you?'

Adam hid a smile. So the old man had been confident he'd agree, had he? And why not? Didn't he owe Vaughn Lacey for a favour given to a young boy in trouble, such a long time ago? He watched as Miriam deftly dealt with the drinks. She wore a black dress with a white collar—clearly some kind of uniform. He hadn't seen such an old-fashioned set-up for years, but, admittedly, he had been living in America, which was altogether a more meritocratic society.

His eyes were drawn to an exquisite Augustus John etching, which hung on the wall, and he pursed his lips together thoughtfully. That piece of artwork alone must be worth a cool couple of million. He wondered how much else around the place was existing on past glories and how well Vaughn and his granddaughter would be able to adapt if any cut-backs were going to be necessary.

But now was not the time to start asking questions like that. He took the drinks from Miriam, and when she had let herself out he handed one to the old man and then raised his own, touching it to the other, the chink of crystal sounding as pure as the ringing of a bell.

'To success. To the resurrection of Lacey's,' he murmured, raising the drink to his lips and wondering just what the hell he had let himself in for.

Vaughn gave a tight smile. 'I'll send for Kiloran.'

CHAPTER TWO

KILORAN smoothed her clammy palms down over her hips, feeling suddenly and inexplicably nervous. The corridor leading to the boardroom seemed to go on forever, a corridor which she had walked down countless times—so why the nerves?

Her grandfather had telephoned her at the house and asked her to meet him. Immediately. It had sounded more like a command than a request and he had spoken in a terse, almost abrupt way, which didn't sound like him at all.

Was he about to tell her that he didn't think there was any point carrying on? That they should call in the creditors? The end of the company and all that went with it?

A cold sweat broke out on her forehead as she pushed open the door of the boardroom, thrown off her guard as soon as she registered that her grandfather was not alone.

For a man stood, surveying her with a lazy, yet judgemental air. The kind of man who would make any woman's heart miss a beat and whose expression would fill her with foreboding.

She turned to the familiar figure in the wheelchair. 'Grandfather?' she said uncertainly.

'Ah, Kiloran,' murmured her grandfather. 'This is Adam. Adam Black. Do you remember him?'

It was like a little pebble being dropped into a pond. Slowly, the ripples of memory spread across Kiloran's mind. She frowned.

Adam Black.

Of course she remembered him.

True, she had only been young, but some men came along who were so unforgettable that their image was scored deep in the psyche, and had been at an impressionable age. Reading stories about knights in shining armour who carried off with them the damsel in distress to some unnamed and yet pleasurable fantasy.

Adam Black had seemed to fit the role perfectly, and—judging from the female workers at Lacey's—Kiloran had not been the only one to think so. Hadn't groups of them found excuses to go to the loading bay, in order to catch a glimpse of the bare-chested man, as he'd effortlessly lifted great boxes of soap into the lorries? Hadn't even her mother remarked that he was a fine-looking boy?

And so it was with astonishing and rather disturbing ease that Kiloran was able to recall Adam Black perfectly.

She turned her head to look at him.

The years had not just been kind to him, they had treated him with the deference usually only given to the chosen few.

The body was lean and lithe, his skin kissed with the faintest tan. The hair was still jet-black—thick and abundant as it had ever been with only a faint tracing of silver around his temples. The grey eyes were narrowed and watchful. He looked—not exactly unfriendly, but not exactly brimming over with *bonhomie*, either, and he was dressed in an immaculate charcoal-grey suit, as if he was ready for business.

She remembered the young man wearing nothing but a pair of faded denims, his bronzed back dripping with the sweat of his labours, and it seemed hard to connect him with *this* man, who stood before her now, a dark study of arrogant respectability.

Kiloran's heart had begun to thunder beneath the thin silk of her dress, but the voice of reason began to clamour in her head.

Why on earth was he here?

And her childhood crush was eclipsed by the sudden crowding in of facts. She suddenly realised just why his name had sounded so familiar—and not just because he had spent one summer doing hard, manual work for her grandfather. She made the connection, and she was even more confused.

Adam Black—*the* Adam Black—was here in *her* boardroom? The man that the investment journals called 'The Shark' because of his cold and cutting ways? She had read about him, in the way that anyone in the business would have done. She had seen him quoted in the papers and read about him in the magazines which covered big mergers and acquisitions. And seen his regular appearances in the gossip columns, too. The camera loved him and so did women, beautiful women, invariably. He had acquired a reputation for loving and leaving—though maybe not for loving, but certainly for *leaving*.

So why was he *here*? She stared at him in confusion.

'You remember my granddaughter?' Vaughn was saying. 'Kiloran Lacey?'

Adam gave a brief, curt nod. 'It was a long time ago,' he murmured.

A very long time ago. Certainly, his snatched, snapshot memory of a girl in pigtails bore no resemblance to the woman sitting at the huge, round table wearing a dress as darkly green as her eyes. Her long, shapely legs were outlined by the thin fabric, but not even her magnificent legs could detract from the lush breasts, the silky material of the dress doing very little to disguise their almost shocking fullness.

He had remembered fair hair, tightly bound in pigtails, but the colour of her hair was as pure as spun gold, although most of it was caught back in a knot. She had her mother's hair, he thought fleetingly. And her mother's eyes—or at least they were the same colour. Because the eyes which returned his stare were cool and intelligent and assessing, not hot and hungry and predatory like her mother's. But women wore different masks, didn't they? Who knew what kind of woman Kiloran Lacey really was?

But outwardly, at least, she was perfect.

Her skin was as pale as clotted cream, which contrasted so vividly with her rich green eyes. She had the kind of natural beauty which, in another age, would have had artists clamouring to paint her.

Her lips were wide and lush and full, and held the merest suggestion of a pout of displeasure as she looked at him as if he had absolutely no right to be there. And that little pout stirred at his senses in a way it had no right to. Or maybe it was the unsmiling look on her face. Adam was used to an instant response from women, and for once he wasn't getting it.

'Nice to see you,' he said shortly.

Kiloran kept her voice steady. 'Would someone mind telling me what's going on?' She gave him a polite smile. 'I don't understand why you're here, Mr Black.'

'Call me Adam.' His mouth thinned into a bland smile. 'Please.'

Something about his superior, almost *arrogant* self-assurance made Kiloran begin to simmer. How dared he look as though he had every right to stand around lording it and as if she—*she*—were in some way superfluous! She felt like calling him something far more uncomplimentary than his first name, but she drew a deep breath. 'Adam,' she managed steadily. 'This is something of a surprise.'

'I've asked Adam to establish the full extent of the embezzlement,' said her grandfather.

Embezzlement. There it was. Such a horrible word, and no less horrible because it was true. A fact. A smooth-talking accountant with a convincing line in lies and she had fallen for it, hook, line and sinker.

'But I've been working on that myself,' she objected. 'You know I have.'

'And you're involved, Kiloran,' drawled Adam. 'So I'm afraid it isn't quite that easy.'

Her heart missed a beat as she stared at him incredulously. 'Are you trying to suggest that I've stolen from my own company?'

He shook his dark head. 'Of course not. You weren't involved in the process itself,' he said blandly. 'But, unlike me, you won't be able to take an impartial overview of the situation.'

'I think you underestimate me,' she shot back and she met the answering look in his eye which said as clearly as if he had spoken it, I think not.

'Why don't I leave the two of you in peace?' said her grandfather hurriedly, and began to manoeuvre the wheels of his chair in the direction of the door.

Kiloran scarcely noticed him leave, her breath was coming in short and indignant little blasts, which was making her chest rise and fall as if she had been running in a particularly fast race.

Adam wished to hell that he had the authority to tell her to put a jacket on, but what reason could he give? That he found the sight of her moving breasts too distracting? That her hair was too shiny clean and blonde and her lips positively X-rated? That the silken look of her white and golden skin made it seem a sheer crime to have it covered in anything other than a man's lips?

Instead he curved his mouth into the sardonic smile which would have made people who knew him well have serious misgivings about his next words.

'Your grandfather asked me to review your financial

position,' he said bluntly. 'And I've had a preliminary look at the figures.'

There was a simmering silence while she looked at him. 'And?'

The grey eyes became as steely as his voice. 'I suspect that it's worse than even he thought.' He paused just long enough for her to realise just how serious it was. And then he remembered Vaughn's kindness, remembered too that this woman was his granddaughter. He forced a smile.

'I'm afraid that we're going to have to make a few changes round here.' The silence became slightly tighter still before he delivered his final blow. 'Because, without a miracle, I'm afraid your company will go bust, Kiloran.'

CHAPTER THREE

Without a miracle, your company will go bust.

ADAM BLACK fixed her with a cool, challenging look and Kiloran stared at him, trying not to be lulled by the stormy beauty of his eyes.

'Aren't you exaggerating just a little?'

He observed the cool, almost haughty look she was giving him and for a moment he almost relished wiping that proud look from her face before plucking a sheaf of papers from his briefcase and flicking a dismissive hand in their direction.

'Have a chair,' he drawled, in the kind of tone which suggested that she didn't have a choice.

'Thanks,' she said stonily, thinking that he seemed to have acquired the ability to make her feel like a stranger in her own boardroom.

He sat down in the chair beside hers and his mouth curved. 'So you think I'm exaggerating, do you? Tell me, have you read these papers?'

'Of course I've read them!'

'Then surely you can be in no doubt about just how bad things are?'

'Do you think I'm stupid?'

He gave a cynical smile. 'Take my advice, honey. Never ask an open question like that. You're giving me the opportunity to say yes.'

'Then say it! I'm not afraid of your answer,' she said proudly.

He sighed with barely concealed impatience even though she looked very beautiful when she tilted her chin like that and the eyes sparked a witchy green fire. This was what happened when you worked with family firms—people behaved as if they owned the place, which, of course, they did. If Kiloran Lacey had been any other employee—no matter what her position in the company—he would have told her to stop wasting his time, to shut up and just listen.

'If anything, you've been guilty of mismanagement,' he said. 'Stupidity would imply that you had ignored advice, and I'm assuming you didn't?' He raised a dark, arrogant eyebrow. 'Or did you? Did anyone warn you that your company accountant had been salting away funds for his own private Swiss bank account, Kiloran?'

'Of course they didn't!'

'And you didn't notice?'

Now he was making her *feel* stupid. Very stupid. 'Obviously not.'

'Indeed.' Reflectively, he brushed the tip of his finger against his lips and subjected her to an unhurried appraisal. 'So what happened? Did you take your eye off the ball? Or weren't you watching the ball in the first place?'

He made her sound like a fool, and she was no fool. Kiloran knew that she had been guilty of a lack of judgement, but she was damned if she was going to have this supercilious man jumping to conclusions when he didn't know a damned thing about her! And looking at her in that cool, studied way, the thick, dark lashes shielding the grey eyes, making her feel she'd been caught momentarily off balance.

'You're full of questions, Mr Black—'

Questions which she seemed very good at evading, he acknowledged thoughtfully. So did that mean she had something to hide? 'I thought you were going to call me Adam.'

'If you insist.'

'Oh, I do,' he responded. 'I do.'

His dark face momentarily relaxed into one of lazy mockery. Kiloran swallowed, feeling out of her depth and it was a curious sensation. Men didn't usually faze her—even exceptionally good-looking men like this one, though she had never met a man quite like Adam Black. The aura of power and success radiated off him, but she was damned if she was going to be cowed by that. 'Perhaps it's time you provided me with a few answers yourself,' she said quietly.

He raised his eyebrows, trying to ignore the way her lips folded into pink petals. So she was trying to pull rank, was she? Hadn't it sunk in just how precarious her situation was? How people's livelihoods were at risk? Or was she just thinking of her own, spoilt little self?

He decided to humour her. Maybe if he gave her enough rope she would hang herself. 'And what exactly do you want to know, *Kiloran*?'

His voice was a steely honey-trap, but Kiloran let it wash over her. 'Just why my grandfather has called you in?'

Dark brows were knitted together. 'I should have thought that was obvious—he wants me to help you get out of the mess—'

'I've created?'

'Helped to create,' he amended.

'Please don't patronise me—'

'Patronise you?' Adam had had enough. 'Listen, if I were patronising you, you'd soon know about it!' He leaned forward by a fraction, then wished he hadn't because she smelt of some evocative scent—something flowery and delicate which shivered over his senses—and he jerked back as if someone had stung him. 'You know damned well why he's called me in!'

'Oh, yes—your reputation for getting things done is legendary.' She paused. 'But that doesn't explain why you've condescended to take on such a lowly assignment.'

His eyes glittered—what had he thought about giving her enough rope? 'Well, well, well—that sounds like a pretty fundamental problem to me,' he mused. 'If you consider your own company to be "lowly".'

'That's not what I meant, and you know it!' He was twisting everything she said! 'Just that you usually deal with far bigger ventures than this one!'

'Maybe I wanted a change.' He looked towards the large French windows, which overlooked the garden, where the view was as pretty as something from a picture, distracting enough, but far less distracting than the whispering movement of her silk as she crossed one bare brown leg over the other. 'A change of scene. A little country air.'

Kiloran felt the breath catch in her throat and it felt as if someone were tiptoeing over her grave. He was uncannily echoing her own sentiments and suddenly this seemed like trespass in more than one way—now he was coveting her land as well as her company! 'How much are you being paid?'

Adam recognised the implied insult. So that was how she still saw him, was it—the poor boy from the wrong side of town who was not worthy to sit at the same table as the princess? But his face remained as coolly impassive as before. 'That's none of your business!' he said silkily.

'Oh, I think it is.'

His smile became bland, and the tone in his voice quietly emphatic. He was damned if he was going to tell her that he wasn't being paid a penny! Let her think what she liked of him. 'Sorry.' He shook his head. 'It's a private deal between your grandfather and me. And while I am in charge, it will remain that way.'

While I am in charge. Kiloran stared at him as if he'd suddenly started speaking in a foreign language!

'You mean—I'm going to be answerable to you?'

'I'm afraid you are.' He shrugged as he saw her green eyes widen with genuine shock and for a moment he felt an unwilling tug of empathy. 'That's what generally happens in situations like this.'

All the control which had seemed to be slipping away from her ever since she had discovered Eddie Peterhouse's defection now slid away from her entirely, and most of all she felt a sinking sense of hurt. Why hadn't her grandfather spoken to her first? Checked whether she would object to having this impassive-faced man waltzing in and taking charge of everything. Including, it seemed—*her*!

She fixed her expression to one of studied calm. Let him see that a one-off error of judgement did not mean that she couldn't be as professional as he was. 'So where do we begin?' she asked coolly.

There was a pause. 'Why don't we start with you telling me something about yourself,' he said unexpectedly.

Something in the way he said it threatened her equilibrium. It sounded like the kind of question a man asked on a date, when he wanted to get to know you better, and this was certainly no date. 'Like what?'

He wanted to know what her golden hair would look like when it was freed to tumble down over the luscious swell of her breasts. He wanted to know if she cried out when she came. He wanted... 'Why, your job history, of course,' he replied evenly.

Some distracting darkening in his eyes made it difficult for her to concentrate. She swallowed. 'I went into the City, straight from university, stayed in my first job for three years and was working for Edwards, Inc. when Grandfather got ill—and the rest you know. The usual route.'

He said nothing for a moment. Usual for most people, maybe—and especially for privileged little princesses like Kiloran Lacey. Nothing like his own hard, clawing journey up the ladder.

'I see.' He leaned back in his chair, his eyes narrowing as he watched her. 'Well, you obviously have *some* experience—'

'You sound surprised!' she observed.

He ignored that. 'And we're going to need to establish the full extent of the embezzlement. Obviously. And then evolve some kind of strategy to resolve it. Aren't we, Kiloran?'

Despite her good intentions to remain cool and professional, Kiloran found it hard not to squirm beneath that grey-eyed scrutiny. It didn't help that he was making her feel incompetent, and neither did it help that he was so overpoweringly attractive.

He was making her aware of herself in a way which was quite alien to her. Since when had her breasts begun to ache and tingle just because some man's eyes had flickered over them in casual assessment? And why was she suddenly and acutely conscious that, beneath her dress, she had nothing covering her bottom other than a tiny and ridiculously insubstantial thong?

Her pulse beat strong and heavy, like a dull hammer at her wrists and temple. 'Wh-what do you want to know?' she asked from between parched lips, wondering if he had this effect on everyone.

'You can help me by giving me a few salient facts.'

'Like what?'

'Tell me about Eddie Peterhouse. How long he worked for Lacey's—general stuff.'

'He'd been with the company five years—'

His eyes bored into her. 'And you joined—when?'

'Two years ago.'

Adam gave a humourless smile. 'Which was around about the time the theft started.'

The accusation buzzed unsaid in the air around them. 'What are you implying?' she said shakily.

He didn't answer, not straight away. Let her work out the implication for herself. 'What did he look like?'

She narrowed her eyes at him in bemusement and gave her head a little shake. 'What's that got to do with anything?'

The movement meant that he could see the tight

thrust of her nipples pushing against the thin green silk, and the erotic thoughts which came tumbling into his head made it hard to concentrate. Hard being the operative word, he acknowledged grimly as he felt his body react to her unmistakable beauty. He didn't like this. He didn't like this one little bit. He shifted in his chair.

'The police will want a description—'

'But you're not the police,' she objected.

'Are you going to answer my question or not, Kiloran?' he snapped, and the grey eyes glittered like a winter sea. 'I asked you what he looked like.'

Bizarrely, she felt like throwing something at him and waltzing straight out of the boardroom, as if she were some reactive, emotional child. But she was not a child, and she did not have the luxury of being able to act on her emotions. She took a deep, steadying breath instead.

'He was tall.'

'You could be a little more specific than that?' he drawled. 'How tall?'

To her absolute horror, she heard herself saying, 'Not as tall as you.'

He gave a cynical smile. 'Not many men are,' he said, matter-of-factly. 'Again, specifics might be a little bit more helpful.'

She ran her tongue over her lips. 'Just over six feet, I guess.' He was still waiting. 'Fair hair. Blue eyes...' Her voice tailed off.

'Go on,' he urged obscurely. 'Was he in good shape?'

She only just prevented herself from saying, Not compared to you, but thank God she bit *that* back in time. Instead, she shrugged, as if she hadn't given it much thought at all—which in truth she hadn't. 'He was okay. He drank a little too much beer, but a lot of men do.'

'Did you find him attractive, Kiloran?'

She stared at him. '*What* did you say?'

'You heard. Did you?'

'No, of course I didn't! Why on earth should you ask me something as outrageous and insulting as that?'

'There's no "of course" about it,' he stated flatly. 'And neither is it outrageous or insulting. Human nature is very predictable and it's a classic scenario, I'm afraid. A man flatters a woman into thinking he's in love with her. And suddenly she's putty in his hands. Is that what happened, Kiloran? Did he seduce you? Ply you with pretty words and compliments? Maybe even take you to bed? Were you willing to put everything in his hands without bothering to check it out? Because that's what sometimes happens when a woman is in thrall of her lover.'

The crude way in which he was talking was having the most disastrous consequences. She could feel her palms growing wet and sticky as he purred out things like 'take you to his bed'. Was that why her heart was racing, because she was imagining *him* taking her to bed? She got to her feet and deliberately looked right down her nose at him. 'I don't have to listen to another word of this!'

'Sit down!'

'No, I won't sit down!' She stayed standing, the position of being able to look down on him giving her a brief feeling of superiority. 'Does my grandfather know the kind of interrogation you're subjecting me to?' she demanded coolly. 'Do you think he would stand for it?'

'Go ahead—ask him.' He shrugged.

'I don't think you'd like that for a moment, Mr Black. He'd have you out of here so fast you'd—'

'I don't think so,' he interrupted icily. 'He gave me a free rein and I intend using it.' But his words conjured up uncomfortably provocative images involving Kiloran on horseback, wearing a tight pair of jodhpurs, and he pushed them away with an almighty effort. 'I need to know whether you let your emotions cloud your judgement, that's all, Kiloran.'

She was about to blurt out that she never let emotions cloud her judgement, until she realised that she would be completely contradicting herself. She didn't blurt. She didn't react. She was calm and cool—so what the hell was happening to her? Quite the opposite. From the moment he had walked in here she had done nothing *but* react. To *him*. And it was time she stopped.

She sat down again, all the fire taken out of her, sucking in a deep breath and hoping it would steady her racing heart. 'For your information, no—I did not find him attractive.'

'Charming?'

'He was not without charm, no,' she admitted carefully.

'Good-looking?'

He was being so persistent! Eddie Peterhouse had regular features and had dressed in handmade Italian clothes, cleverly cut to disguise the slight swell of his beer-belly, but compared to Adam Black... 'Not particularly.'

He twisted a slim gold pen between long, slim fingers. 'So what would you say was the most overriding characteristic he possessed?'

She wanted to be truthful, even though her instincts baulked at having to tell this man *anything*! 'He seemed to know what he was doing. He exuded confidence.'

That figured. 'Con men always do. That's why people believe their lies and their evasion.'

'Do you put everyone in a snug little compartment?'

'Human nature being what it is, I usually find it works.'

How cold he sounded—more like a computer than a man. She wondered what compartment he had put *her* in, and then decided she would rather not think about it.

She gave him what she hoped was a calm and pleasant smile. 'Isn't wondering just why it all happened a bit of a waste of time?' she queried. 'What's done is done—surely what we need to do now is to rectify it?'

At last, he thought. A little common sense instead of the impenetrable maze of feminine logic! 'Yes.' The gleam from his grey eyes was one of challenge. 'Think you're up to it, Kiloran? It's going to be a lot of hard work.'

'I've never shirked from hard work.'

Looking at her, he doubted it. She looked as if nothing had troubled her more in her life than what moisturiser to use on that porcelain skin of hers. Or which item of clothing she was going to cover that delectable body with. 'I'm pleased to hear it. And the sooner we get started the better. I'll be back first thing on Monday morning.'

He began to collect the papers which lay on the desk in front of him, signalling, thought Kiloran, that the interview was at an end! He had grilled her, while she was left feeling as though she knew precisely nothing about the man who would now effectively be her boss! Just who *was* Adam Black?

'You come from round here, don't you?' she asked casually.

In the act of putting the papers into his briefcase, Adam paused, his eyes narrowing.

'That's right.' He wondered how much she knew and how much her grandfather had told her. And then asked himself did he really care what a spoilt little rich girl thought about him?

'Have you still got family living locally?' Kiloran persisted.

'Not any more,' he answered, but there was mockery in his eyes now as he enjoyed her feeling of powerlessness—that the man who would temporarily be calling the shots could just please himself. He gave a quick glance at his watch. 'I'm afraid I really do have to move.'

Leaving Kiloran feeling like someone with nowhere to go. She watched as he ran his fingers through his thick, dark hair and gave her a swift and not particularly friendly smile.

'I'll see you first thing on Monday,' he said. 'Goodbye, Kiloran.'

CHAPTER FOUR

WITH icy politeness, Kiloran showed Adam out, watching as his powerful car shot off down the long, winding drive, spraying gravel in its wake. Like a bat out of hell, she thought as the car became a pinprick in the distance, and then she went to look for her grandfather.

She found him in the library, and he looked up from his book as she burst in.

'Kiloran.' He smiled, but his eyes were wary.

'Grandfather, how *could* you?'

'How could I what, my dear?'

'Ask that...that...high-handed megalomaniac for help!'

'He might be high-handed,' he conceded, 'but he's no megalomaniac. Men like Adam Black don't have delusions of grandeur—they don't need to. His success speaks for itself. We're very lucky to have him.'

Lucky? It didn't feel lucky—it felt like... Kiloran couldn't define exactly how it did feel, but all she knew was that he had stirred her up into a state where she would have liked to have smashed something. She remembered his cool, dark good looks. His censorious face as he had taken her to task about her mismanagement!

Can't you face the simple truth, Kiloran? a voice

mocked her. Or is it that you simply can't bear the fact that you had to hear it from *him*?

'Well, if he's so wonderful—then why is he here? There must be a million other places he could be giving the benefit of his superior knowledge to!'

'He's doing me a favour,' said Vaughn slowly.

'Why?'

Her grandfather looked at her. 'That's the way it goes in business sometimes.'

Something in his voice was warning her off, and for the first time in her life Kiloran felt excluded, as if she were trying to dip her toe into a man's world, which she had no right to enter. And something in her grandfather's eyes told her not to bother trying.

'Relax, Kiloran,' said the old man gently. 'We couldn't be in better hands.'

How that phrase mocked her—and not just mocked her, but filled her with a strange kind of excitement as her mind was dazzled with disturbingly sensual images of being in Adam's hands. Of his experienced fingers playing sensual havoc all over her. And that was all part of the problem, she realised.

He wasn't the kind of man you could look upon with any kind of indifference. He dominated the space around him with such intensity that he seemed to leave a great, gaping hole in the atmosphere when he was gone. And how on earth was she going to co-operate with him and give of her best if all she could think about was how infuriatingly gorgeous he was?

Just stop it, she told herself fiercely.

Stop it.

Was that one of the reasons behind his success? That formidable presence? She remembered the way his face had become shuttered when she had asked if he still had family living close by. What really did she know about Adam Black, besides his successful professional reputation?

Nothing, that was what, and her grandfather obviously wasn't going to tell her anything either.

The party she was going to that night suddenly lost some of its allure. A fact borne out by the evening itself, when a perfectly acceptable man—who might normally have made a pleasant companion for the evening—left her feeling something she hadn't felt for a long time.

Restless.

Too restless to sleep. As if something had been woken in her that she could not put a name to, something which taunted her from the edge of her dreams, only to disappear when she opened her eyes. She tossed and turned into the small hours, drifting off only to wake up and find that it was still dark. And when she went down to breakfast, it was with an almighty headache.

She pushed the food around her plate like someone convalescing from an illness. She had known that things were bad, but somehow Adam Black's terse and critical assessment had made them seem a million times worse. Maybe rural living had blunted the edges of her judgement. Maybe her grandfather should never have appointed her in the first place.

Racked with self-doubt, she stared out at the summer garden—at the splashed colour spectrum of the roses and the bright blue spears of delphinium. What else could match a view like that? Certainly nothing that London could offer.

She had come back to live in the country for everything that view represented—a pace of life which was so much more relaxed than the hurly-burly of the city. Here, values seemed more grounded and there was time to do the things she enjoyed. Simple pleasures, far removed from the smoke-filled clatter of City bars. She rode her horse, played tennis and mixed with a set of people with similar tastes and passions.

No, maybe passion was the wrong word. Passion meant strong and uncontrollable emotion and Kiloran could certainly never have been accused of *that*.

Hers had been an uncertain childhood and her mother's moods capricious as she had sought happiness in the arms of a series of men until she had finally hit the jackpot and married her millionaire. Kiloran, in contrast, had strived for nothing more ambitious than balance, vowing never to go the way of her mother and look for happiness in someone else. She would find it within herself. She wanted nothing more than safety and security. Of knowing that she could survive on her own.

But a life which had seemed safe and predictable now looked anything but, and not just because the business was threatened. No, Adam Black had stormed into her life like a rampaging hurricane and, just like land left in the wake of a hurricane, she now felt distinctly flattened.

And distinctly disorientated.

In his London apartment, Adam stood beneath the jets of the shower and rubbed soap into his long, tanned legs, feeling the water beating warm and strong against him as it cascaded over his hair-roughened skin. He had been trying to wash away the memory of Kiloran Lacey and her pink and white beauty, telling himself that an unwilling sexual attraction was no basis for a close working relationship with the woman. But what choice did he have? He hadn't been *expecting* to be bowled over by that cool, insouciant air—it had just hit him out of the blue.

It hadn't happened like that for a long time—actually, never quite like *that* before—and never with anyone he worked with. She was off limits, he told himself. Strictly off limits.

He rubbed soap into firm, hard muscles but the physical contact only awakened feelings he would prefer to be subdued and, abruptly, he terminated the shower and roughly towelled himself dry. He slung on a pair of jeans and a T-shirt and flicked the message button on his answering machine, where the message light flashed the number eight onto the small screen.

Eight messages. He frowned. Had he really given his number out to that many people or had word just got around? He had only been back in England a month and yet already it seemed that he was in demand as the 'must-have' guest at every party. Single men were as rare as virgins, he thought wryly.

But he was tempted by none of the invitations on

offer as the machine beeped and whirred its way through the tape. He didn't want to be teamed up with a gorgeous accessory of a woman who would look at him and his lifestyle and wonder why he wasn't married and immediately set about righting that.

Nor have to fend off the attentions of the hostess who was invariably feeling jaded with marriage and on the lookout for a quick fix of sexual excitement.

And it seemed that dissatisfaction went hand in hand with affluence. Once, affluence had seemed like the answer to everything, but maybe that was because when you didn't have something you strove and strove until you did. Or, at least, he did. And then when you got it—what then?

Another challenge, he guessed. Something like Lacey's. A little, old-fashioned ship, bobbing around on the pirate-infested sea of big business.

He gave a slow smile, enjoying the analogy, even if Kiloran Lacey somehow and distractingly got into the picture, tied to some mast with the waves plastering her clothes to her body.

He groaned as he felt the unwelcome throb of desire and, annoyed with himself, picked up the phone on the first ring instead of letting it go directly to the answering machine.

'Adam?' came a breathless, eager voice. 'It's Carolyn.'

It took a moment to fit the face to the voice and when he did, he nodded. She was beautiful and amusing enough to take to the theatre with him, surely? 'Carolyn,' he murmured. 'Good to hear you.'

*   *   *

While the Lacey factory lay on the outskirts of the small, nearby town, the administration block had been built by Kiloran's great-grandfather within the grounds of the mansion itself. He had been a man ahead of his time in more ways than one and he had wanted to see as much of his children growing up as possible.

Kiloran had always enjoyed the easy access between work and home, but when she walked into her office on Monday morning to find a horribly familiar figure sitting at *her* desk she felt as though she were being invaded on all fronts.

Long legs were stretched out in front of him, the soft fabric of his suit stretching over the hard muscle of his thighs, and she found herself thinking how broad his shoulders were when viewed from this angle.

The jet-dark head was lifted and the face which was raised to greet the sound of her entering could by no stretch of the imagination be described as welcoming, but that didn't stop her heart missing a beat.

Kiloran swallowed. 'Good morning, Adam,' she said carefully. 'What are you doing here?'

'What does it look like?' he questioned coolly. 'Working.' He gave a pointed look at the expensive gold timepiece which gleamed discreetly above an immaculate white cuff. 'What's this?' he questioned sardonically. 'Your half-day?'

She felt so unsettled at seeing him, particularly seeing him sitting looking so arrogantly territorial, that she immediately went on the defensive. 'It's nine o'clock,' she answered. 'The time when most normal people start working.'

He put down his pen with a clatter. 'These are not normal times, Kiloran,' he returned. 'I thought you realised that! And, besides, I'm always at my desk by seven-thirty.'

Well, bully for you, she thought. 'How did you get here?'

'I flew.'

'Seriously?'

He gave a click of irritation. 'Of course I didn't—the nearest airfield is miles away. That was what was known as irony, Kiloran.' Though he doubted whether she would know irony if it got up and performed a little dance for her. 'I drove.'

'This morning?'

'Very early this morning.'

It must have been virtually daybreak when he had started out—because even when the roads were empty, the journey still took two hours from London. That would probably account for the smudges of faint blue shadows beneath those magnificent eyes. Or had he spent his weekend engaged in pursuits which would guarantee a lack of sleep? Probably, if the newspapers were to be believed.

She felt at a loss. 'Would you like coffee?' she asked.

Silently, Adam counted to ten. 'No, Kiloran,' he said steadily. 'I would not like coffee. What I would like is for you to take the weight off those pretty feet and grab yourself a chair—'

'You're sitting in it,' she said stonily, bristling at the 'pretty feet' bit. 'This is my office, remember? My desk. And my chair.'

'And have you sorted a room out for me?'

'Not yet, no.'

He shook his head, as a teacher would to a child who had not presented their work on time. 'You knew I was coming—you've had two days to organise something.' He leaned back and studied her. 'So why haven't you?'

She couldn't ever remember being spoken to in such a way—not even in her very first job, when she had been the most junior of juniors. 'I'll do it straight away!'

'Not straight away, no. Here—' He gestured towards the swivel chair beside him. 'Come over here and sit down.'

She felt like Little Red Riding Hood being enticed by the big, bad wolf, but there was something so authoritative in his tone that she found herself doing exactly what he said.

'There,' he murmured, a glimmer of amusement sparking in the depths of the stormy eyes as she perched on the seat next to his, noting the awkward set of her shoulders and her frozen posture. She really didn't like him one bit, did she? he observed wryly. 'How's that?'

It was awful. Or rather, it wasn't. It was the opposite of awful. She could never remember being so aware of a man in her life. This close, she could catch traces of some subtle musky aftershave, which only drew her attention to the faint shadowing at his jaw. He must have shaved so early, she found herself thinking inconsequentially—and yet already the new growth was visible. The breath caught in her throat; she knew that it would be rude to look away from the grey eyes, and feared that if she did he would sense her discomfiture.

And realise the cause of it.

'Perfect,' she said lightly. 'But only as a very temporary measure.'

Yeah. He wasn't going to argue with her about *that*. This was more than a little too close for comfort, that was for sure. He tried to rationalise her appeal, just as he had been trying to rationalise it since the moment he had seen her again—telling himself that the woman he had spent Saturday evening with had been just as beautiful.

So what was it about Kiloran Lacey? What was so special about those green cat's eyes and the shiny blonde hair? Was her appeal strengthened simply because she *was* off limits?

He let his eyes drift over her. The simple summer dress she wore dropped in a floaty little hem to her knees. Sweet knees, he found himself thinking reluctantly. Her bare arms were strong and toned and lightly tanned and he found himself wondering if she was an exercise fanatic. Probably, he decided. It wouldn't surprise him if she had had her own high-tech gym installed somewhere in the bowels of this enormous house. An extravagance incurred at the expense of the company, no doubt, and his mouth flattened into a thin line of disapproval.

'Right.' With an effort he brought himself back to the subject in hand, drawing out a sheet of cream-coloured writing paper from the sheaf of documents in front of him. 'Let's see what we have here.'

Kiloran took one brief glance at the distinctive, spidery handwriting and her heart sank.

'Recognise this?' he asked shortly.

She nodded. 'It's from my aunt Jacqueline.'

'It certainly is. But she's more than just your aunt, isn't she, Kiloran?' He saw her shift a little in her chair. 'She just happens to be the second biggest shareholder of Lacey's soaps and—'

'And let me guess—she's angry?'

'Angry?' Adam's dark lashes shielded his eyes as he lowered his glance to scan over the letter. 'To say that she is angry would be something of an understatement. And I have to say that I have some sympathy with her.'

Well, he would—wouldn't he? 'May I read it?'

'You won't like it.'

'Oh, I'm tough enough to take Aunt Jacqueline's...' But her voice tailed off as she began to read. Angry wasn't the word for it. The words seemed to sizzle off the page.

The letter didn't pull any punches. And there was a particularly wounding paragraph.

I have no wish to apportion blame, Vaughn.

Of course you don't, thought Kiloran wryly.

But nonetheless, someone must take responsibility for the theft. If Kiloran had had the courage to admit that she was out of her depth, then none of this might have happened and as a consequence, my financial security and that of my daughter might not now be threatened.

Kiloran read on.

I have been comforted by your news that Adam Black has been brought in and I must congratulate you on having hired a man of such formidable reputation.

Kiloran wondered fleetingly how Adam Black felt about having been described as 'hired'.

In fact, I should take some comfort in a meeting with him at the earliest possible opportunity, and I would be pleased if you could arrange this for me.

She put the letter down. 'Perhaps it would make everyone feel better if they just lined me up in the stocks and threw things at me—that's what they used to do in days gone by, isn't it?'

'Self-pity won't help, Kiloran.'

'No.' Is that what it had sounded like? Suddenly, the thought that this man might be judging her and finding her wanting was too much. Let him see that she wasn't going to crumple and go to pieces. She lifted her head and met the assessing gaze full-on. 'She wants to meet with you.'

'So I see. It's not a bad idea—put everyone in the picture. I'm going to arrange a meeting of all the major shareholders—'

'When?'

'Just as soon as we've made some headway.' There was a pointed silence before he continued. 'And we won't make any just so long as we sit around doing nothing.'

'Are you always such a hard taskmaster, Adam?' she questioned softly.

Adam's throat dried as the words came out like some sultry provocation, conjuring up an image which was uncomfortably erotic. Did she do that deliberately? he wondered. Was she aware that, when she said things like that, most red-blooded men would melt?

'Only if I need to be,' he answered silkily, trying to ignore the lush thrust of her breasts and the hint of lace behind the thin fabric of her dress. God, he couldn't stand a minute more of this than he had to! 'I want you to organise an office for me,' he shot out. 'I need e-mail, phone links and a fax machine.'

'I'll get one of the secretaries to do it.'

'Better had,' he agreed evenly. 'Because in the meantime I'm going to have to stay right here.'

If anything could be designed to make her act swiftly, it was the thought that this man would be intruding on *her* space for any longer than was absolutely necessary. The office, which by any standards was a large and spacious room, seemed suddenly to have constricted to the dimensions of a shoebox.

On legs which felt like cotton wool, Kiloran rose to her feet. 'I'll go and see to it straight away.'

'Thanks.'

He watched her graceful movement as she swayed out of the room, the pert line of her bottom thrusting with tantalising appeal against the floaty material of her dress, and wondered what kind of life she led outside the office. Wasn't she lonely, living out here in the back of beyond? Or was there a man who ran his fingers through the thick, shiny splendour of her hair in bed at night? There must be. A woman like that did not look as though she was born to be celibate for long.

A thoughtful look stayed on his face. He was puzzled at the progression of his thoughts and he did not like to be puzzled. Yet he had worked closely with beautiful women before, and not once had he wasted time thinking about what they did or didn't get up to in the bedroom.

His mouth flattened. There was a very good rule for not mixing business with pleasure, he remembered. It meant that you could keep your mind on the job. He picked up his pen and viciously began to underline various paragraphs on the page in front of him.

After a couple of minutes Kiloran came back into the office. 'Everyone's talking—I think the office staff ought to meet you.'

He looked up. 'Oh?'

'They know something isn't right and now there'll

be rumours circulating because some mystery man is demanding an office!'

'What do you want to tell them?'

'That you're our knight in shining armour?' Now what on earth had made her come out with something like *that*?

Bizarrely, the image pleased him and he gave a slow smile. 'Is that how you see me, then, Kiloran?'

She could have bitten her words back, but, stupidly enough, yes, it was. Childhood memory became fused with adult reality and the result was perplexing because the perception remained exactly the same. Yet he looked nothing like a storybook character. He was dressed in a beautiful charcoal suit, which provided the perfect backdrop for the glittering grey eyes, and he looked the personification of the modern executive.

But there was something about the steely determination which hardened the corners of the lush mouth and something about the shadowed jaw which meant that the clothes and the setting counted for nothing. Adam Black had the age-old looks and charisma of the conquering hero.

'Hardly,' she said lightly. 'You've forgotten your horse!'

He resisted a smile. 'I think we'll just tell the truth, shall we? That way there can be no misunderstanding.'

She nodded, her throat still dry. 'I'll go and call them in.'

Kiloran left the office hastily, before he had a chance to say anything else, or to look at her again with that coolly quizzical stare, which made her feel as if she'd never been looked at by a man before. And before he could see the colour which had made her cheeks feel as if they were on fire.

Now what was *that* all about? she asked herself as she headed for her secretary's office. No one was denying that he was potent and powerful and attractive, but she knew the dangers of men like that. Men who could just snap their fingers and any woman would go running straight into their arms. She liked gentle men—*gentlemen*—not men who looked as though they would drag you to their beds and then kick you out when they'd had their fill of you.

'Are you okay, Kiloran?' Heather, her secretary, was looking at her anxiously. 'You look like you've seen a ghost!'

Not a ghost, thought Kiloran grimly. Ghosts didn't exude so much sex appeal that it positively radiated off them. 'Come and meet our newest member of staff, Adam Black,' she said, forcing a smile.

'Is that the man who looks like a film star?' sighed Heather.

'Too rugged to be a film star,' said Kiloran automatically, before turning to her secretary in surprise. 'Have you met him, then?'

'No, but the cleaner did, first thing,' confided Heather. 'Said she thought she'd died and gone to heaven!'

More like hell, thought Kiloran, but she forced a smile.

'And then he *made her a cup of coffee*!'

Heather made it sound as though an angel had suddenly materialised and started boiling the kettle! 'Did he, now? Well, liberation is obviously alive and well and waiting in my office!'

'I'll go and get the others!'

The staff trailed in to meet him and Kiloran watched as Adam rose to his feet as if he owned the place, then graciously shook them each by the hand until he had them virtually eating out of his.

'I'm going to be very frank with you,' he said winningly, 'because I believe that honesty is the best policy.' He paused, looking around, his stormy eyes assessing their curious expressions. 'Most of you will know that Eddie Peterhouse has left the company, but what you will not know is that funds are missing and unaccountable for, and we would very much like to question him.'

There was an audible gasp and then a buzz of chatter.

He looked around the room and every voice fell silent. 'The police are looking for him, and we are co-operating in every way we can,' he said smoothly. 'Everything is in hand. I will be working here in collaboration with Kiloran until we get things back on their feet as quickly as possible. Until then, things will carry on as before—but in the meantime I will be at the helm. Is that understood?'

They all nodded, visibly captivated by his tough, no-nonsense air of determination.

'Good,' he said and treated them to a devastating smile. 'Well, that's all, then, unless anyone has any questions they'd like to put to me?'

No one did, he seemed to have said it all, and they filed out as obediently as lambs being sent off to slaughter. But once they had gone Kiloran turned to him, and, try as she might, she couldn't hide the shaking hurt in her voice. 'Did that make you feel better?'

He didn't react to the green fire sparking from her eyes. 'What?'

'Telling them about the missing funds!'

'Like I said,' he drawled, 'I believe that honesty is the best policy.'

'And then virtually conducting a coup right in front of me! You really put me in my place, didn't you, Adam? "I will be at the helm!" Does it give you pleasure to always be in the driving seat?' She wished she hadn't said it, and as soon as the words were out of her mouth she regretted them, for they took on an unmistakably sensual undertone, and, from the darkening of his eyes, the fact had not escaped him either.

'That's the way it goes, Kiloran. That's what was agreed with Vaughn.' He fixed her with an impatient air. 'There's no room for egos at a time like this. Once I've gone, you can play Managing Director to your heart's content.'

She opened her mouth to reply and then shut it

again, for what could she say which wouldn't make things degenerate into a shouting match?

He gestured to the pile of papers. 'And now, if you've quite finished discussing office hierarchy,' he said sardonically, 'we've got work to do.'

CHAPTER FIVE

ADAM worked like a demon.

All morning long he crunched numbers, building financial models on Kiloran's computer while the fax machine worked overtime. His single-mindedness was impressive, and Kiloran sat beside him, trying not to stare at the way his hair waved thickly around his ear and to concentrate on answering the series of questions he shot at her so rapidly that she felt as if she were taking part in a televised quiz show.

During the morning his jacket came off. Then the tie. A little later the top two buttons of his shirt were impatiently opened and Kiloran observed these with a horrified kind of fascination. What next? she thought. Would he start peeling off his trousers? Would he soon be sitting there wearing nothing but a pair of—undoubtedly—silk boxer shorts?

He looked up and frowned. 'Is something the matter, Kiloran? You're looking quite flushed.'

'It's...hot in here,' she managed.

'Yeah. It is—why don't you open the other window?'

She was surprised he didn't tack on *like a good girl*, but she was glad of the excuse to turn away and to allow the summer air to wash over her heated cheeks. She prayed that he couldn't read her mind as she turned back to pick up a sheaf of papers and begin to work through them.

At one point, Heather poked her head round the door. 'The canteen's closing soon,' she announced. 'And they want to know are you eating lunch?'

He didn't even look up. 'Get them to send some sandwiches and coffee over, would you, Heather?'

Heather raised her eyebrows expressively in Kiloran's direction as if to say, *Tyrant*. 'Sandwiches all right for you?'

'Fine,' said Kiloran shortly, and got to her feet as Heather disappeared. 'But if I don't get some fresh air soon, I'll expire. I'm going to take a walk in the garden, if that's all right with you, Adam?'

He looked up then, saw the strained expression on her face and wondered if he had been working her too hard. She lifted her hand to push away a stray strand of blonde hair and her wrists, he noted inconsequentially, were tiny, as delicate as the slender ankles. *She* looked delicate. So delicate she might break. He gave a frowning glance at his watch. And it was getting on for two o'clock—they had worked right through without a single break.

He rubbed his eyes. 'Sure.' He removed his hand from the mouse, stretched, and yawned. 'I might come with you—you can give me a guided tour of the grounds.' His voice deepened. 'Show me your beautiful garden, Kiloran.'

The soft tone momentarily disarmed her even more than the yawn, which gave her a glimpse of a rare moment of relaxation. Did he always drive himself so hard, she wondered, and if so—why?

She smiled. 'Is that an order?'

'Mmm.' It was, he realised, the first time she had really smiled at him. She should do it more often. Definitely. But there again, maybe she shouldn't. Not if he wanted to stay sane. 'Come on.'

She led him outside and Adam stood, momentarily dazzled by the bright light, thinking that the garden seemed too humble a word to describe the sprawling Lacey grounds which surrounded the grand, old mansion. He felt as though he had stepped into an exotic paradise where brightly coloured blooms dazzled in the flowerbeds and perfect lawns were broken only by trees and shrubs. There was a sense of permanence and of timelessness which seemed to seep into his senses and for a moment he almost envied her.

'It's beautiful,' he said slowly.

'Yes.' She looked around her, and contentment stole over her. 'It is.'

'I've never seen some of these flowers before.'

'Probably not. A lot of them are extremely rare.'

'Who planted them?'

'My great-great-grandfather. He lived in India for the early part of his life and, when he came home, he brought back all the shrubs and trees and flowers he could. We had hothouses specially built. Some of the plants failed, but some of them flourished. The flowers were used to make the basic scent for the soaps, and the rest you know.'

She watched for some kind of reaction, but the

sculpted profile remained as unmoving as if it had been carved from rare black marble. For a moment she saw it through *his* eyes.

'It's more than just a business, you know, Adam,' she said suddenly. 'It's a way of life. It *is* a life. *Our* life. The way that Laceys have always lived.' Unconsciously, her voice took on a low conviction. 'Can't you understand why it's so important that we don't lose it all?'

He began to walk towards a confection of water, shaded by trees, so that the sunlight dappled and glinted on the surface. She had something he never would have, he realised—not if he became the most powerful man in the universe. A sense of continuity, of generations going back as well as the generations who were yet to come. And through it all the house remained, solid and enduring—a symbol of past and present and future.

He watched as Kiloran walked over to join him. The sun was behind her, shining through her, so that she looked like someone caught in a spotlight. The brightness haloed her hair with a golden shimmer and outlined the lush, young body beneath the summer dress she wore. She looked exquisite—like a goddess, with the world at her feet—and hadn't that always been the way of it?

She took it all for granted, this beautiful woman to whom the gods had been so generous. And what would she be without all these trappings? he wondered. Would she still have that tantalisingly aristocratic air about her?

His mouth curved with disdain. 'God, Kiloran—is that all you can think about?' he demanded. 'Your family? And your family's position in society, as land-owners and employers?'

'But that's just the whole point,' she appealed.

'What—status?' he snapped back.

'It's nothing to do with status! People round here rely on us for jobs—they always have done! Why, you did yourself—once.'

Adam felt his nerve-endings tingle. So she wanted his gratitude, did she? Was he supposed to fall to his knees in front of her? 'Oh, your arrogance and your pride, Kiloran,' he said softly. 'Are you seeking to put me in my place? Or simply to remind me of your position of ownership?'

'You make me sound like a snob,' she said bitterly.

'And you're not?'

'No! Never!'

'Do you know why your grandfather gave me a job?'

'No.'

'He hasn't told you?'

She shook her head. 'He refused.'

So she had asked, had she?

He hadn't intended to tell her, but suddenly it became important that he did. Just how important was her position in society to her? he wondered. She had denied being a snob—well, let him see the evidence for himself.

'I come from a single-parent family,' he said, staring out to where a cypress tree had darkened the lawn with its shadow.

'Well, so, as a matter of fact, do I!'

'It's not quite the same. Your mother was a widow.' He nearly said 'respectable' because that was usually the word associated with widows, but Kiloran's mother had in no way been respectable. 'Mine didn't even know who my father was.' He said the words matter-of-factly. *'He could have been one of many.'*

She returned his gaze steadily. 'I see.'

He had been watching her face for shock, or some kind of condemnation, but there was nothing but a calm acceptance and perversely he *wanted* shock. *Wanted* condemnation. He wanted her to judge him and find him wanting, for then—couldn't he do the same with her? Wouldn't it make life a hell of a lot easier if he could imagine her like her mother—with her mother's shallow values? Instead of those emerald-bright eyes gazing up at him and threatening to melt him with their understanding green fire.

'I grew up in Barton Street—do you know it?'

'I know *of* it—I've never been there.'

'No,' he said shortly. 'I don't imagine that you would.' He watched as a bird splashed around in the water. 'My childhood was spent with a succession of "uncles" filing through the house.'

He spoke as if he were reciting share prices, as if he didn't care. Was his heart as hard as his face suggested? 'That must have been—awful.'

He looked at her. It probably sounded as if he were describing life on Mars to her. 'Awful? Yeah—you could say that. It became harder to tolerate as I grew older. But I had a way out. I was good at school and I worked hard. I worked hard at my Saturday job, too. I used to work at the baker's, in town. Know it?'

'Of course.'

He had never told anyone this, he realised. He had suppressed it for years. So was it being back here that made it all bubble to the surface again? And why *her*?

'I'd saved my wages ever since I'd started,' he said. 'I knew I was going to need every penny I had to help get me through college.'

Kiloran watched him. 'What happened?'

'I had the key to the bakery because I used to work some nights.' There was a pause. Long and heavy and pregnant. 'One night my mother's lover stole it. He broke in and he ransacked the place. Took everything there was to take—including a till full of money. The following morning they had both gone.'

'Your mother, too?' she breathed, aghast.

'That's right.'

'What happened?'

'They sacked me. Of course. Threatened to go to the police unless the money was paid back. Yet how could I get a job to pay it back when people thought I was dishonest? That's when Vaughn stepped in.' His eyes were very bright and very hard. 'Do you see now the debt I owe him—that he trusted me when no one else would give me a chance?'

Kiloran nodded, shaken by what he had told her. 'And your mother? Do you still see her?'

'I never saw her again,' he said flatly. At first he

had had no desire to—her betrayal not seeming to warrant it. And as time had gone by he had buried it; it had seemed easier all round to do that. Besides, he had a high-enough public profile—shouldn't she have come to *him* after everything that had happened? 'So how does that make you feel now, Kiloran? Powerful?'

'Powerful?' She shook her head. 'Why should I? None of us have any control over the circumstances in which we were brought up.' She bit her lip as she remembered her mother's indiscretions—the way she had blocked them out. Ignoring them and hoping that they might go away. It had taken her mother's marriage for her to eventually start behaving like a grown-up. 'And anyway, as you have just pointed out—if there's any position of authority at the moment, then it's yours. You're the one calling the shots!'

Her words made him focus on the now, rather than on the then. 'Do you really think that the success of small industries such as yours are set in stone?' he questioned gently. 'It isn't your God-given right to own all this and to oversee it. Society is about flux and change as much as stability. And people have to adapt to the times.'

'You're saying it's hopeless, is that it?'

He shook his dark head, her dark, haunted eyes stabbing remorselessly at his conscience. Why was he doing this? Was he unconsciously trying to punish her because she made him want her more than he was comfortable with? Or maybe for having the roots he lacked? And if that was the case, then he was being neither honest, nor fair.

'I'm not saying it's hopeless. If I thought that, then I wouldn't be wasting my time here, would I?'

'Thanks,' she said drily.

'You're going to have to learn to start listening to the truth, Kiloran,' he said roughly. 'And the truth is that I don't have any answers for you, not yet. The company might be salvageable; it might not—and until I have every available fact and figure in front of me, we can't possibly know that.'

'And if I'd been keener, more alert—then I'd have spotted Eddie's deception and everything would have been just perfect, is that it?'

He turned to face her. 'I can't answer that either,' he said honestly.

'You mean it might have been?'

'You don't need me to tell you that.'

'Oh, God!' She turned away, hugging her arms to her chest as if she were standing there in the dead of winter instead of on a bright, summer's day. 'What have I done?'

He heard in her voice the hopelessness he had once felt himself, and a feeling like that was never forgotten, so that empathy reared an unexpected head. 'Kiloran—'

She turned back, and all she could see were the hard planes of his face, the sunlight casting shadows over his features, his eyes glitteringly bright as he stared down at her. 'What?'

'Let's just see how it goes, shall we?'

She nodded, biting on her lip and hoping he didn't notice the hint of tears which threatened to spring up at the back of her eyes. For a moment, neither of them moved and Kiloran felt the slow burn of unwanted desire.

Because the frustration at the situation she found herself in was bubbling up into another kind of frustration. She had never felt this way about a man and never before had she wanted so much for someone to take her in his arms and blot it all out.

He gazed down at her, the message in her eyes unmistakable, and Adam was too experienced in the ways of women not to have read it correctly.

She wanted him.

Her softening lips told him, as did the darkening of her eyes. He didn't need to glance down towards her breasts to know that their buds would be exquisitely tight, longing for the teasing caress of his fingers or his lips. And they were alone...not a soul would know...

She wanted him, and for a moment he was more than tempted. To tumble her down onto the soft grass and to tangle his fingers in the silk of her hair.

But he moved away from her.

'Come on. We'd better go and eat lunch,' he said abruptly, and willed the dark hunger of longing to leave him in peace.

It was gone eight when he finally switched the computer off and looked at her, and Kiloran had been wondering whether he intended working right through the night.

'Had enough?' he asked.

More than enough—but she gave him what she hoped was a coping smile. 'Sure.'

He rose to his feet, towering over her like some dark, avenging angel. 'Then I'll be going. I have to drive back to London.'

It seemed stupid not to say it—if it had been anyone else she would have said it. 'It's a long drive after a hard day. Do you—do you want a bed for the night?'

His senses sprang into life and just for a moment he allowed himself the fantasy. She wasn't offering *her* bed, but that didn't stop him imagining it. In his mind, he laid her down on a big bed, then slowly drew off the green dress, picturing the lush perfection of her body clothed in nothing but silk and lace. The secret curves and shadows hidden by outrageous items of underwear. He would not remove them, not at first. He would allow his eyes to feast before his lips and his fingers and...

'I don't think that's such a good idea, do you?' he questioned softly.

'I guess not,' she agreed, but she didn't ask him why, and the air was tight with a tension so tight that she felt she could snap it.

CHAPTER SIX

'I've arranged a meeting of the shareholders,' Adam announced as Kiloran came into his office with her arms full of files.

She put the files down on his desk. 'When?'

'A week next Sunday in London seems to be the only time we can get everyone together at such short notice. I've arranged to use my new offices,' he said, leaning back in his chair and narrowing his eyes. 'That okay with you, Kiloran?'

What could she say? That she would prefer to be out riding her horse rather than having to endure a grilling by the shareholders? And why was he glowering at her like that—hadn't she been sweetness and light all day? All week? 'Sunday's fine.'

And he now had all the figures at his disposal, thank heavens. The end was in sight, though he knew that he was going to miss the sight of *her*. Maybe even miss her feisty little ways and that occasional stubborn pout. He ran his fingers through his thick dark hair. 'I think we're in business.' He yawned. 'Do you want to hear my recommendations?'

'Better had.'

She drew up a chair—one delicious thigh resting uncomfortably close to his. Surreptitiously, he shifted his leg away. 'It's exactly as I first suspected—you're lagging way behind the times. You need to take a serious look at your overheads—and I'm not talking about production here.'

She raised her eyebrows. 'Meaning?'

He glanced down at the wad of papers. 'For example, hiring a part-time designer would be a lot more cost-effective than using expensive design agencies as you are at the moment.'

Kiloran nodded. It made sense. Such simple sense that she wondered why she'd never thought of it herself. Had she been guilty of burying her head in the sand?

'But that will increase my wage bill,' she said, biting her lip.

He saw her stricken face. 'Yes—but you've got enough work so it will be cheaper in the long run,' he said gently.

'Yes.' She looked at him steadily. 'Anything else?'

'You could sell some of your own shares. Plough some of the proceeds back.'

Kiloran nodded. 'Okay.'

He had expected to have to fight her on this and her easy agreement uncharacteristically took the wind right out of his sails. 'You know, you've done many good things—'

'Thanks,' she said drily.

'No, I mean it—the way you've kept abreast of trends—diversifying into the aromatherapy line and the scented candles.'

His praise meant more to her than it should have done, but they weren't sitting here with the intention of boosting her ego. They were here to seek solutions. 'Anything else?'

His face grew closed. 'Well, yes. The way you live will really have to be curtailed if you want Lacey's to carry on.'

'Curtailed?' She narrowed her eyes. 'What's that supposed to mean?'

'Just that the business is helping fund a self-indulgent lifestyle.'

'Self-indulgent?' She spat the words out indignantly.

'Sure. You rattle around in that great big house—'

'If you're even thinking I'd agree to sell it, Adam, then think again—Grandfather would never agree to—'

'Let me finish,' he said coolly. 'I said nothing about selling, did I? I know how much it means to you— but you could think about utilising the space. Letting out some of the bigger rooms for conferences can be lucrative.'

'Make the house into a kind of business, is that what you're saying?'

He ignored the squeak of horror in her voice. 'Lots of people have to do it. Or maybe you consider yourself too special to deign to try?'

That hurt. 'Is that what you think?'

He shrugged. 'You don't seem very willing.'

'Well, you can hardly expect me to embrace the suggestion with whoops of joy. And it would take a lot of organisation.'

'But it can be done.' He cradled his dark head in

the palms of his hands as he watched her from between narrowed eyes. 'As for the cash flow problem,
which needs to be solved in the interim—' he paused,
anticipating her reaction to *this* '—you could sell one
of your paintings. That Augustus John etching you've
got hanging in the boardroom is very saleable.'

'I didn't know you knew we *had* an Augustus John.'

'Or just surprised that I recognised it?' he queried
sardonically.

Their eyes met and he saw the colour rise in her
cheeks.

'Are you serious?' she demanded.

'For heaven's sake, Kiloran,' he said impatiently.
'You've got loads of pictures hanging around the
house. Surely you can lose one of them?'

'You make it sound like they're posters you buy in
the local art shop!' she protested. 'Don't you realise
that—?'

'If you're going to start telling me that you've had
them since for ever and that they are very special to
you, then please don't bother,' he retorted. 'I'm not so
dense that I can't see that—but you asked for a solution to your problems and I'm coming up with a fairly
painless one.'

'*Painless?*' Selling her shares she could cope
with—but the etching was part of her past, her life. It
symbolised something that was deeply important to
her and yet Adam Black was dismissing it in a single
word.

'You've got a better idea? Then please do enlighten
me,' he snapped, and then, with an effort, levelled out

his voice. 'Listen, Kiloran—you put a highly saleable painting on the market and you walk into the shareholders' meeting with that knowledge. Money in the bank, end of story. They'll be full of questions but you've got your answer all ready. Takes all the angst away. Simple.'

Simple? 'And there's really no other way?'

'You tell me.'

She felt like telling him that it felt as though he were tearing her life apart, shred by excruciating shred, but he was only there as an impartial arbitrator, after all. How could he be expected to feel passionately about an inanimate object he was not connected to? She wondered if he felt passionately about anything.

'I guess I have no choice.'

But he shook his head. 'Oh, yes—there's always a choice.' He was losing his patience now. 'You could choose not to take my advice and watch the company fold—but if you think some damned etching is worth all that, then go ahead. Keep it!'

Slowly she raised her head and met the assessing grey stare. 'Very well, I'm happy to sell it—but I'll have to get my grandfather's approval,' she said flatly.

Briefly, he wondered if he was being a little too Draconian—but what other way was there? She was fighting to hold onto a lifestyle she could no longer afford, and she was stubborn—even her grandfather had told him that. And stubborn women were like horses—you had to work them hard to make them realise who was boss.

He expelled a breath. 'Good. The other thing which might interest you is that my job is done now, and that after the meeting of the shareholders you need never see me again.' He allowed a smile to linger. 'I know how much that will please you, Kiloran.'

It should have done, it really should. But unfortunately, you didn't always feel the way you were supposed to. Why was she filled with a sinking certainty that Lacey's was going to seem a very dull place without Adam Black? 'Best piece of news I've had all week,' she agreed blandly.

And hoped that the lie didn't show.

CHAPTER SEVEN

THE meeting of the shareholders was held in Adam's prestigious new offices close to Fenchurch Street station in the middle of the hustle and bustle of the City, set right in the middle of the capital's most high-powered heartland.

Kiloran found the offices easily enough and a uniformed security guard let her into the towering building, where a vast marble foyer glittered beneath the deflected light of crystal chandeliers.

'Take the lift to the thirtieth floor, miss.' He smiled.

The lift mimicked the feeling in her stomach as it rose smoothly to the top of the building, and when Kiloran stepped out she followed the low hum of voices which drifted out from an open-doored room. As she walked in, ten faces turned to look at her, eight male and two female.

But the face she noticed above all the others belonged, predictably, to Adam. He sat with his tie loosened, his black hair ruffled and the grey eyes glittering with an intensity which made the chandeliers seem muted in comparison.

It had been little over a week since she'd seen him yet her heart began to hammer hard and strong beneath her suddenly heavy, aching breasts. As if his physical presence had set up some clamouring interior recognition which lit a touch-paper to her senses.

He looked up, unsurprised by the rush of pleasure at seeing her standing there. She would make any man with a pulse feel like that, he reasoned. 'Kiloran,' he said evenly. 'Good. Everyone else is here.'

'Waiting,' said the woman beside him, with a rather pointed little smile.

Jacqueline was Kiloran's aunt, pretty and blonde and very like her mother to look at—with what looked like the entire contents of a cosmetics counter applied to her face.

'Hello, Aunt Jacqueline,' said Kiloran.

'You're looking a bit peaky, dear,' said her aunt, with a brittle smile, as she held a pale cheek up for a kiss. 'Been dieting?'

Having Adam Black around had made food seem like a necessary evil, but she certainly wasn't going to say *that*! 'Not intentionally.' She smiled.

'Come and sit down,' said Adam, pointing to the one empty space, directly opposite his.

And then Kiloran noticed who had claimed the other seat beside him. It was her cousin, Julia—as dark as her mother was blonde—and very, very beautiful, in a sloe-eyed, Madonna type of way. She was dressed expensively in a scarlet dress, and her raven hair fell in two gleaming wings on either side of her face. She was also, Kiloran noted, staring at Adam and looking as smug as a cat who had just found an unexpected saucer of cream and had decided to keep it all to herself. She couldn't blame her.

'Hi, Jules.'

Julia tore her eyes away from Adam and gave her cousin a conspiratorial grin. 'Oh, hi, Kiloran.'

They hadn't seen each other for getting on for a year, not since Julia's last birthday party—always a lavish affair—which Kiloran sometimes suspected that she was invited to mainly to admire the showcase of her glamorous London life.

'This is an amazing place, isn't it?' asked Julia, glancing around at the ornate, high-ceilinged room. 'Makes Lacey's look like a doll's house!'

'It's certainly impressive,' said Kiloran drily.

Julia picked up the silver pot which stood in front of her, as if she were the hostess at a coffee morning. 'Can I get anyone a coffee? How about you, Adam? You look as if you could use one.'

He shook his head, watching Kiloran as she sat down and smoothed back her hair, so that it looked as if she were wearing a sleek, blonde cap. She had faint blue shadows beneath her eyes and he wondered if she had been spending sleepless nights. You and me both, honey, he thought grimly.

'No, thanks,' he said shortly. 'There's no point in hanging around and, now that Kiloran's here, I think we just ought to crack on with things.' He paused and then raised his voice, so that everyone stopped chatting and looked at him. 'The first thing I want to say is that the situation is not quite as gloomy as it could be—'

'Really?' Aunt Jacqueline raised her eyebrows disbelievingly. 'You mean that the missing money has been returned?'

Adam gave a patient smile. 'Unfortunately, no. But we *do* have a contingency plan.'

'Really?' said Jacqueline again.

'I have already made recommendations to Kiloran, which she has agreed to implement.'

The grey eyes met hers in a questioning look, which she answered with an imperceptible nod, and every face in the room was turned curiously towards her.

'These involve the letting-out of some of the larger function rooms in the Lacey house for business conventions.'

There was a little buzz of comment and he paused.

'Kiloran and her grandfather have also agreed to sell the Augustus John, which you may be aware is solely their property. The profit raised will be channelled directly back into the business.' He looked around, gauging their reaction. 'I cannot see that anyone here today could have any objections to either of those two strategies, particularly as Kiloran and her grandfather have agreed to them, and they are the people who will be hardest hit by either.'

Aunt Jacqueline gave a giggle. 'Heavens! You'll be running an up-market guest house! What does your mother have to say about *that*?'

'She understands that there's no alternative,' answered Kiloran, in a low voice. She had rung her mother late last night to tell her.

'But hasn't she offered her rich husband to bail you out?' asked Jacqueline mischievously.

Adam's mouth curved, glad to be reminded of reality rather than hormone-driven fantasy. Was that the philosophy among the Lacey women, then? Men as open cheque-books? Flutter your eyelashes and they'd always help you out in a fix. Though, if that were the case—then why hadn't Kiloran tried it? He didn't imagine that she would have *any* trouble netting a rich sugar-daddy.

Kiloran saw his brief look of distaste and winced. 'That wasn't an option,' she said quietly. 'I'll be opening the function rooms for business conventions—just as stately homes do these days.'

'I think it's a wonderful idea,' breathed Julia, and, when Adam turned to look at her, her mouth fell slightly open, gleaming and parted provocatively. 'I never liked that old drawing anyway—*much* too dark!'

Kiloran looked down at the polished table, despairing at her cousin's reaction. Old drawing, indeed! She loved that etching—both subtle and yet highly erotic. It showed a woman drying herself after a bath; the economical lines used by the artist managed to perfectly convey the gleaming, wet flesh.

It had hung in that room for as long as *she* could remember, and it had hung there during her mother's childhood, and her grandfather's—and before even that. Was it so wrong to want to safeguard the past?

She glanced up to find Adam watching her, surprising a disconcerting flash of understanding in the grey eyes.

'I don't think any of us underestimate the sacrifice

in parting with something so deeply cherished,' he said quietly. 'Now, shall we take a vote on it?'

The rest was a mere formality. The vote was carried and passed and the meeting broke up to adjourn for the drinks which stood waiting on the side.

It all seemed a bit of an anticlimax and Kiloran wanted to leave, and to leave as quickly as possible, but she knew that would have been rude. The shareholders would be expecting their pound of flesh, and that included talking to her. She kept her chatter bright and enthusiastic, trying not to focus on Adam, but that would have been like trying not to notice a meteor which had come crashing through the ceiling.

You couldn't miss him, or his low, murmured laugh. And neither did she miss the fact that Julia was commandeering his attention, or that he was letting her, though she guessed she shouldn't be surprised. Julia would turn most men's heads with more than just her looks—she had the kind of kittenish compliance which most men found irresistible.

She belonged to the school which thought that men should be flattered and cajoled and pampered. An old-fashioned view that men were always right—their jokes listened to attentively and laughed at whether they were funny or not. Julia had been engaged three times before changing her mind at the last minute, leaving broken-hearted swains in her wake, so the submissive attitude clearly worked.

And Adam obviously thought so, too—judging from the way he was responding. Unwillingly, Kiloran looked at them. His dark head was bent as Julia raised herself up on tiptoe to whisper into his ear and he laughed at something she said.

Kiloran put her glass down. She was damned if she was going to stand and watch while those two heads grew ever closer, while Julia moved in for the kill, with Adam the willing victim.

Taking a deep breath, she walked towards them and her cousin shot her a 'lucky-me' look.

'Adam, I'm going now.'

Adam thought how pale she looked and wondered if this meeting had been a trial. Perhaps she considered it a complete waste of her time—to have travelled up to London just to have his plan rubber-stamped—but common courtesy had insisted that she be there. And it had all been resolved very smoothly, hadn't it? So why was her face so tense? Her green eyes looked almost haunted and there were tiny goose bumps on her bare arms.

He found himself transfixed by the golden cross attached to a fine gold chain which hung around her neck and which dipped tantalisingly towards the hollow created by her breasts. He hadn't been able to get her out of his mind, and now he found he didn't want to let her out of his sight.

And when he spoke, his voice sounded husky. 'Kiloran, you can't possibly leave yet. Stay for another drink.'

It was tempting, particularly if she drank with him, but then she noticed that both he and Julia were drinking champagne—and what had she got to celebrate?

'No. Honestly. Thanks. I must get back—I've got a lot to do.'

'Yes.' There was something so ethereal about her at that moment, she looked as if a puff of wind might blow her away. He remembered how the sunlight had illuminated her blonde hair like a halo in the garden, how he had told her things which might have been best left unsaid. A confession which had troubled him, but more because of the fact that he had made it—and to whom—than because of its content. He held his hand out. 'Goodbye, then, Kiloran.'

She shook his hand, revelling in that one, brief moment of contact and wondering, if circumstances had been different, whether she might have got to know him on an altogether different level. 'Goodbye, Adam. And thank you.'

She gave Julia a kiss on either cheek, said goodbye to her aunt Jacqueline and ran for the tube, but as the train raced through the dark tunnels she couldn't get him out of her head. Stop building him up into some kind of romantic fantasy, she told herself. What would be the point? Just forget him.

For the next few weeks she did her best to do just that.

The first thing she did was to contact an auctioneer with a view to selling the etching by auction, and the delightful if rather foppish man who came to see it grew very excited.

'Oh, this is very special,' he breathed. 'Very special indeed. We shan't have any problem finding a buyer for *this*.' He looked at her. 'Shame to have to sell it?'

Kiloran nodded. 'It *is* sad,' she agreed. 'But it's not the end of the world.' She gave him a bright, determined smile. It was more than just wanting to put things right—she was going to show Adam Black that it *could* be done—and that she could do it.

Next she rang up the Council to find out what she needed to do about letting out rooms. There was lots to discuss—planning permission, health and safety, building regulations. When all the paperwork had been done, a very officious woman came to the house to tell her that there would have to be slight modifications made to the vast Lacey kitchen and that the bathroom facilities would have to be extended, all of which could be quickly accomplished.

She thawed a little when Kiloran gave her tea and lemon cake. 'You might as well start advertising in the business journals straight away,' she suggested as her large teeth bit into a piece of lemon icing. 'No time like the present!'

Photographs were taken of the house and gardens and a full-page spread was placed in *Investment Today!*

'Don't scrimp on advertising,' warned the magazine. 'It's a false economy. Targeting the right client is essential.'

Building work began and Kiloran persuaded her grandfather to make a trip to see her mother in Australia. He had been meaning to do so for a while, and having scaffolding and debris around the place finally goaded him into action.

'I can't keep putting it off,' he said to Kiloran rather wistfully.

She understood what he was saying. He was an old man. He could not keep putting things off. You had to live for the moment, she thought as she drove him and his nurse to Heathrow, while the memory of Adam's smile swam into her mind to haunt her.

The police were no closer to finding Eddie Peterhouse, but suddenly that no longer seemed to matter. Lacey's was safe, the staff had lost their edge of worry. Adam had shown her a way out, and she was taking it.

She thought about him, of course—even though she had vowed not to. Someone that dynamic wasn't easily forgettable. And even though she fell into bed exhausted at the end of every day, she dreamt about him, too—and dreams she had no control over, unlike her thoughts. The unconscious mind was so powerful, and so, too, were the sensual, erotic dreams which made her sleep fitful, and left her waking shaken.

The first tang of autumn was in the air when an envelope fell through the letter box. It was an invitation to Julia's birthday party and Kiloran put it on the mantelpiece and forgot all about it, until she got a phone call from Julia herself.

'Well?' she demanded. 'Are you coming?'

'Oh, heck,' groaned Kiloran. 'I've been so busy, I forgot all about it. When is it?'

'Saturday.'

'Saturday?' Kiloran frowned again. '*This* Saturday?'

'That's what it said on the invitation!'

Kiloran sat on the edge of the desk. She had been working almost non-stop since Adam had left. Maybe a party was just what she needed.

'Yes, I'd love to come, Jules.'

'By the way...' there was a pause '...I've invited Adam.'

Kiloran's heart raced. 'Oh?' she said, hoping that her tone conveyed just the right amount of noncommittal interest, but inside her stomach was sinking. All the signs had been there—was Julia going out with Adam?

'Yes.' There was a sigh. 'Wish I hadn't bothered really, but there's nothing I can do about it now.'

'Oh,' said Kiloran again.

Another sigh. 'I made a bit of a play for him and, for the first time in my life, found a man who wasn't willing to take the bait—not just unwilling, but not *interested*, either! Did my ego the world of good, I can tell you,' Julia added wryly.

For some inexplicable reason, the answer to her next question was terribly important. 'And you're heartbroken, right?'

'Wrong!' Julia laughed. 'For about a minute maybe! Then I found myself a suitable replacement. Well, he's tall and he's rich and he's handsome! He's not Adam Black but maybe that's a good thing. I like a man you can tame and he doesn't strike me as a tameable man—not by any stretch of the imagination. You like him, don't you, Kiloran?' she added casually.

'My views on Adam Black correspond pretty much to yours,' said Kiloran slowly.

'So we'll definitely see you on Saturday?'

'Yeah. Looking forward to it.' Kiloran replaced the receiver with a heavy feeling in her heart. She didn't want to face him; she didn't—but having said she would go, she could hardly back out now, could she? What if Julia told him that she had agreed to go and then changed her mind when she had heard that *he* was going? Why give him that pleasure?

What the hell? She *would* go! And I can slip away early, she decided. No one will notice.

She dressed for the party with inordinate care, using clothes as an armoury.

She wore scarlet. Deliberately. Bright and bold and dramatic. The colour of blood and of life and against it her blonde hair contrasted as pale as the waning moon.

The dress was not especially revealing, but it clung like a second skin, moulding itself to her hips and the lush swell of her breasts, the skirt swirling a little when she walked in a pair of deliciously high-heeled black shoes. She piled her hair up on her head and secured it with glittery scarlet pins, so that tendrils of it tumbled and twisted around her face. With her green eyes and her scarlet lips she thought that she looked more like a doll than a living, breathing woman, but she didn't care.

She took the car. At least that way she would be independent. No need to stay the night in town, or to be reliant on a train which might or might not run on time.

But once she hit London, the traffic was absolutely atrocious. She sat for what seemed like an eternity in a jam and, by the time she drew up close to Julia's house, was nearly two hours late and wished she had the nerve to turn around and go straight back again.

Oh, for heaven's sake, she told herself crossly. Since when did you decide to start acting like a love-lorn schoolgirl? He probably wouldn't even *be* there now. And it wasn't even as though she had anything concrete on which to pin her fantasies, was it? Apart from a sexual attraction which only a fool would have denied—this was the way which every woman on the planet probably felt towards him. He had done absolutely nothing to encourage her.

With a heavy heart, she got out of her car outside the Chelsea town house to hear music spilling out, and she had to ring twice before anyone heard her.

A girl she had never seen before answered the door, clutching a tumbler of lurid-coloured cocktail. 'Hi!' she said brightly, and peered at her rather drunkenly. 'Who're you?'

'I'm Kiloran—Julia's cousin.'

'She's inside somewhere,' said the girl vaguely. 'Come on in.'

Inside, the music was throbbing and there were people everywhere. Kiloran looked around for Julia, but couldn't see her. In fact, she couldn't see a single soul she knew and that only increased her feeling of isolation.

She headed for the kitchen, where she managed to fight her way through the scrum to find herself a glass of wine, and then made her way back towards the party.

The first reception room was crammed to bursting, with couples glued together under the guise of dancing.

The second was still crowded, but there was at least room to stand and, in an effort to find Julia, Kiloran began to push her way forward, when she froze.

Because he was there.

Difficult to see, true, because he was surrounded by a nucleus of glamorous women who seemed to be straining towards him, drawn like iron filings to a magnet.

But his presence was as unmistakable as it was remarkable. That tall, wide-shouldered yet lean body. The jet-dark hair and the glittering stormy eyes. And before they could be trained in her direction Kiloran fled—making her way back through the kitchen and out into the garden, like someone seeking sanctuary.

The air was surprisingly clean and pure and scented, with only the faint drone of traffic reminding her that she was in the city. Kiloran took a sip of her drink, but the wine almost made her choke when she sensed, rather than heard, someone behind her and she spun round to see the tall, dark figure watching her, unmoving, the grey eyes unreadable, and she stood, rooted to the spot, as if she were part of the garden itself.

He had seen her, of course. Through the smoke and

the cloying perfume and the dazzle of the party outfits he had noticed her pale blonde hair and scarlet dress immediately.

And a small smile had lifted the corners of his hard mouth as he had observed her hurried departure from the room. Had she known, or expected—that he would follow her?

Well, he had.

'Hello, Kiloran,' he said softly.

Kiloran swallowed. 'H-hi.'

He felt his heart accelerate as he moved towards her. The colour of the dress she wore was as hot as a flame and yet she still carried with her that cool and untouchable air about her, which was ironic really, considering that she looked as though she had been born just for a man's touch. His touch.

His mouth tightened as he drank in the lush curves, the whisper of silk against the endless legs—pale and slim—made longer still by the outrageously high heels she was wearing.

He had tried not to think about her, and yet had done nothing *but* think about her. Yet she seemed to represent some inexplicable danger and he couldn't work out why. Was it because circumstances had made him tell her something of his past? Allowed her access to a side of himself he usually kept concealed from the world?

But as the days had gone on the danger had seemed to become something to be faced rather than to be avoidable. He hadn't realised how much he had been waiting for this moment until now.

Kiloran's heart thudded at the expression she read in his eyes—predatory, sensual, full of promise.

'You're looking very...spectacular,' he said carefully.

So was he. Oh, so was he! 'It *is* a party,' she said equally carefully. This close she could see the faint shadow around his jaw, the dark crisp sprinkling of hair revealed by the couple of buttons of his white silk shirt which he had undone.

He put his glass down on the table. 'I hear things are going very well for you.'

She gave him a cool smile. 'I like to think so. We've sold the etching.'

'So I gather. Well done. It must have been a wrench.'

She gave him a quick glance, sensing sarcasm, but the expression on his face made him look as though he had meant it.

Kiloran thought how different he seemed tonight. In the office she had caught only glimpses of his devastating sensual nature, but tonight that man was revealed in all his unmistakable glory.

'Miss me?' he mocked.

She met the challenge in his eyes. 'What do you think?'

'I think that maybe you do.'

'You really are unbelievable, Adam,' she murmured.

'So I've been told.'

'That wasn't what I meant and you know it!'

Her eyes were lit with green fire and her mouth was

a soft, scarlet invitation. How he had hungered for her, and now his appetite was growing by the minute.

'It wasn't such a terrible assumption to make, was it, Kiloran? It's just that I missed you and thought that perhaps the feeling might be mutual.'

Her heart skipped a beat. 'You—*missed* me?'

'Mmm.' He wanted to reach his hand out and free her hair, clip by scarlet clip. 'I wasn't expecting to, but I did.'

'Is that supposed to be a compliment?'

His grey eyes shone as he shook his dark, ruffled head. 'Only if you take it as one. It's the truth—nothing more, nothing less.'

There was something ominous about that. Nothing more, nothing less. As if he was setting out some guidelines. Instinct told her to get away from him while she still had the ability to do so, but some unfathomable emotion tempted her to stay. 'Well, now I'm here.'

'Yes.' His eyes drifted over her and when he spoke the one word was delivered so softly that she could barely hear it.

'Look.'

She followed the direction of his gaze as he positioned his finger a hair's breadth away from the tiny goose bumps at the top of her arm and traced an imaginary line right down to her wrist. He wasn't even touching her and yet inside she felt as if she were turning to jelly. She stared at him.

'See?' he whispered. 'The evening is warm and yet you're cold and trembling. And your eyes are flashing a complex message at me. On the one hand you look as if you would like me as far away from you as possible, while, on the other, as if there was nowhere else you'd rather be. So which is it to be, Kiloran?'

'The former,' she breathed.

'No,' he contradicted.

'Oh, yes. I nearly pulled out when I heard you were coming,' she told him.

For some reason, this stirred him even more. 'Well, I did the opposite. I came because I knew you would be here. Because I wanted to see you again and thought you might look very beautiful. And you do. Very.'

Kiloran despised the frantic beat of her heart which raced in response to the honeyed caress of his voice. 'You could have rung me up any time, if you'd wanted to see me.'

'But I prefer the unexpected,' he said softly. 'I wanted to see the look on your face when you saw me, and I wasn't disappointed.'

Oh, Lord—did that mean she had completely given herself away?

His eyes were drifting over her now—unashamed predator. He still carried with him the indefinable air of control, but tonight the mask had slipped slightly.

'Stop it.'

'But why,' he questioned softly, taking the glass from her unprotesting fingers and placing it on the table next to his, 'when you don't want me to stop it?'

'Yes, I do,' she whispered, but he must have read the lie in her eyes and on her lips.

'I don't think so. It's been tough at work—but we're no longer at work. I've left and we're free to do what the hell we want. We've been fighting it and I don't want to fight it any more. I know what you want, honey.'

'Stop it,' she whispered again, but he took no notice, just gave a low laugh as he caught her by the waist, drawing her behind the scented seclusion of the thick, scrambling honeysuckle and into his arms.

'Say it once more—with feeling,' he whispered.

Say it? She could scarcely breathe, her senses were so full of him and the heady perfume of the flowers. He pulled her closer and bent his head to look down into her face, his dark features leaning over her with a look of desire which she had dreamt of. But the reality far outstripped the dream. Dreams were cold, comfortless illusions while reality pulsed with life and promise.

But wasn't desire on its own wrong? Shouldn't there be something more than that? 'Don't—' The protest was blotted out by his kiss, her word drowned by that first sweet, melting contact, and she said his name in a kind of broken assent. 'Adam.'

'I know.' His words were a shuddering sigh as he cupped her face between the palms of his hands and plundered more deeply, coaxing her mouth open with the tip of his tongue until she could bear it no more and her lips finally parted to let him dip inside, into a sweet moistness that made him groan.

Kiloran felt as if she had strayed unawares into an unknown country where sensation ruled supreme.

Every nerve-ending was screaming in sensory alert, her body flowering into instant life beneath the urgent possession of his mouth. Her blood growing thick and heated. Her heart pounding, threatening to leap out of her chest.

She gave herself up to it—it simply wasn't within her power not to as her eyelids fluttered to a close. Somehow her hands had drifted up to grip the broad, hard shoulders, feeling the sinew beneath the thin silk of the shirt he wore.

One hand had moved from her face to cup her buttock, moving her body closer still, so that they were moulded unbearably close together, her skin on fire where it touched his, her mouth making an involuntary moan as she felt the stark, hard power of him where the cradle of his masculinity pressed unashamedly against her.

The kiss went on and on until Adam drew his mouth away, staring down into the huge, haunted green eyes, at the soft, dark blossom of her lips.

'Maybe we'd better stop this,' he managed unsteadily.

Her breathing was ragged as she gazed up at him in befuddlement, just wanting him to carry on kissing her.

'Come home with me, Kiloran,' he urged softly.

It took a moment or two for it to register exactly what it was he was saying and when she did it was powerful enough to annihilate the terrible longing. Just like that! The cold, hard, commitment-phobe Adam Black thought that one kiss would have her in his bed within minutes! And if she had been drowning under his kiss, then now was the time to come up for air. And fast.

She smoothed her ruffled hair back. 'Isn't it mandatory to at least buy a woman dinner first?' she questioned drily.

His eyes glittered. The untouchable look was back, and somehow that turned him on even more. 'You're hungry?'

'You really do have the most colossal nerve, don't you, Adam?' she demanded icily.

'No man has ever kissed you at a party, is that it?'

Not like that, they hadn't, no. 'That's not the point!' she snapped. 'Most women require a little more wooing than one kiss followed by the careless suggestion they might like to share your bed!'

'You want me, Kiloran,' he said unsteadily. 'Deny that and I'll call you a liar!'

She wasn't stupid enough to deny what was as plain as the faint outline of the moon which was beginning to appear in the still-blue sky. 'I might want a diamond necklace—but that doesn't mean I'm automatically going to rush out and rob the first jeweller's I see!' He began to laugh as she pushed one of the dangling tendrils away from her cheek and began to turn away, afraid that her face would reveal more than he knew. More than even she knew, because, surely to goodness, a single kiss shouldn't make her feel like this— as if she had never known what it was to really *feel* before? 'Goodbye, Adam.'

'And where are you going?'

'Home. Back to Lacey's.' Back to where she was safe—safe from a man with nothing to offer but his exquisite body. She turned back then, surer of herself. 'And please don't try following me!'

He didn't point out that her eyes belied her words. No woman wanted to be made aware of her own weaknesses.

'No, I won't follow you,' he murmured softly. 'Not tonight. I've done enough deals in my life to know that you should only act when the moment is right, and that moment isn't now. I'm good at waiting—I always have been. And I'll only come when you're ready for me, Kiloran.'

CHAPTER EIGHT

WITH Adam's mocking words ringing in her ears, Kiloran drove back to the house in a highly charged state of arousal and indignation.

So he would come back when she was ready, would he? As if she were some package just waiting for him to open her! As if he could walk into her life and find her waiting there with open arms.

But the memory of his kiss burned on her lips as if he had branded her. As if he had made her his with just that one stamp of possession.

She fought it all the way home, telling herself that she was completely in control. He had coaxed her body into glorious and responsive life, but that didn't mean that she was going to leap into bed with him. In fact, when he came—*if* he came—she would just show him the door.

But he didn't come.

And somehow, instead of dampening the fire he had ignited, his failure to show only fanned the flames and it was hard to think of anything but him, even though she tried.

She threw herself into her work as more and more was accomplished on the conversion of the house. The newly revamped kitchen looked almost unrecognisable and the reception rooms gleamed with new paint.

And although she was spending long hours in the office, Kiloran forced herself to accept every invitation which came her way. There were cocktail parties and dinner parties and balls, and when she wasn't socialising she rode her horse until her muscles ached and exhaustion claimed her and the memory of him grew fainter.

Until one evening, nearly six weeks later, when she returned from the stables to find him waiting for her, and her heart missed a beat for it was like every fantasy come true.

A silver sports car was parked directly in front of the house, and a dark figure dressed completely in black leaned against it. Her throat dried as she met that laconic, glittering gaze and she felt like someone who had spent days in the desert as she drank in the hard, cold features and the luscious, carved mouth.

He had come.

She walked towards him, her heart pounding, wondering if her excitement showed, feeling her palms grow damp and clammy as she gave him what she hoped was a noncommittal smile.

'Adam,' she said. 'This is a surprise.'

'I said I would come.' He had kept her waiting until he himself could wait no longer. A smile glimmered its way to the corners of his mouth. She was wearing riding clothes! Excitement began to fizz its way through his veins as he took in the tight jodhpurs, the long, leather boots and the silk shirt, clinging damply to her breasts. 'And here I am.'

'So I...see.' The dark jeans emphasised the long,

muscular legs and the fine cashmere sweater matched his dark, ruffled hair. He was so damned sure of himself. And his arrogance and conceit filled her with a new strength.

She raised her eyebrows questioningly. 'Why?'

'I thought you might like to have dinner with me.'

'Dinner as a precursor to sex, is that what you mean?'

He feigned outraged surprise. 'Kiloran,' he murmured. 'You shock me.'

'Then you're easily shocked,' she retorted. 'Don't tell me you want to have dinner because you want to get to know me better as a person.'

'Yes,' he said unexpectedly. 'I do. Now who's looking shocked? What's the matter, Kiloran—do you think I'm so crass that I just want to take you to bed and that's it?'

'That's what you suggested the other night.'

'I was a little carried away by the heat of the moment.'

'And if I'd said yes? One night of bliss and that would have been that?'

'I'm flattered you anticipate bliss,' he purred, before giving his dark head a shake of exasperation. 'But, no, I'm not into one-night stands.'

'But you're not into commitment either.' Now why on earth had she said *that*?

'Not if you're talking wedding bells and happy ever after,' he agreed.

'Stop twisting it round,' she protested. 'I'm not proposing marriage!'

He laughed. 'I'm very relieved to hear it.' His eyes drifted across her face, lingering longest on her lips, wanting to kiss them again. 'So how about dinner, Kiloran?'

She thought about what it would entail. The drive to the nearest pub or restaurant. The fussing around with drinks and menus. A waitress disturbing their conversation. Onlookers when she wanted to be alone with him. 'I'm not hungry,' she said truthfully.

There was a heartbeat of a pause. 'No. Neither am I.'

Kiloran's tongue flicked out to slick at her parched lips. There was something so *blatant* about the way he was looking at her. No other man could have got away with such unashamed hunger. 'You know...' she swallowed '...you wouldn't win any prizes for subtlety.'

'I'm not looking to.' His eyes narrowed. 'And subtlety isn't my style, Kiloran. I prefer honesty. I see what I want and I go all out to get it. And I want you.'

She gave a shaky laugh. Men didn't come out and say things like that—they might think it, but they didn't *say* it! 'Just like that? Is this the line you spin to every woman?'

'I don't usually have to.' Most women would have gone straight back to bed with him the night of the party.

'They make it easy for you?'

'Or easy for themselves?'

'Arrogance!' But she laughed in spite of herself.

'Just truth.'

He leaned against the car and the jut of his hips was like an open invitation. Kiloran looked him straight in the eye. 'I'm not interested in being one of a long line of willing victims.'

He thought that *victim* was an unusual choice of word. 'I'm not as indiscriminate as you seem to imply, Kiloran,' he said softly.

'No? So when did you last have a lover?'

He frowned with memory, and the wry knowledge that, having admitted honesty, he could not now refuse to answer her question. 'Back in the States—a little under a year ago.' He met her eyes. 'Hardly evidence of a man who's engaged on a mission to seduce every woman in sight—no matter what my reputation. Satisfied, Kiloran?'

It was an ironic and poor choice of word. Satisfied was the last word she would use to describe herself, not when he was looking at her with those smoky grey eyes, his thumb hooked lazily into the belt of his trousers. Promising everything, promising nothing.

'This isn't what I'm used to,' she admitted. It felt too sophisticated, too calculating. Too lacking in emotion. For him, certainly. But that didn't stop her wanting it. The only question was, did she dare run the risk of getting hurt?

He nodded. 'You want me to send flowers, is that it?'

'I have all the flowers I need, Adam.'

'So are you going to play games with me, honey? Tease me a little longer? Play the dance of convention? Or are you going to come over here and put us both out of our misery?'

He ran his eyes over her with a proprietorial air which made her heart begin to race erratically. She wanted to run straight into his arms, but an instinct for self-preservation stopped her. 'Just what are you offering me, Adam?' she asked quietly. 'Honestly?'

'Honestly?' Her directness was almost refreshing— if it wasn't such a bloody challenge! 'A relationship— if that's what you want, and I think you do. No strings. No demands. No ties. No questions.'

'Fidelity?'

His eyes narrowed. 'Always.'

'And if I hadn't turned up to Julia's party, what then? Would someone else have done?' But deep down she knew the answer to this. And it was not ego but a sure sense of her own self-worth that made her realise that he was not just looking for a willing body. He could have had scores of those.

'No, Kiloran, no one else would have done. It would have been another time, but I would have still ended up having exactly this conversation with you.'

'I should kick you out right here and now,' she whispered.

'But you aren't going to. Are you?'

No, she wasn't. But neither was she going to fall like a ripe plum from a tree straight into his arms. Even though the taut, hungry set of his body told her that this was what he expected. 'Would you like to come inside?' She gave him her politest smile. 'And have some tea after your long drive?'

She was putting him in his place, and for a moment he enjoyed the unfamiliar sensation of subordination. 'Served by one of your army of staff?' he questioned drily as he fell into step beside her.

She pushed open the back door. 'Hardly an army, Adam. Though, as it happens, I've been cooking for myself since Grandfather went to Australia.'

'Have you now? I'm impressed.' But she had bent over to pull off one of her riding boots and he thought that he might explode when he saw the jodhpurs tighten over the curve of her bottom. It seemed like an eternity before both boots were kicked off in a muddy heap and they tramped through into the kitchen.

'Indian?' she asked, pulling the elastic band confining her damp hair and shaking it free. 'Or China?'

The movement of her breasts as her hair came down entranced him and he knew that tea would choke him. She turned to face him and he met a look of startled recognition in her eyes, a hunger which matched and fed his own.

'You don't want tea,' he said huskily and pulled her into his arms. 'Any more than you want dinner. This is what you want, isn't it, honey?'

Of course it was—but still some small voice of sanity tried to reason with her. Pull away, she told herself. Even though he's strong, he won't stop you. Even though he's aroused, he will let you go. But she didn't pull away. 'Adam,' she said threadily.

'Kiloran,' he mocked, but his voice was thick with need as he drove his mouth down on hers with a kiss which ignited all the pent-up longing which had been eating away inside him. 'Kiloran,' he breathed against her mouth. 'I can't wait any more.'

For so strong and so powerful a man, it was an unexpected note of surrender, and surrender where it was least expected had a potent power of its own. It sealed what the kiss had started, and the slow blaze erupted into flames, setting her on fire where their bodies touched.

She caught his shoulders, her fingers sliding luxuriously against the sensual black cashmere, making a mixed moan of protest and delight as he began to unbutton the thin silk shirt which clung damply to her breasts, peeling it away so that her breasts were revealed, the golden-white flesh spilling over creamy lace.

'Oh, my,' he murmured as he gazed down at them, bending his head to flick a lazy tongue over where a raspberry-dark nipple protruded, hearing her tiny little gasp of pleasure as he felt it peak against his tongue.

Her hands burrowed up beneath the cashmere, feeling skin as silkily sensuous as the sweater itself, the muscles hard and firm beneath the oiled flesh. She could feel the slick rush of heat and her heart was racing out of control as his mouth whispered a slow, erotic trail of delight over her breasts. 'Adam,' she managed.

'Are we alone?' His breath felt warm against her skin.

It was what they called the sixty-four-thousand-dollar question. She nodded. 'Completely,' she whispered.

He lifted his head to stare down at her. The cool, untouchable Kiloran Lacey was barely recognisable. Her eyes were huge, so glitteringly black that the emerald rims were barely visible. Two flares of rose-pink defined the high, aristocratic cheekbones and her mouth was like a crushed rose. He ran his finger along the curve of her jaw and felt her tremble in instant response and knew that he could have her here. Now. On this great big wide oak table which looked as if it had been here since the beginning of time.

But he needed something to calm him, something which would not have him acting as if he had never made love to a woman before, which was exactly how he felt.

With a swift, decisive movement he bent and scooped her up into his arms and her head fell back.

'What's this?' she whispered.

'You look like some old-fashioned stable wench,' he managed unsteadily. 'So I might as well play my part, too. Shall I carry you upstairs to have my wicked way with you?'

'W-wicked?'

'Very wicked. Does that suit you, Kiloran?'

Oh—yes! At that moment he was the master and she the slave and she had never felt more deliciously weak. His curved smile of expectation was tinged with danger, and the glitter of his eyes indicated that he, too, was on a knife-edge of control.

In a silence broken only by the sound of their

breathing, he carried her upstairs. The irony of the fact that he was playing the dominant role and she the subservient one didn't escape her—but the fantasy was impossible to resist. At that moment he *did* dominate—by the sheer force of his personality and his formidable sexuality, and Kiloran Lacey rejoiced in the feeling that a man could make her feel like this.

He was staring down into her hot face, at the hectic glitter of her eyes. 'Where?' he shot out.

'In—there.' She pointed a shaky finger at the second door of the west wing and he pushed it open with his knee, depositing her in the centre of the four-poster, and then looked down at her, a fierce and intense look of longing darkening his features.

'Am I your master?' he questioned silkily.

The fact that he had clicked right into her own fantasy made her want him even more. 'Yes,' she whispered, from between parched lips.

'Then take my sweater off,' he instructed.

But she felt so weak that she couldn't have moved from the spot, drowning in sweet anticipation. 'No.'

He smiled. 'So you're going to defy me, are you, Kiloran? You're going to force me to strip for you?'

The roles were now reversed and, wordlessly, she nodded, watching with unbearable excitement as he peeled the sweater off and tossed it aside, then began to unbuckle the belt of his black jeans, his eyes not leaving her face.

He kicked his shoes off, then unzipped the trousers slowly, provocatively, wincing very slightly as they rasped down over the undisguisable evidence of how aroused he was, and despite her hunger, her excitement, colour flared in Kiloran's cheeks and he smiled.

'Am I making you feel shy?' he purred.

'A little.'

He slid the jeans down over the hard, muscular shafts of his thighs, kicking them off impatiently, until he was wearing absolutely nothing but a pair of boxer shorts, their silken sheen emphasising the hard outline of his erection.

With a sinful smile he slid them off and Kiloran gave an involuntary gasp.

Totally unselfconscious in his nakedness, he came to lie on the bed beside her, but he didn't touch her and she turned to him, a little pout of frustration crumpling her lips.

His eyes were slitted, the thick, dark lashes hiding all but a steely gleam. 'Your turn now.'

'But I want *you* to undress me—'

He shook his head. 'Next time,' he promised.

'No. This time.'

He leaned over her, sensing the battle and wondering whose nerve would break first, and recognising from the implacable light of determination in her eyes that it would be him. For a man used to winning, it excited him beyond reason and his mouth curved almost cruelly.

'So that's the way you want it, is it?' he murmured.

His touch seemed to burn sweet, pure fire on her skin as he began to remove her clothes with enchanting yet frustrating precision. The damp shirt was discarded and then he unclipped her bra, tossing the flimsy piece of lace aside, his fingertips lingering on each breast, ignoring her sighing little objection when they did no more but whisper and tease.

He eased the jodhpurs down over her pale, milky thighs and then skimmed the lacy little thong the same way. And only then did he lean over her, blotting out the light which streamed in through the windows, promising so much with the lean, hard contours of his body, yet his tense face yielding no emotion as he stared down at her.

'You are every man's fantasy come to living, breathing life,' he said unsteadily.

But the beautiful mouth was unsmiling as he bent his lips to her breast.

A pierce of longing so sharp that it came close to pain shot through her, her head falling helplessly back against the pillow, her eyes closed as his fingertips began to weave their magic on her body.

'Adam,' she choked, and wondered if she sounded as vulnerable as she felt at that moment.

'Tell me,' he urged, lifting his head. 'Or show me.'

Blindly, she reached her arms up to him, pulling him down, wanting his kiss, and when it came it was everything a kiss should be—seeking, urgent, satisfying and yet curiously unsatisfying, leaving her wanting more. And more still. Giving her a fleeting premonition that whatever Adam Black gave her it would never be enough.

His hand moved over the slight swell of her belly and then down to the juncture of her thighs, finding the moist, heated centre of her, hearing her helpless little cry.

She was like malleable clay beneath his expert touch, but he was doing all the giving and suddenly the game of power and control seemed unimportant. She reached out and took him in her hand, enjoying his automatic little jerk of pleasure as she began to move her palm softly over his silken hardness.

'What are you trying to do?' he gasped. 'Kill me?'

If 'orgasm' was translated from the French as 'a little death' then, yes, she would like to give him the most slow, pleasurable one imaginable, but he shook his head, his face tight with tension.

'Not now.' He wanted to join with her, to feel the most basic communion of all—the melding of flesh and of senses.

He pushed into her before she was expecting it and her eyes flew open, a delicious slow heat beginning to spread over her.

'Adam—'

'What?' he whispered back and began to move slowly, his eyes locking hers, a soft smile making him look almost vulnerable.

She had forgotten this intimacy—it had been a long time—but she had never been roused to this kind of pitch before, either, not even within the context of a long-term relationship. She had said 'I love you' to a man before at just this moment, but now she realised that those could be words said as convention, not because you felt as though you would die if you didn't say them.

She wanted to say them now, to Adam, and she had to bite them back, telling herself that she couldn't possibly love him. She didn't know him well enough to love him—it was just great sex, that was all.

'Adam!'

'Mmm?'

Did he sense that already she was so close to the edge? Did her body relay that to him and he respond with long, hard strokes which felt as though they were piercing her heart itself?

'Adam, it's—'

It was too late, for her and for him. He felt the great, swamping rush of pleasure before his world exploded, to the sensation of her sweet, pulsing flesh and her choked little cry, and the astonishing sound of him saying her name, over and over and over again.

Kiloran watched the man who slept beside her. The rumpled duvet lay skimming his narrow hips, leaving his torso naked, and his chest rose and fell with the deep, rhythmic breaths of a truly relaxed sleep.

She stared at his face. The dark lashes formed two perfect arcs which rested like feathers on the sculpted features and his lips were very slightly parted, almost begging to be kissed.

But she didn't lean across and kiss them. After what they had just shared that seemed like an intimacy too far. A wave of dark hair curled over his forehead and she wanted to wind it round her finger.

But she didn't do that, either.

She knew the big things about him—that he was

intelligent and dynamic and powerful and that he was
an achiever. That he drove a fancy silver car and lived
in London and had experienced loss and betrayal in
his youth, which probably accounted for why he had
never settled down.

The big things, yes, but not the little things. Like
whether he hated being woken from sleep, or whether
he drank tea in bed in the mornings. Or whether...

Grey eyes flickered lazily open and he gave a slow
smile, running a reflective finger along the curved outline of her naked body. It was a moment before he
spoke and, when he did, his voice sounded reflective.
'That was pretty amazing, Kiloran.'

Suddenly, stupidly, she felt shy—as if she were being given marks out of ten for performance.

The finger moved to tilt her chin. 'Wasn't it?' he
prompted.

'You know it was.'

'But you're regretting it?'

She felt her body stiffen. 'Why should I?'

'Because you look a little...wary...I guess.'

That was because she was. She had taken as a lover
a man who she could see as being nothing more than
that. A passionate man with coolly assessing eyes
which promised everything and yet promised nothing.
Was she setting herself up for automatic heartbreak?
Shouldn't she have given it more thought than she had
done, rather than letting him kiss away any lingering
doubts? But passion was a strange and capricious emotion. Normal rules did not apply. And, besides, it was
too late now.

'Do I?' she said lightly.

'You know you do—now wipe that frown away and come here.'

He caught hold of her and brought her face down to kiss him, so that her hair dangled and tickled at his chest and Kiloran remembered that she had come straight from the stables. 'I must look a fright,' she groaned, jerking her head back.

'You look gorgeous.'

'Liar!'

'But I never lie,' he reminded her softly.

'Do I smell of horses?'

He rubbed his nose against her neck and breathed in. 'Mmm. A little.'

'Why didn't you tell me?'

'It turned me on, if you must know.'

'I could have taken a bath,' she said shakily, because something in the way he was looking at her was making her feel so *wanton*.

'There wasn't time.' His eyes grew smoky as they captured hers. 'We could take one now, if you like.'

She felt him grow hard against her and slid her arm around his waist. 'Okay,' she said breathlessly.

'And then you can show me your newly acquired cooking skills. And then we can make love again.' Idly, he began to stroke at a rosy nipple and felt it spring into instant life. 'And then we can co-ordinate our diaries.'

Kiloran's hand stopped stroking the satin skin in the small of his back. 'Diaries?' she asked stupidly.

'I want to know when I'm going to see you again.'

CHAPTER NINE

CO-ORDINATING their diaries.

It wasn't the most romantic way to begin a relationship, though Kiloran supposed that it was the practical way, particularly in view of the fact that Adam had recently started a new job—doing what he had been brought in to do at Lacey's, only on a much larger scale.

'I'm going to be pretty tied up next week,' he had said as he'd bent his head to kiss her goodbye. 'But I'll ring you.'

And immediately she was catapulted into that unwilling state of waiting for the phone to ring.

He didn't ring until Wednesday, which she supposed was about right for the kind of relationship they were obviously going to have and the kind of man he was. Monday would have seemed like the behaviour of a man in love—which he wasn't. Tuesday, ditto. Thursday would have made her seem like an afterthought and Friday an insult.

So Wednesday it was.

'Kiloran?'

'Hi!'

His voice was soft. 'How are you?'

Imagine if she told him the truth—that she had spent the last three days worrying that he wasn't going to ring at all! 'I'm fine,' she said lightly. 'How's the new job?'

'Busy.'

'Oh.' She waited.

'Going to come up to London and see me this weekend?'

'You don't want to come down here?'

'Can't. I have a big, glitzy ball to attend on Saturday night—it's a work-related thing and I wondered if you might like to be my guest?'

She gave it just the right amount of consideration. 'I'd love to.'

There was a pause. 'And you'll stay?'

'If you like.'

Adam gave a wry smile. She certainly wasn't over-eager. 'I'd like that very much,' he said evenly. 'Let me give you my address.'

Kiloran felt stricken with nerves as she drove to London on Saturday evening, having tried on about seven dresses before finally deciding on the one she had started with.

Adam's flat was in Kensington—the first two floors of a period town house in one of the smartest roads.

He opened the door to her knock, looking nothing short of devastating, even though his dark hair was still damp from the shower and the snowy shirt, which contrasted with black, tapered trousers, wasn't buttoned up.

Kiloran's nervousness increased tenfold as his eyes narrowed. Maybe all the other women would be wearing long and she would be the only one in a knee-skimmer? Would it have seemed gauche and naïve to have checked with him first?

She smoothed her hand down over a silver-silk-clad hip. 'Will this do?'

'Do?' He pulled her into his arms and resisted the temptation to let his hand slowly travel the same route, because if he started doing *that*, then they would never get out of the door.

She looked as exquisite as some cool, gleaming moonstone, with not a hair on her shiny blonde head out of place. He liked the don't-touch-me air—the contrast between the ice-queen of now and the firecracker she would later become. 'Oh, yes, you'll *do*. In fact, you look so gorgeous that I imagine I'll have to chain you to my side all night.' He smiled and dropped a light kiss on her lips. 'Mmm. Better not spoil your lipstick. Come and talk to me while I finish getting ready and then I'll pour you a drink.'

It was an urbane and sophisticated line but this was not what Kiloran wanted at all. She would have preferred if he had dragged her straight upstairs and ravished her to within an inch of her life—but she couldn't just rely on sex to stop her feeling insecure, could she? She had fallen for the urbane and sophisticated man—so she could hardly start complaining that he wasn't acting like a caveman!

'That sounds lovely,' she said calmly and followed him through to a large, airy sitting room. There were squashy sofas and restful water colours on the walls and a bottle of pink champagne stood cooling in an ice bucket.

'I'll just get my tie.'

She nodded, watching while he went into the bedroom, where he picked up a bow-tie and began deftly knotting it.

He could see her reflection in the mirror as she looked around the sitting room. 'Like it?'

She turned her head towards the sound of his voice and she could see that the bed was invitingly yet dauntingly vast and there were fresh flowers beside it. But he wasn't asking about the bedroom and so she concentrated on the view over the square in the sitting room instead. 'It's lovely. Peaceful and pretty.'

'Isn't it? I'm only renting until I decide where to buy. This is on the market, but I don't know whether it would be big enough.'

For what? For a resolutely single man who had the occasional visiting girlfriend? She focussed like mad on a tree, aware that if she spent the whole time concentrating on how completely separate their lives were, then it wouldn't work at all. And this was only the beginning, for heaven's sake.

He finished knotting the tie and came into the sitting room, and Kiloran's stomach flipped. If there was any chaining to do, then she imagined it would be entirely mutual.

'Shall we have a glass of champagne? There's a car collecting us at seven.'

'Yes, please.' They were, she realised, acting as if they had just met. And why hadn't he kissed her properly—lipstick or no damned lipstick?

He popped the cork, poured two glasses and handed her one. 'What shall we drink to?'

'Success?'

He shook his head. 'No. To beauty.' His eyes glittered with unspoken promise. 'To you, Kiloran,' he said softly, and chinked his glass against hers.

The compliment made her feel quite dizzy, and the wine, taken on an empty stomach, only added to it, but at least it relaxed the knot in her stomach a little bit. 'Why, thank you,' she murmured.

The ball was predictably glamorous and there was a giant ice sculpture of an eagle, keeping pounds of finest beluga caviar at just the right temperature.

'Slightly over the top,' whispered Adam as he guided her by the elbow to their table.

So were most of the women—wearing dresses which made her own feel positively understated. Some of the women gave her openly envious looks and Kiloran was glad that Adam was newly arrived back from the States—she would have hated to have been classified as girlfriend number twenty-two.

She played her part of sophisticated partner to the full. She chatted animatedly and laughed at jokes—some funny, some not. She delicately but politely fended off the advances of a senior banking figure who had been hitting the bottle hard for most of the evening.

Adam watched her, a pulse beating steadily at his temple. She had barely looked at him all evening and the novelty factor of that was driving him crazy. Not that he needed any added incentives. He glanced at his watch surreptitiously.

'Kiloran?'

She looked up, caught in the crossfire of his grey eyes. 'Mmm?'

'Ready to go home now?'

'Sure.'

In the darkened seclusion of the car, he drew her into his arms as he had wanted to do all evening, drinking in her perfume and revelling in the softness of her skin. 'God, that evening dragged, didn't it?'

With his lips on her neck it was hard to think about anything, but she maintained the demure air of the corporate companion. 'I rather enjoyed it.'

'Did you?' He slipped his hand beneath her coat to cup her silver-satined breast, his mouth against her hair as he whispered, 'Tell me what else you enjoy, honey.'

And it was madness itself on the one hand to have wished that he had kissed her instead of talking to her at the beginning of the evening, and then to wish that he would talk to her now instead of kissing her! What the hell did she want from the man?

Kiloran gave up thinking—it was much easier to go under the spell of his kiss and slip into a relationship which gave her some, though certainly not all, of what she wanted.

Weekdays separated them—they met on Friday and parted on Sunday. Sometimes Adam came down to Lacey's, but more often than not Kiloran went up to London, where Adam wanted to rediscover the city he had left behind eight years earlier. And Kiloran found herself seeing a different city from the one she was used to, because she saw it through Adam's eyes as well as her own, and it slowly crept up on her that they were the eyes of a woman falling in love.

At first she tried to deny it, and then to talk herself out of it, asking whether it was possible to fall in love if it was very definitely one-sided. But it was. Of course it was. Unrequited love—the biggest heart-breaker in history and as old as time itself.

She was headachey one Sunday evening, when she was driving back to Lacey's, having just spent a sat-isfying yet ultimately dissatisfying weekend at the flat. There had been a dinner on Saturday, a lazy Sunday morning in bed, then the papers and brunch and a walk in the park. They had gone back to bed and then the telephone had rung and Adam had been speaking to someone in America, and Kiloran had slipped out of bed to shower and wondered whether he had even no-ticed her going.

She found herself wondering about the natural term of his relationships, and wondered, if she finished it, how long it would take him to replace her with some-one else whom she found as attractive. And why was she even thinking about finishing it, when to all intents and purposes it was the perfect relationship?

Perfect like a diamond—glittering yet cold.

And that was Adam. His charm could not disguise the fact that he was a man who viewed any kind of commitment as he would a deadly cobra.

She had been looking at a huge, double-page spread in one of the Sunday glossies, all about the Caribbean.

'Doesn't that look blissful?' she questioned, her finger stabbing at white, bleached sand and sea the colour of crystal peacock.

He looked up from the financial section, more captivated by her green eyes than any damned beach. 'Mmm?'

'This. Look.'

He glanced down at it. 'Very pretty.'

'Have you ever been to the Caribbean?'

'Once. A long time ago.'

Getting information about his past was like getting blood out of a stone and for once—just for the hell of it—Kiloran decided to ignore the I-don't-particularly-want-to-talk-about-it vibes.

'When?'

He put the newspaper down. 'About five years ago.'

'Who with?'

His face became shuttered. 'I'm sorry?'

She was hardly demanding to know all the secrets to his heart! 'I just asked who with.' And then rushed on incautiously. 'Was it with a woman?'

Now he really *was* starting to get irritated. 'Why?'

'No reason, especially.' Kiloran shrugged, feeling on the defensive. 'It's just—'

His eyes glittered. 'Just what, Kiloran?'

'Well, it's quite interesting to know about other people you've been out with. Don't you think?'

'No, I don't. I have no earthly desire to find out when you went out with Johnny, or Dickie, or Harry—

or whoever else might be clogging up the romantic files in your memory. Why should I?'

Why, indeed? His voice sounded cold, clipped—she hadn't heard it sound like that in all the time she had been going out with him.

But something made her probe away—with the poorly applied knowledge of someone who continued to pick a spot: that it always left a scar.

'It's called wanting to get to know someone better, Adam.'

His eyes gleamed out an unspoken warning. 'Or intrusion, perhaps?' he questioned easily, getting up from his chair and going to stand behind her, his fingers beginning to rhythmically massage her shoulders. 'I know everything I want to know about you, Miss Lacey.'

She closed her eyes as she felt her body respond to his touch. Instantly turned on by him and furious with herself for being so. She tipped her head back, so that she caught the upside-down version of his face, and from this angle his features were distorted.

'You can't keep relationships in aspic,' she objected.

He sighed, and stopped what he was doing. 'I told you right from the beginning what this relationship was likely to entail, Kiloran,' he said shortly. 'You knew where you stood and you agreed to that, didn't you?'

She nodded. He made it sound like a business merger.

His voice softened. 'Do you enjoy being with me, or not?'

Did the sun rise in the skies every morning? She nodded again.

'Well, then—don't let's spoil it.'

She didn't say anything.

He looked at the frozen set of her shoulders. Why could women never be satisfied with the status quo? Why, if there was a boat drifting along on perfectly calm and pleasant waters, did they always want to rock it? Well, let her sulk if she wanted to sulk! 'I'm going to take a shower,' he said shortly.

And that had been that. She had been left feeling foolish, frustrated, and wishing that she had kept her mouth shut, but on the drive home she questioned whether their so-called relationship could continue like this. Relationships had to grow, didn't they—or they withered and died?

Maybe that was what Adam wanted. Natural wastage.

He rang on Thursday to say that he had to fly to Rome. 'And I won't be back until late Saturday.'

'But you were supposed to be coming down to see me!' She knew as she was saying it that she was playing it all wrong, but that didn't seem to stop her and, besides, why *should* it be a game?

'I know I was—but there isn't really going to be enough time.' A look of determination came over his face. She had to accept what he was offering her, because he wasn't going to offer more than that. 'Let's leave it this time, Kiloran, shall we?'

It seemed she didn't have any say in the matter. 'Fine,' she agreed, resolutely cheerful and yet somehow despising herself.

His voice softened. 'Listen, I'll come down next weekend and make it up to you. How about that?'

But she felt like a child being fobbed off with an inferior toy at Christmas.

She had thought that she would just love being with Adam so much that she would be prepared to go along with the kind of grown-up relationship he had outlined right at the start.

But she was slowly beginning to realise that it wasn't enough—and if it wasn't enough *now*, then what did the future hold?

Adam did what he always did when emotions began to wreak their usual havoc—he buried himself in his work, winning two deals which made him the toast of his new offices.

Success was just as heady as power—for the onlookers, at least, he decided. Two senior female executives had been fawning over him all morning and the more stunning of the two had invited him for a drink after work.

He wasn't remotely tempted. He was tired and he thought of Kiloran, with her grass-green eyes and her fall of moon-coloured hair and a body which took him to places he hadn't realised existed.

And then he remembered the ugly little scene on Sunday.

'I'm pretty tied up at the moment,' he prevaricated.

'I'm completely into rain checks,' smiled the executive, and popped her card into the jacket of his suit. 'Let me know when you're free.'

Rome was crowded and the man he was dealing with a complete incompetent. By the time he arrived in the UK on Saturday evening, Adam had a splitting headache which was not helped by the fact that the airline seemed to have misplaced his bag.

The pretty ground stewardess smiled at him anxiously. 'If you'd like to wait—'

'I've been waiting at the airport for two hours,' said Adam, trying to keep his voice steady. It wasn't *her* fault, after all. 'Just have them send it to me, will you?'

'Certainly, sir.'

To cap it all, it was raining—a driving, relentless rain and he felt full of a pent-up kind of anger, unable to pinpoint the cause of it.

He got into his car, half expecting it not to start, but the powerful engine roared into life immediately and he thought about driving back to London, to an empty flat and an empty bed.

And then he thought about Kiloran and his body responded as instantly as the car had done.

Hadn't he been a little harsh with her?

What if he drove down to see her—surprised her—gave her the perfume he'd bought her in Rome? And then spent the rest of the weekend lost in her arms?

Anticipation caused his face to tighten as he indicated left out of the airport, instead of right.

The drive was one of the worst of his life. The narrow lanes were clogged with mud and the hedgerows seemed to be closing in on him. The radio was playing some loud and intense choral piece which seemed to darken his mood even more and Adam automatically clicked it off, so that for a moment there was silence.

Only a moment.

A car came suddenly in the other direction, hidden until that moment by a sharp bend. Adam's powerful headlights illuminated the vehicle and for just a moment he saw a man driving, one hand on the wheel, the other holding a mobile phone to his ear.

The car was coming towards him. Adam slammed on his brakes and jammed his fist on the horn and his car slowed right down, but it was too late, because the other just kept on coming.

As if in slow motion, Adam saw a frightened, startled face staring at him through the windscreen of the other car and then a loud crash, a jolt of pain.

And then, thankfully, nothing.

CHAPTER TEN

THE telephone rang at midnight, waking Kiloran from a deep and troubled sleep, and she sat up with a start, glancing at the bedside clock in alarm and wondering who would be ringing at this time of the night, and why.

Was it Grandfather?

She snatched the receiver up. 'Hello?'

It was a man's voice, a voice she did not recognise, a low, husky voice. 'Is this Kiloran Lacey?'

'That's me. Who is this, please?'

'This is the police.'

Kiloran began to shake. The *police*?

'Are you a friend of Adam Black's?'

Something in the way he asked the question alerted every fearful instinct in Kiloran's body. It was as though someone had constricted her throat with a tight metal band.

'I'm his...yes,' she struggled the words out. 'He's a friend of mine. Something's happened to him, hasn't it?' she managed to get out.

'Yes. I'm afraid that he's been involved in a car crash. He's been badly hurt.'

Kiloran gave a little moan of distress, her fingers gripping onto the receiver as if it were a lifeline.

'Yours was the last number he had dialled on his mobile and—'

'Adam!' It sounded like the keening wail of a wounded animal. Kiloran's hands began to shake. 'Where is he?'

'In hospital. The Tremaine Hospital—it's near you—do you know it?'

'Yes.'

'Are you all right to drive, or would you rather we send a car round for you?'

'No. No—I can manage. Th-thank you.' Kiloran slammed the phone down and jumped out of bed, grabbing a pair of old jeans and the warmest sweater she could find, her fingers shaking so much that she could barely do her bra up.

Calm down, she told herself. For God's sake, calm down, or you'll end up crashing your own car. A jolt of pain ripped through her. Just how badly hurt was he?

She forced herself to drive at an exaggeratedly slow pace all the way to Tremaine Hospital, but she left her car skewed in the hospital forecourt and ran into the reception as if the hounds of hell were snapping at her ankles.

'Can you tell me where Adam Black is, please?'

'When was he admitted?'

'I don't *know*!'

'Just a moment.' The woman ran her eyes down a list and then looked up, her face folded into a deliberately calm expression. 'He's in the intensive care unit, he—'

But Kiloran had already gone, taking the stairs instead of the lift, running all the way to the isolated and sterile unit right at the very top of the hospital wing.

A nurse in a white uniform looked up from the desk. 'May I help you?'

She felt like crying that it wasn't *her* that needed help, but Adam—but she took a deep breath. Hysteria would help no one. She must be strong. 'I've come to see Adam Black.'

'Are you a relative?'

'No.' She wanted to say, I'm all he's got, but that wasn't true, not in the real sense. 'I'm his girlfriend. He has no next of kin.'

'I see.' The nurse got to her feet. 'If you'd like to wait here for a moment.'

The moment felt like eternity but eventually the nurse came back with a colleague.

'My name is Sandy,' she said gently. 'And I am Adam's nurse. Won't you sit down for a moment and I'll tell you what is happening with him?'

Another moment. Another eternity. Kiloran forced herself to concentrate.

He was concussed. He was in a coma. There didn't appear to be any major internal injuries and he had just undergone a brain scan. The good news was that he hadn't broken any limbs.

That was the *good* news?

Kiloran gave a ghostly smile. 'When can I see him?'

'I'll take you to him now.'

It was like some surreal nightmare as she followed

the nurse through the spotless, soundless and gleaming unit until they finally stopped outside a cubicle.

Through the glass, Kiloran could see Adam lying as still as death on the bed and she jammed her fist into her mouth and gave a soundless little cry. Her Adam— her strong, powerful Adam—with all that vitality just zapped away.

'What can I do?' she whispered. 'To help him?'

'Talk to him. Stroke his hand. Remind him of things you've done together. Try to bring him back.'

Remind him of things you've done together. The words haunted her as she fearfully made her way towards the bed, towards that still and silent figure.

What shared memories did they have which might stir his sleeping mind? But the only ones she could think of were not the deep and meaningful memories which would arouse a man from a coma. Great sex and glitzy restaurants were not the kind of profound or precious memories which would arouse the sleeping mind. Were they?

She could, of course, say that she loved the way that his mouth sometimes softened when he was about to kiss her. Or that it felt as if she had just won a prize if something she said made him laugh aloud. Or that when he was sleeping she could see the boy in the face of the man and that he could look almost vulnerable.

But not this time. She flinched as she looked at the bruised and battered face. There was no vulnerability in Adam's face today. It was barely recognisable as a face—man or boy—it was so distorted and discoloured with bruising. And besides, those were not the kinds of things he wanted to hear, not from her and not from any woman.

So what the hell was she going to say to him?

She sat down beside the bed and began to stroke his hand. What did he like most about her? He liked the strong and in-control Kiloran, and that was what she would be.

She took a deep breath and smiled at the nurse. 'Adam Black,' she said, very softly. 'You are nothing but an old attention-seeker! I've been woken up out of a deep sleep to come and see you, and you haven't even the decency to open your eyes and say hello.' And then her voice cracked just a little. Oh, what the hell? 'Wake up, Adam,' she pleaded softly. 'Wake up, darling.'

For nearly two days he lay there while the nurses turned him and washed him and took his observations.

And for nearly two days Kiloran remained by his side, except when they forced her to go and rest in the small side room especially reserved for 'relatives'.

It was when the sun was going down on the second day that he finally stirred.

Kiloran had been talking to him, still in the new, soft voice which she seemed to have specially acquired for this heartbreakingly one-way conversation.

'The business rooms are fully booked for the next six months,' she was saying. 'And the weirdest thing of all is that someone spotted the photos of the garden and showed them to an expert, and *he* said that he had never seen such a big collection of unusual shrubs and trees. And—'

She drew a deep breath and wistfully stroked the back of his hand, remembering a snapshot image of the day the two of them had stood in the garden, that first day he had come to work at Lacey's. They had been bathed in sunlight and Adam had looked so strong—as if he were the most alive person on the planet. And then he had told her about his mother, about Vaughn giving him the job. Knowing him now, as she did—or what little he allowed her to know— she realised that it had been a strangely intimate thing for him to have told her. Never to be repeated.

'And some terribly up-market magazine wants to do a feature on it! Imagine! They especially loved the lily collection, and you know your favourite—the pink and white one? They want to put that on the cover!'

Through the heavy grey mists of a wasteland he seemed to have inhabited since the beginning of time, Adam heard a soft, sweet voice talking of lilies and he thought he had died and gone to heaven.

He tried to move his mouth.

'Nurse!' Kiloran stumbled to her feet and knocked the chair over. *'Nurse!'* She bent over him. 'Adam— oh, *Adam*! Darling, can you hear me?'

Something, or someone had superglued his eyes together, but with an almighty effort Adam forced them open by a fraction, but such a fierce and piercing light scorched them that he let them snap shut again.

'Nurse—he tried to open his eyes—I swear he did!' Nurse? *Nurse?*

'Just move aside for a minute, would you, Kiloran?'

Kiloran? Was that a name, for God's sake? Or some kind of mountain? His mind fuddled along.

'Come along, Mr Black—try to open your eyes for me!'

A voice infinitely less soft and sweet was speaking to him again. A bossy kind of voice. 'Come along, Mr Black—open your eyes.'

With an effort, he obeyed—only to have Bossy-voice shine some God-forsaken light in them. If he could have groaned, he would have done, but his vocal cords seemed to have let him down.

'Yes, he's conscious.'

'Oh, thank God! Thank *God*!'

Sweet-voice sounded close to tears—a sound so poignant that he wrenched his eyes open. A beautiful face was staring down at him, with hair the colour of sunlight and green eyes that swam like the ocean. It was all too confusing and Adam let himself slip grate-fully back into that grey wasteland.

CHAPTER ELEVEN

'SO HOW are we feeling this morning, Adam?'

Adam opened his eyes. 'Where's Kiloran?'

The nurse smiled. Men were a bit like animals—if the first thing a duck saw was a tiger, then it forever believed that the tiger was its mother! And Kiloran, in this case—was the tiger!

'Kiloran's just bringing the car round to the front of the building—and I'm here to help you get dressed.'

'I can get myself dressed!'

'Not yet, you can't,' the nurse fussed. 'You're as weak as a kitten, although I must say that you don't particularly *look* as weak as a kitten!'

'Why can't Kiloran help me?' he demanded, his heart sinking as he saw the nurse begin to roll her sleeves up over her rather hefty forearms. He'd much rather that golden-haired angel be at hand.

The nurse coughed. 'Well, she was a little taken-aback when you didn't recognise her, of course—but, as I told her, that's perfectly normal in these circumstances.'

'You mean I know her?'

The nurse helped him on with his jeans and began to get rather pink around the neck.

'Yes, Adam,' said Kiloran, in an odd, strained kind

of voice as she walked into the cubicle. 'You do know me—you just can't remember.'

Adam was still feeling groggy, but not too groggy to wonder how well he had known her.

'Here.' Kiloran began to slide a sweater over his head, her fingers automatically colliding with the silken flesh, and she saw him still, their eyes meeting, his full of confusion, and something else, too—some fleeting look of sensual awareness.

Kiloran would have been shocked if she hadn't already noticed Adam's body responding in the most elemental way possible—even when he'd been deeply unconscious.

It had happened on the second morning, when she had been helping the nurse to wash him. It had been a little embarrassing—for Kiloran, in any case.

But as the nurse had cheerfully explained, 'Oh, I wouldn't worry about *that*, my dear! Men are very basic creatures. They would need to be at death's door before their bodies stopped reacting.' She withdrew the sponge hastily from his chest. 'It's an automatic response,' she added hastily. 'It's not me, or anything.'

Kiloran had managed to smile. The nurse in question was of pensionable age and although she was very sweet—she did not imagine that she was really Adam's type.

But now, the look she surprised in his eyes was not simply an automatic masculine response to the touch of a young woman, of that she was certain. There had been the glimmer of memory there, she would have sworn it.

Did that mean he was starting to remember?

Because up until now, his mind had been a complete blank. He seemed to recognise his own name, but that was all. He didn't know why he had been driving so near to Kiloran's when he had specifically told her that he was going straight home to his apartment. Nor did he have any knowledge of any relationship between the two of them.

Though that, accepted Kiloran wryly, might say more about the definition of their 'relationship' than any memory loss.

And she was taking him back to Lacey's, assured by the medical team that he needed only rest and recuperation and not any high-powered nursing care. All of which she was perfectly capable of administering.

She wanted to do it; she loved him, but she knew that even if she hadn't she would have done it, anyway—for who else did he have?

That had been the most profound shock of all—of realising that such a strong and powerful man was, after all, as vulnerable as the next person.

'Let me help you—' She moved to help his arms into the sweater, but he tried to push her away.

'I can do it—'

'No, you can't! Are you always this stubborn, Adam?'

'No, honey—you're the one who's stubb—'

Their eyes met in a long look. He had called her 'honey' and he had called her...

'Yes, that's right,' she said slowly. 'I *am* stubborn.'

'You mean that's memory?' he demanded, as if he

had just discovered the secret to the universe. 'Not guesswork?'

She smiled. 'It certainly seems that way. Now stop worrying about it, about anything—I'm going to take you home.'

'You're bossier than that nurse,' he complained, but he was wondering exactly where home was.

It was not what he imagined it would be—a huge and beautiful mansion, set in acres of exquisite grounds.

'This is where I live?' he questioned as the car crunched its way up the gravelled drive.

'Some of the time,' she replied evenly, because the doctor had told her to simplify things. And he *did* spend weekends there, with her, some of the time.

'With you?'

She nodded. 'Yes, with me—though we don't live together, as such.'

He wondered why. Through eyes newly focussed on the brightness of life after the greyness of his coma, he thought that he had never seen a more beautiful woman than Kiloran.

'You have an apartment in London,' she went on, staring at him for some kind of recognition. 'In Kensington.' But there was none—nothing other than the blank kind of acceptance which greeted each new fact which she recounted. It made her realise how many subtle interpretations of a 'fact' there could be. If you told someone that you spent weekends together, it could sound like quite a commitment—while noth-

ing, of course, could be further from the truth. Not
that Adam was into subtle nuances right now.

'Come on, now,' she said gently, thinking how
much she wanted to use a term of endearment, like
'sweetheart' or 'darling'—but that was something she
had only done when he'd been in a coma and she
hadn't been able to help herself. And now was very
definitely not the time to carry on with it. She was
supposed to be helping his memory to return by keeping things much as they'd been before the accident.
And besides, the doctor hoped that the amnesia would
only be temporary—imagine Adam's icy horror if his
memory suddenly returned, to find her acting lovesick
all over him!

'You're very tired,' she whispered, slipping her arm
around his waist as she took in the dark shadows beneath his eyes and the lines of fraught tension on his
face.

Some autopilot reaction made him try to push her
arm away. 'I'm fine.'

She ignored him, knowing that he didn't have the
strength to resist. She tightened her grip on him and
reluctantly he leaned on her as they went into the
house.

She had asked Miriam to bring tea and crumpets
and buns to the library, where a fire had been lit and
was roaring. She had wanted the most English of teas
to see if that would nudge some kind of memory, because they'd sometimes had tea in here, just like this,
after riding. She shot him a glance to see his reaction.

He looked around the room, taking in the very cosy

scene in front of his eyes. It felt as though someone had muzzled his brain with cotton wool and he shook his head in irritation as he sank down into a chair in front of the fire.

'How would you like your tea, Adam?' asked Kiloran, lifting up the heavy silver pot.

'Just lemon, please,' he replied automatically and saw her smile. 'What is it?'

'That's how you always take your tea.'

'So my brain is sorting out the most important things, right?' he questioned drily and she smiled again.

'At least your sense of humour hasn't completely deserted you.'

'You mean I have one?'

'Sometimes.' She was about to tease him when she drew herself up short. 'Don't tire him,' the doctor had told her—and perhaps teasing would qualify as tiring him. 'Have a sandwich.'

He shook his head. 'I'm not hungry.'

She nodded. She wasn't going to force it, but he looked so pale, so unlike her glowing Adam that if she could have persuaded him to eat she would have done. 'Okay.'

Adam drank his tea. It was very comfortable here by the fire—warm and welcoming. If only his head didn't feel as though someone had jammed it in between a giant nutcracker, and in the process managed to take away all the thoughts and associations and familiarity which made him what he normally was.

But how did he know what he normally was?

He put the cup down and looked at Kiloran, which was halfway to a cure in itself. She was wearing a soft wool dress, the colour of blueberries, and her hair was loose—like the moon against the backdrop of a nearly dark sky. Her long, slim legs were spread in front of her and she had kicked her shoes off. He might be only two days out of a coma, but that didn't mean that *all* his senses were dead. He might have a little difficulty wanting food as he usually did, but the stirring leap of awareness and the pounding of his heart made him thank God that a very important part of him was still very much alive.

'Kiloran?'

She had seen him watching her, studying her in a way she had not seen him do before, except perhaps when they'd been in bed together. Never usually that openly. His eyes had darkened and suddenly she was reminded of how long it had been since they had made love. 'What?' she said huskily.

For a moment, he almost forgot the question, but with a steely determination he dragged it back out of the reach of growing desire. This was too important to wait. He would not forget anything else; he had forgotten enough. And then it occurred to him that his ability to make love might have been affected. His mouth hardened. Like hell it would! 'How would you describe me? Normally?'

Kiloran saw the perplexing pattern of emotions which had flitted across his gorgeous face—expressions she had never seen there before. There had been uncertainty and concern and then the familiar steely resolve. 'Six-two, black hair—'

'Not the way I look—hell, Kiloran! I can see in the mirror and have enough imagination to realise that my face isn't usually black and blue and swollen to twice its size! I mean, how would you describe me—the man. If you're my lover, then you must know me better than anyone else.'

The irony of his remark didn't escape her. If she told him that she suspected no one *really*, *really* knew him, because he always kept something of himself back—then would that sound like a criticism? And what right did she have to criticise him? She loved him, didn't she, in spite of that? She couldn't make him into a more emotionally giving person just because that suited her template of what her true-love should be. You couldn't control the way someone was, or adapt them to suit your fantasies.

'What kind of a person are you?' she mused. 'Well, you're very hard-working. And disciplined. And focussed. You're very successful—one of the top five investment bankers in the world, probably. People respect you—'

'You make me sound like a machine,' he said, and a note of something like bitterness crept into his voice.

Her voice softened. 'Oh, you're no machine, Adam—I can assure you of that.' She drew a deep breath, because this kind of thing wasn't easy to say, out cold, from the other side of the room—to a man who technically was your lover but who didn't remember a thing about you. 'You're a warm, giving lover.' She swallowed. 'The best lover I've ever had.'

As a testimony it was curiously lacking, and his mind was too tired and too befuddled to put his finger on exactly what it was.

Kiloran rose to her feet, an anxious look on her face. 'You've tired yourself out. You need to rest—'

'I'm not a damned invalid—'

'Well, yes, Adam,' she said firmly, coming to stand over him, a stern expression on her face. 'Actually, you are at the moment. And if you want to get better, you're going to have to do exactly as I say. The doctor told me to tell you that.'

'And if I refuse?'

'Then I'll hire a nurse to look after you. Someone like Sandy.'

He shuddered as he remembered Bossy-voice and imagined just how much *she* would crack the whip. He stared at Kiloran. There was something awfully appealing about such an ethereal-looking beauty coming on to him like a school-marm, but something here definitely did not compute. The felt curtain across his mind twitched by just a fraction. 'I'm not used to being told what to do by you, am I?'

She shook her head. 'Not by me, not by anyone.'

'Am I a tyrant, Kiloran?'

For a moment she forgot that he was an invalid. 'I'm not the kind of person who would go out with a tyrant,' she said drily. 'No matter how gorgeous he happened to be.'

'So you think I'm gorgeous, do you?'

It was, she realised, the first time that she had ever dared tell him *anything* about the way she felt. 'You aren't bad,' she said grudgingly. 'When your face isn't bruised and battered.'

He laughed. 'And I'm definitely not a tyrant?'

She pretended to consider this. 'Out of ten on the tyrannical scale, you would score a fairly modest rating of three.' She took a deep breath. He seemed to want to hear the truth, so surely she should give it to him.

'You're master of your own kingdom, Adam,' she said slowly. 'That's all. You live life entirely on your own terms.'

'Doesn't everyone?'

'Maybe not to such a great extent.'

He wanted to ask her more. Like why—but an overwhelming lassitude had started to seep into his bones. He closed his eyes and yawned.

'Now you really *are* going to bed,' she said severely.

The eyes flew open and there was a mocking look glinting in their depths which made Kiloran's heart turn over. Come back to me, Adam, she pleaded silently. Please come back to me.

Until the awful thought occurred to her that this new Adam was infinitely softer, more malleable, and far easier to relate to.

What if the old Adam came back and she found that

she was no longer prepared to cope with the relationship on the old terms?

But that was jumping ahead a step too far.

'Bedtime,' she said unsteadily.

For the next couple of days Adam recuperated, using
the most powerful method of recuperation which
existed.

He slept. For hours and hours at a time, tucked up
in Kiloran's big four-poster bed.

The first time she had taken him up there, she had
watched him carefully, to see if there was some kind
of reaction, some recognition that they had indulged
in so many pleasures of the senses here in this room.

But there had been none. No stirring of memory—
though that did not mean that he'd been indifferent to
the bed. No way. He had laconically raised his dark
eyebrows over tired eyes.

'Going to join me, Kiloran?' he yawned.

Kiloran bent her head to pull back the duvet, not
wanting him to see any trace of vulnerability, or sadness. What she wouldn't have given to have climbed
in beside him, wrapped her naked body next to his and
hugged him tight. Not wanting sex from him, just
closeness and wanting to give him comfort in return.

But she could not envisage a scenario where they
went to bed without making love—it was not that kind
of relationship. Adam loved sex. Well, so did she, for
that matter—especially with him—but sometimes she
found herself wishing for the intimacy which came
without having sex.

Not for them the lazy familiarity which came from
being totally relaxed in each other's company. There

had always been reservations, barriers between them. Her wishing he would let his guard down and him always being wary of giving too much away.

And although their relationship had been satisfying—there had never, not once, been a shared vision of a future together. With Adam it had never been more than what they had today. And while that made her appreciate what she *had* got, it also made her long for what she had not. Commitment—and that was one thing she would never get from him.

'I'll sleep next door for the time being. I think you need a little space,' she said lightly.

And so did she.

He pulled a face of objection, but he was too tired to object too much. He lay down on the bed and it felt like heaven.

'Okay,' he yawned. 'If you say so.'

But within a couple of weeks he began to show very definite signs of improvement—physically, at least. The sleep showed in the renewed brightening of his eyes and the familiar healthy glow of his skin. Often she took him outside, to sit in the restorative spring sunshine and to sit quietly in the haven which the garden provided. He was eating proper meals, too—the freshest, most delicious food that Kiloran could conjure up.

She put two plates of salmon down on the table one evening and a dish of new potatoes, and crunchy, bright green mange-tout. He smiled. 'Mmm. Who cooked this?'

'I did.'

The curtain twitched. 'But...you don't cook,' he said slowly.

She looked up from spooning a potato onto her plate. 'No, that's right. I didn't used to cook,' she agreed calmly.

'But you do now?'

'That's right. I quite like it, actually.'

'So what changed?'

She knew and he knew that they weren't in the remotest bit interested in her culinary conversion. This was a scent on the trail to recall. A trail that she yearned to complete and yet dreaded at the same time. 'You changed me.'

'*I* did?'

'Uh-huh.'

He stared at her, thinking how exquisitely pure the black velvet dress made her look. 'I complained?'

She shook her head. 'Not really. But you were obviously disapproving of the fact that I had servants and let them take care of me.'

He nodded, digesting this. So she had sought his approval, had she? Now why was that? 'Kiloran,' he said suddenly, and something in his voice made her go very still.

'Yes, Adam?'

'Just how do I know you?'

CHAPTER TWELVE

KILORAN put the spoon down with a hand which had suddenly begun to tremble and stared at Adam.

'How do I know you?' he repeated.

The doctor had told her this might happen; she was only surprised that it hadn't happened sooner. He had said that Adam's mind might naturally fill in some or all of the gaps by itself. Or that he might require assistance to do so.

The challenge was going to be telling him the truth. In confronting reality, however painful. For she was astute enough to recognise that by telling him this particular story, she would automatically give away a lot of her own feelings, if she was going to be brutally honest.

And that might frighten him.

'We met when my grandfather asked you to come and help our ailing business,' she said succinctly.

'How long ago?' he shot out.

She frowned. 'Almost nine months ago,' she said. Heavens above—was it really that long? And how ironic. It was longer than she had realised and yet it also seemed a ridiculously short time. But a human embryo could grow into full and sustainable life in exactly that time. 'Though I had actually met you years before.'

Now it was his turn to frown. 'When?'

'You worked here when you were eighteen,' she explained slowly. 'You grew up around here.'

'What about my mother?' he demanded. 'And father?'

Now she was in the most terrible dilemma. He had confided in her the truth about his background back at the beginning, back in that sunlit garden, which now seemed like a lifetime ago.

Could he take hearing this? Something which he normally chose to suppress.

'Keep nothing back,' the doctor had urged.

'But what if it's painful?' had been her response.

'The past often is, Miss Lacey. So is life. Protect against pain and there is no growth. And without growth, we die.'

'You never knew your father, Adam. And you haven't seen your mother since that summer, all those years ago.'

The felt curtain which was blocking recall now blew gently as a dark wind began to whisper across his mind. He was taken back to a morning long ago. A kitchen. Unwashed dishes in the sink and a note on the table. She wasn't coming back. She had gone. Gone and taken something with her. His hopes and his dreams and, unless he did something about it—his reputation.

Adam flinched and stared at her, his eyes dark with pain. 'I remember,' he said slowly. 'I remember. The house. The emptiness.' There was a long, raw pause. 'My mother had gone.'

She heard the finality in his voice and moved so that she was close enough to touch him, close enough to grip his forearm as if willing him to bring it all back to mind. 'But what else do you remember, Adam? What else?'

He shook his head. It was like swimming in cloudy water. Sometimes the light appeared on the surface, but then once again the mud obscured it. He stared into her green, green eyes and let his gaze travel down to lips as soft and as luscious as ripe strawberries.

And suddenly he did not want the past—he wanted the present, with all its infinitely more pleasurable associations. Why elect for pain when this beautiful woman was touching him, reminding him with dizzying recall just how wonderful pleasure could be? 'Kiss me, Kiloran,' he said softly.

She shook her head. 'Not now. It's too soon.'

'Kiss me,' he repeated, and something of his old mastery returned.

She moved her face closer, frozen in that position for one breathtaking moment, their eyes locked in glittering question. At that moment she had never felt closer to him.

'Now,' he murmured.

She lowered her lips onto his. A tender brush which became a tiny kiss. She felt his sigh warm against her and their lips parted by a fraction, melding in a sweet, exploratory kiss which felt like two teenagers trying one out for the first time.

It felt as if she had never really kissed him before, Kiloran thought with a jolt, and her breath quickened.

He reached his hand up to touch her neck, wonder-
ingly, as if he had never felt skin before, but in a way
he hadn't. His senses had needed to die in that coma
to spring to life as never before. The heavy throb of
desire beat its silken heat in his blood, but for once
there was no urgency to consummate. He wanted to
make this last all night.

He drew his mouth away. 'Let's go to bed.'

She shook her head, her heart thundering. 'You
aren't well enough.'

'Says who?'

'I don't know what the doctor would say—'

'Damn the doctor!' He scraped his chair back and
took her hand.

'Adam, we mustn't.'

'Kiloran,' he said simply. 'We can't not.'

She felt her cheeks flame, for the words seemed like
an avowal of something she had long hoped for, until
she reminded herself that they weren't. They were a
declaration of fact. And of intent. His body and his
mind had been very nearly lifeless, and now they
wanted to celebrate life itself in the most basic way
possible. Just as his hunger had returned to help him
heal, so too had another, different kind of hunger.

'Okay,' she agreed softly. 'Bed it is.'

She felt as shy as a virgin bride on her wedding
night as he took her by the hand and led her upstairs,
walking like a man who had never known a day's
sickness in his life, let alone one whose life had, just
a few weeks earlier, been hanging on by a thread.

The bedroom door closed behind them, Adam took

her into his arms, bending his head so that his mouth was very close to hers. 'What do you like me to do best?' he asked softly.

'Kiss me,' she murmured.

He needed no second bidding, groaning as he sweetly plundered her lips, on and on and on, as if the kiss were a fountain of life and he were drinking greedily from it.

And only when she felt as if he had sucked her dry did he draw down the zip of her dress, letting it fall into a pool of rich, dark velvet onto the ground.

He sucked in a low breath of appreciation as she stood before him wearing nothing but flimsy underwear of soft green lace, her golden-white skin gleaming like silk. Her breasts spilled over the low-cut bra and the matching knickers made her legs seem to go on and on forever.

He must have seen her like this before and yet it seemed as though he had never really looked at her. Never appreciated the satin fall of the blonde hair which tumbled all over her shoulders.

'Dear God,' he murmured. 'You are unbelievable. Unbelievable.'

'No, I'm real.' She began to unbutton his shirt. 'You're wearing all this, while I'm not wearing nearly enough,' she complained.

He gave a low laugh, sucking in his breath as her palms skated light, sensuous circles over his nipples. 'You're wearing too much, oh, Kiloran—' This as she unzipped his trousers and teased her fingertips over his straining hardness. He slid his hand between her thighs and her eyes widened in helpless pleasure as he began to move his fingertips against her. 'Like that?' he whispered.

'You obviously haven't lost all your memory,' she groaned. 'You know I do.'

'Maybe it's just instinct,' he husked.

Instinct made it sound too functional, she thought briefly. Her head tipped back and she moaned again with an unbearable feeling of expectation and excitement and yet it was tinged with a sensation of apprehension.

Sex had always been so wonderful between them, but she couldn't ever remember feeling quite this defenceless—as if it would be impossible to hide the way she really felt about him, deep down. What if she cried out her love for him at the height of it all?

'Come here and stop looking so worried,' he murmured as he drew her down onto the bed beside him. 'I'm the one who should be worried. What if the accident has left me being unable to make love?'

At the same time, their eyes were drawn to his naked body, where the very visible proof of how much he wanted to make love was clear to see.

'I don't think so.' She smiled, and nibbled at his ear lobe.

But it was different. He knew that. This was a test, but not just a test of his physical ability—there was something else going on and it perplexed him. He sensed Kiloran's reservations and he was damned sure that it had nothing to do with his skill as a lover. No, there was something else.

He stroked her breasts, which was infinitely easier than analysing something which seemed determined to evade him.

Kiloran sighed, wrapping her arms tightly around his back, smoothing the flesh which covered the powerful shoulders.

He moved his hands all over her body, as if reacquainting himself with familiar yet undiscovered landscapes, and she responded instantly, her heat moist and warm against his fingers.

'Take me,' she whispered, when the longing became unbearable. 'Take me.'

The unexpected and old-fashioned entreaty was like fire ripping through his veins. He moved on top of her, his hardness threatening to obliterate him if he didn't do something about it soon.

'Oh, Adam!' she cried as he pushed into her and filled her. He began to move and a kind of sob was wrenched from Kiloran's throat. 'Adam!' she whispered shudderingly.

For a moment he stilled, reluctant to stop when something was this amazing, but he sensed that this was not the way it usually was. He smoothed the hair back from her face and looked down into her eyes. 'Tell me,' he invited softly.

Never tell a man you love him, not unless he says it first, she thought. She bit the words back and shook her head. 'It feels so good.'

Now why on earth should her testimony disappoint him—make him feel strangely hollow? But then she had begun to move beneath him, her hips writhing in expert rhythm which took him up and beyond...

'Kiloran!' He choked her name out just as she began to moan and the feeling just went on and on and on until both were spent.

And afterwards they lay there, their arms wrapped tightly around each other, neither saying a word—though both for different reasons.

He lay there, watching the moon as it rose in the night sky to flood the bed with a kind of silver radiance. Could he live the rest of his life like this? he wondered. In touch with his present, but not his past. He sighed.

Kiloran turned onto her side. A sigh was a wistful, yearning thing—she had never heard him sigh before, she realised. 'Adam?'

He turned his face. Her hair was tumbling down over her breasts and in the moonlight she looked like some creature from another world. And maybe she was, for she inhabited his past more surely than he did. 'Mmm?'

'How do you feel?'

He pulled her against him, revelling in the collision of warm, soft skin and thinking that nothing could beat this. 'How do you think I feel? Pretty amazing.'

'I wasn't talking about the sex.'

Well, neither was he, but he registered her sudden defensiveness. Was she insecure, he wondered—and had he contributed to making her that way?

'You want an update on my state of recovery at this precise moment, do you, honey?' he drawled.

She shook her head. 'Not really. I mean, I presume that what we just did—'

'Make love, you mean?' he enquired helpfully.

Why was she blushing? Why did she feel about sixteen—with all those stupid, foolish dreams that sixteen-year-old girls had? Why, if she had a schoolbook right now, she would be writing his name on it and drawing a heart round it!

'Adam, you mustn't be flippant!'

'How am I being flippant?'

'You've been very ill. We've just made love and it was probably too soon.'

He captured her hand, guiding it slowly down the front of his hair-smattered chest, and beyond and heard her tiny little gasp. 'I don't think so, honey. The body recovers from trauma very quickly, it seems.'

'But what about the mind?'

He stared at the ceiling. The mind was a different matter. 'It's still blocked,' he admitted.

'Don't you care?'

'You mean, don't I *mind*?' He laughed, but opened his eyes again and saw the anxious look which had pleated her brow into a little frown. 'Kiloran, what can I do? I can't force it—it has to come when it comes, when it's ready to come.'

But they both became silent once more.

Right now he felt at peace, and something was nagging at him, telling him that it was an unusual state for him. What if he unlocked the door to his past and found it full of demons? Would he know this kind of easy peace again? And yet, a man could not live without a past, no matter how much it might haunt him.

With an effort, he forced himself to concentrate on their conversation during a supper they had not eaten.

The memory of the dirty kitchen and the note on the table came gritting back like sand being rubbed into his eyes.

'Kiloran,' he said slowly. 'I'd like to go back.'

She stilled. To London? 'Back where?'

'To the place where I grew up. I want to go back.'

CHAPTER THIRTEEN

KILORAN waited another couple of days before she took Adam to his childhood home. She told herself that was because he was still weak, that the shock might prove too much for him, and all this was true.

But she did not deny to herself that there was a self-seeking reason behind the delay. What if she took him back and memory came with it, snapping into clarity, like a blurred picture suddenly coming into clear and bright focus?

She had grown used to this new Adam and she couldn't help wondering if she would be able to tolerate the insecurity and the emotional repression which had been necessary to maintain a relationship with the old one.

The morning she chose was as perfect a spring morning as she could imagine. The sky was an eggshell blue, unclouded and peerless and pure. Birds sang with heartbreaking fervour in the hedgerows and the banks were studded with pale lemon primroses.

Spring, thought Kiloran—a time of rebirth. But birth was painful, nobody could deny that—just as they could not deny that it changed everything. Everyone. Nothing was ever the same again.

She shot a glance at Adam. He had recovered well, the indomitable strength and vitality of the man had served him well. Outwardly, at least, he looked the same as the man she had fallen in love with.

She narrowed her eyes. Though, on closer examination, maybe that wasn't quite accurate. He *had* changed. The grey eyes were no longer so restless. The glittering, predatory eyes of the shark had gone.

But a jolt to his memory might bring them back, surely? And the coldly ambitious Adam Black might re-emerge from the chrysalis of his coma.

'Ready?' she asked.

He drifted his hand over the silken-gold of her hair and followed it with the butterfly touch of his lips on the back of her neck. 'Maybe we should go back to bed for a while?' he murmured.

Kiloran closed her eyes, tempted. If there was one thing that Adam *had* recovered quickly, it was his prowess as a lover. 'But we've only just got up!' she objected.

'The doctor said that I was to rest as much as possible.'

'I think that your idea of rest and the doctor's are not quite the same thing.' Reluctantly, she pulled her neck away. 'Shall we walk or shall we drive?'

'Walk.'

'You won't get too tired?'

'Kiloran,' he sighed. 'I'm fine. You know, this isn't going to work if you continue to nurse me all the while.'

'I was only trying to help.'

'I know you were, honey, but the time has come for you to let go. I'm in good shape physically and I can take care of myself. And the rest I can deal with myself. I have to.'

Kiloran nodded, but she turned away on the pretext of getting a soft, woollen cardigan for the sunshiney spring day had a deceptive bite to the air. *Let go.* The two words chilled her right through and she was glad to snuggle into the cardigan. Already he was cutting her out. That was *without* any nudges to his memory.

But this wasn't about her and *her* feelings—it was all about Adam and what he needed to make him whole again.

And he would not be whole without memory, she realised sadly. She could not have a relationship with a man—especially not this man—on the superficial basis of a newly relaxed persona. That was only part of Adam.

True, he was softer and sweeter, but she couldn't keep him that way just for her benefit.

He needed to know who he really was and she needed to know whether he still wanted her once he had discovered that. And she him.

'Shall we go?' she asked.

The Lacey gardens had never looked more beautiful—the lawns were freshly cut and the scent of newly mown grass brought back a lifetime of different springs. For a moment she became the child who had run across these sunlit lawns and thought how uncomplicated life had seemed then.

Or had it?

Didn't memory always play tricks? Didn't it always look perfect when you looked back, your mind cleverly editing out all the bad bits? Wasn't that nature's way of making life seem bearable? Her mother's moods and erratic behaviour had affected the atmosphere in the house, but all Kiloran could remember was a happy little girl, running through the flowers.

They crunched their way up the gravel path to the sound of birdsong and the gentle whisper of the breeze as it rustled its way through the new leaves.

'You're very quiet,' observed Adam.

'Mmm.' She glanced up. Was it her imagination, or were the grey eyes already a little more distant? Would she, too, soon be nothing more than a memory to him? 'Can you remember the way?'

It seemed that he could, his feet taking him automatically on a route he had not trodden for years. Paths of familiarity were worn deep into the mind, he realised, and some things you found you knew on an unconscious level.

They passed the bus stop and he came to a halt. 'I caught the bus there,' he said slowly. 'To London. The day I left Lacey's.'

She nodded, seeing a contemplative look cross over his face. 'Tell me.'

He dug his hands deep into the pockets of his jeans. 'It was a grey day.' As grey as the wasteland of his coma. 'I had a pocketful of money I'd earned at Lacey's.' He remembered a feeling of lightness, of no longer being encumbered by the burden of debt, but there had been a feeling of emptiness, too. Now why was that—*why was that*?

There had been a girl on the bus. She'd had some

beads round her neck which had spelt 'love' and the kind of dress which should have ideally been worn at a ball—a floaty concoction of gossamer-gold which had contrasted with her raven-dark hair. She had been going to London, too, and she had shared her bag of fruit with him on the journey.

He had stayed with her for a month, maybe two, and for a while she had filled some of the emptiness he'd felt. But then he had moved on. He'd always kept moving. Like a shark, moving, moving, moving.

'And?'

Kiloran was looking at him expectantly and her sweet, innocent expression drove a knife of remorse through him. He must not hurt her, he realised. And he could. He could hurt her very badly. He kept the memory of the girl to himself.

'I went to London and made my fortune,' he said lightly. 'Just like Dick Whittington.'

'But you didn't have a cat, I presume?'

He laughed. 'No. No cat.'

'Here's the shop,' said Kiloran.

The village shop had changed—it had gone from selling mainly fresh vegetables and produce from local farms through to an ugly incarnation as a brightly lit and plastic supermarket. And now it was back to selling local produce. Kiloran glanced at the sign in the window which read: 'Organic vegetables and free-range eggs on sale here!' What goes around comes around, she thought.

Everything seemed so heavy with significance today, but maybe that was as it should be. By attempting to discover his own past, Adam was inevitably making her look to her own.

She had come full circle by moving back here, but she hadn't given any thought as to whether she would stay. She had never given a thought to the future before, but now she was beginning to realise that everyone had a part to play in shaping their own destiny.

Did she really want to spend the rest of her life at Lacey's? She asked the question, knowing that, deep down in her heart, she did.

His footsteps took him past the shops and beyond where the cottages were picture-box pretty with their fresh whitewash and their roses growing around the doors. And Adam recalled the nagging ache of envy. These were the places where real families lived. There had always been lights on in these houses, and families sitting around tables together, eating a meal. Glowing Christmas trees in the window. And he had been the boy outside in the cold.

Soon the houses became closer together. Here and there a drift of garbage floated by on the spring breeze and a group of boys stopped their chatter and stared at them with too-knowing eyes. He stared directly at one, saw the wariness and suspicion in the face of someone who had never known the innocence of childhood. I was that boy once, he thought.

They turned a corner and halfway down the road Adam stopped in front of a narrow terrace.

The house had changed. The front door was newly painted in a bright yellow colour. Not his choice, but at least someone had made an effort. On the window sill was a planter filled with a few straggly daffodils which matched the door colour. The flowers were dusty and in need of some water, but they lived—they *grew*. They gave hope.

The stone that was his heart stirred. 'It was here,' he said huskily. 'Right here.'

He stared down the narrow street and through a man's experienced and analytical eyes he saw for the very first time the other side of the story. His mother's.

What must it have been like for her? he wondered. He had been quick to judge and condemn and maybe that was natural after she had betrayed him. But what of her own struggle to survive—to clothe and to feed him?

He tried to imagine Kiloran—or any other woman he knew—in the same situation. Alone and pregnant, with no skills to find work and no access to child-minders. Things weren't a piece of cake for women even in these days, but back then being a single mother must have been a nightmare. Nothing but grinding poverty and condemnation from society.

Could he really blame his mother for using her only asset—capitalising on her youth and beauty to fruitlessly seek out a man who would love and provide for her?

Or judge her because the very nature of her circumstances had meant that the only men she'd come into contact with had simply not been cut out for that role.

And *he* had been a major factor in contributing to those circumstances, through no fault of his own. He had been born. A child binded and restricted you—

and all through his childhood she might not have been the best mother, but maybe she had been the best she *could* have been.

He glanced down at Kiloran, who was still staring at the house.

He saw her face and his mouth curved into a smile which held a trace of the old cynicism. 'Pretty tiny, isn't it, Kiloran?'

She felt her cheeks grow warm, but she turned her head to meet his gaze. 'Yes, it is. But big or small, it doesn't matter—it's what's inside a house that makes it a home.'

He heard something of her own wistfulness. Kiloran might have been rich, but her life hadn't been a bowl of cherries either. Her mother's behaviour had been reprehensible at times and it must have been deeply embarrassing to an impressionable young girl.

And at that moment he realised that where he had come from didn't matter; that the man he was today was what mattered. But what kind of man *was* he today? Would he like him? Would she? The questions crowded him with claustrophobia, and suddenly he knew he had to get away.

'Let's go,' he said abruptly.

'You don't want to knock?'

He turned to meet the innocent question in her eyes. 'Why would I?'

'Maybe they know where your mother—'

He shook his head. 'Kiloran—look around you. These houses are for people with transient lives, they always were and they still are.'

She rested her fingers lightly on his arm. 'Have you remembered any more?'

He shook his head, trying to clear it because the memory was there, gnawing away insistently at the corners of his mind. But something kept nudging it back.

They walked slowly back along a different path, and it was when they came to the old baker's that Adam stopped, staring in at the fake wedding cake which stood in the window, which had been there ever since he could remember.

And it was then the floodgates opened and everything came back, in a dark tide which swamped him.

'Adam?' She lifted her hand to his face and tentatively touched his cheek, seeing the sudden whitening of his face and the tension which had tightened his features. 'Adam, what is it?'

He shook his head, locked in some strange kind of limbo as past and present whirled together in a terrifyingly vivid kaleidoscope.

His mother had gone and he'd had no one—cut adrift and rudderless. As if his body were hollow and he had had to fill it with something.

She didn't know how long they stood there for, only that when Adam eventually nodded, as though something had been completed, he met her eyes and she knew without having to ask the question that his memory had returned. It was as if someone had flicked a switch.

'You remember?' she whispered.

'Oh, yes, I remember. That's the reason I went to

work at Lacey's. My mother had left debts. My reputation was worth nothing.'

'Adam—'

He shook his head. He couldn't take her sympathy or her understanding. Not right now. 'I'm fine.'

It was as though a shutter had come down, effectively keeping her out. She stared at him. 'Adam,' she whispered. 'Talk to me.'

'There's nothing to be said,' he said flatly.

She waited for a moment, her eye drawn to the dusty bride and groom who stood on top of the faded cake, seeming to mock the whole institution of marriage. 'What do you want to do now?' she asked quietly.

He gave a smile, but some of the softness had gone.

'I'd like to go back to Lacey's,' he said. 'And I want to make love to you.'

She understood that. The need to obliterate pain through the sweet oblivion of the senses. But although her body responded instantly, her heart felt wary. There was something different about him—it was as though someone had coated him with a hard, protective veneer.

All vulnerability had fled and been replaced by the passionate predator who felt a million miles away.

Not a word was spoken on the journey home. Adam seemed completely preoccupied with his thoughts and, on a rational level, Kiloran didn't blame him. If his memory had suddenly come back and he was sifting and filing information in his head, then what right had she to chatter on about inconsequential things? His face was closed and forbidding enough to stop her trying to ask him anything really important and she tried to tell herself that he would elaborate when he was ready.

But her throat was dry with dread and longing and when they arrived back at Lacey's he wordlessly took her straight upstairs, where he proceeded to take her clothes off so slowly and so teasingly that she came when he first touched her.

And couldn't miss the fleeting look of dark triumph in his eyes as he groaningly entered her while she was still pulsing.

He made love to her as if he were being judged on it—surpassing even his usual skill and finesse and Kiloran lost count of the times she shudderingly cried his name out loud. It was the most mind-blowing experience of her life, but yet it left her feeling that something was missing.

And when it was over, they lay together, coupled like sweat-sheened spoons, their frantic hearts racing.

'That was…' Kiloran swallowed. 'That was something else.' She thought of how long he had just spent making love to her. 'But, darling, you mustn't over-tire—'

'No, Kiloran.' He rolled over, so that he was lying on top of her once more, and his expression was hard, almost grim. 'Your nursing duties are completed, and I mean that. I give you leave of absence.'

Fear rose in her throat. 'What's happened, Adam? Why are you looking at me that way?'

'What way is that?'

How could she possibly say that his expression was no longer soft and giving? Not when this cool, sardonic flicker of interest looked far more like the man she was used to. He was blocking her and it seemed to be deliberate.

'How much have you remembered?' she asked slowly.

'Everything.' The one, stark word spoke volumes.

She sat up in bed, her heart sinking, knowing that she could not go back to the way things had been. It was impossible. And no matter how painful it was going to be, she could not accept a relationship on Adam's terms. It was not so much as second-best—it was probably as much as he *could* offer. But it was not enough. Not for her. She would live in fear of it ending, afraid to give as much as she wanted to for fear of frightening him away.

And no relationship could survive on fear.

'Do you want to talk about it?'

'And say what? That I recall exactly why I came to Lacey's in the first place? Your grandfather's kindness to me.'

'Your kindness to him in helping him out of a fix?'

He carried on as if she hadn't spoken. 'I know that I lived in America and about my new job. I know that I'm renting a flat in Kensington—'

'And us?' she ventured.

'Us?'

She thought that he spoke it like a word he was unfamiliar with. 'Yes, us.'

He smiled, but Kiloran thought that it was a cool

smile, even though he touched the tip of her nose with his lips.

'I know that we've been having a relationship and that it's a very agreeable relationship.'

Very *agreeable*? He made it sound like a piece of classical music playing on the radio!

'I see.'

He wondered if she did, but in the sweet afterhaze of making love his mind had been busy. 'Shall we get dressed and go and find ourselves a drink?'

If it had been anyone else, she might have thought he was searching for Dutch courage, but Adam was not the kind of man who needed alcohol to spur him on to say something, no matter how unpalatable.

She sensed that the end was coming, and that, if it was, she would face it calmly and with dignity. 'I'd love a drink,' she said lightly. *He* might not need courage, but she certainly did.

They dressed in silence, bending to pick up discarded pieces of clothing and shaking out the creases. Kiloran was aware as she climbed into her knickers that he was not watching her, the way he usually did. Feasting his eyes on her with an unashamed appreciation as she covered her body with clothes.

No, he seemed preoccupied as he zipped up his trousers and she caught him giving his wrist-watch a quick glance.

'What shall we drink?' she asked, once they were downstairs. Was there still a foolish part of her that thought he might suggest champagne, as if they were celebrating together?

'A very small Scotch, please.'

She nearly asked him whether he thought he should, but thought better of it. He had already told her un-equivocally that he did not want her to nurse him any more. And with her nurturing role gone, she felt oddly superfluous.

She never drank spirits, just poured herself a glass of wine and then sat down on one of the sofas, and waited.

She didn't have to wait long.

The grey eyes were narrowed as they looked at her. 'Kiloran, I have to go back,' he said.

'Back where?'

'To London.'

'You aren't going straight back to work?' she questioned, alarmed.

He shook his head. So that was the measure of his work-ethic, was it? That he would throw himself straight back into the thick of it when he had only regained his memory just a few hours earlier.

'Not straight away, no. I need to see a neurologist and get him to check me out.'

'And after that?'

'I haven't decided.'

The word *I* had nothing to do with the word *us*, did it? She wanted to say, *When will I see you?* But if he wasn't going to say, then neither was she going to ask. She wouldn't beg, or plead—and she would not ask for what was not freely given.

'When will you leave?'

He glanced at his watch once more. 'I can just about make the last train.'

'Or I could drive you in?'

He shook his head. 'Thanks, but no, thanks. It's sweet of you, Kiloran—but I've imposed on you for long enough.'

Imposed? Now he sounded like a weekend guest who had overstayed his welcome!

'You'd better hurry up and pack, then,' she said abandoning her barely touched wineglass. 'I can run you to the station at least.'

She waited while he went upstairs and packed the clothes which she had arranged to be sent from London. Just as she had arranged to have his mail delivered to his solicitor, in case there had been something urgent which Adam wouldn't have been well enough to deal with. And once he had started to make headway, there had seemed no need to disturb the rare opportunity for peace and quiet.

Yet there were so many questions she had never got around to asking because she hadn't wanted to tire him, or to add to his stress. It had never seemed the right time. She still didn't know why he had driven here when he wasn't supposed to.

She could ask him now, and if he knew then he would answer her truthfully, but suddenly she didn't want to know. What was the point?

He came downstairs, suitcase in hand.

'Ready?' she said brightly.

He thought how much he owed her. 'Kiloran,' he began.

But she pre-empted him. She couldn't bear it if he began to say stilted goodbyes—as if she were some aged old retainer who was about to retire. 'Don't say it, Adam, please—it isn't necessary.'

'I want to thank you from—'

'Don't *say* it,' she repeated angrily. 'Please! I don't need your thanks. I was pleased to do it. I would have done it for anyone.'

He nodded. Suddenly she seemed a million miles away. He could take her in his arms and kiss her better but wouldn't that only be postponing things? He couldn't live a jigsaw life, with one of the pieces missing. And that was how he felt right now. Something was missing.

'Well, if we're going to catch that train…'

Goodbyes were always difficult, she told herself. She hoped that the train would be on time and that she wouldn't be subjected to a long wait with him while she tried to bite back her tears.

But the London express screeched into the station bang on time, and, perversely, *that* didn't please her either.

'Goodbye, Adam.'

'Just come here.'

He pulled her into his arms and swiftly brought his mouth down for a kiss which went on for longer than either of them had intended. It was bittersweet and unbearably beautiful and it felt like a closure. And when he reluctantly raised his head in answer to the urgent whistle of the guard, his eyes were filled with something like regret.

'I'll ring you,' he whispered. 'Okay?'

When will you ring me? she wanted to say, but she could not place any more burdens on his shoulders. She was not going to play jealous or needy—in fact, she wasn't going to play anything. A relationship wasn't a game—and if you had to make it into one in order for it to survive, then maybe it wasn't worth keeping.

Perhaps she should make it easy for him. Tell him that there was no obligation and that she understood his need to get away. Would that show she had some pride left and ensure she would get over him more quickly? But wasn't that just thinking about *her* feelings, and not his?

She opened her mouth to say something, but nothing seemed right, and when the guard blew his whistle again she was both relieved and sad. The moment had come. He was going, only this time it was not like a normal farewell. 'Goodbye, Adam,' she whispered back.

He squeezed her tightly one more time and then climbed onto the train and waved at her through the grimy window, his grey eyes strangely sombre.

And she stood watching the train, not moving from that spot until long after it had disappeared.

CHAPTER FOURTEEN

AFTER he'd gone, Kiloran spent the evening wandering around the house like a lost soul, unable to settle to anything, and her heart nearly leapt out of her chest when the telephone began to ring.

She snatched it up. 'Hello?'

'Kiloran?'

'Oh, Adam!' She breathed a low sigh of relief, appalled to realise that she had half expected never to hear from him again. But that would have implied a lack of courage on his part, and he was certainly not lacking in courage. 'Are you okay?'

Okay? He looked around him, at the luxurious flat which was his home. It didn't feel like home. It felt like some gloriously appointed but sterile hotel suite. True, he didn't own it, but it was more than the fact that he was renting. There were no little bits and pieces which had stamped his personality on the place. And no photographs, he realised suddenly. No snapsnots of his life and all the memories which meant to make up that life. But who did he have to photograph, apart from a mother he didn't know was alive or dead? No girlfriend had ever meant enough to him for him to want to have her displayed in a silver frame, standing on a piece of furniture.

'I'm fine,' he said heavily.

'You don't sound fine.'

What did she expect? 'I'm tired, I guess.'

'There'll be no food in,' she said automatically.

'Kiloran, I'm a big boy now,' he reminded her softly.

And she wondered whether her nurturing role might have blown all hope away. For a big, strong man like Adam to have been so dependent on a woman— mightn't that threaten his masculinity? She had seen him at his weakest and most vulnerable and that might make her a thorn in his flesh, niggling away with the thought that for a while she had seen him helpless and stripped away of all defences.

'Well, I'm glad you're home safely,' she said guardedly.

'Yes.' There seemed nothing more to say and he felt an immense sense of sadness. 'I'll ring again.'

The words rushed out as she forced herself to say them. 'Don't feel you have to. Only when you're ready.'

'Yes,' he said thoughtfully. She was intelligent enough to know that a series of superficial phone calls would serve no purpose. To either of them. 'Take care, Kiloran.'

'And you.' But this time she really *did* doubt his words. She put the receiver down slowly. Oh, he probably *meant* them, but she doubted that he would ring tomorrow. Or the next day. He would ring when he was ready, and that might be when he decided to tell her that it was over.

For there could be no going back to how they had

been, and no going forward to a future he had never promised her. Which left them in some kind of emotional limbo which was not a good place to be.

But she felt some of her own strength and resolve returning. That night she slept with surprising soundness and awoke refreshed, even though her heart was aching. The responsibility of looking after him and the worry of whether or not he would recover had been more of a strain than she had realised.

She couldn't mope around the place mourning something that had never been more than a hopeless dream. She needed to move on—that was what the self-help books always told you.

And moving on wasn't easy when you had little desire to do so. When staying put in an increasingly distant illusion seemed the more preferable option. But she found an inner core of strength and determination and she slowly eased herself back into normal living. She owed it to herself to do so.

At least she had plenty with which to occupy herself—things which only she could deal with and which she had neglected while she had been caring for Adam.

The letting-out of the function rooms was flourishing, and soon they began getting bookings from further afield.

Grandfather even rang from Australia to tell her that they had read about Lacey's in a financial section of one of Sydney's newspapers.

'Before we know it, the soaps will be a sideline!' he joked.

But she had good news on that side as well. 'I don't think so, Grandfather. We've been approached by one of the big department store chains,' she told him. 'They want us to design an exclusive soap especially for them.'

'I'm impressed, Kiloran,' he said. 'You've done well.'

'And we have Adam to thank, of course.'

'Ah, yes,' her grandfather sighed. 'The boy wonder.'

She didn't tell him about Adam's accident. No point in trying to explain why she had been looking after him; he hadn't known about their relationship and there was no earthly reason to tell him—not now, when it looked increasingly certain that it was over.

She forced herself to keep busy, and not to hang around the telephone like a love-struck schoolgirl.

She even went out a couple of times, but her heart wasn't in it, though as the weeks passed it became easier to sit in a pub with people she had known since her schooldays, and tell herself she was having a good time.

Spring turned to early summer and there had still been no word from Adam. She was vacillating between calling him some very uncomplimentary names underneath her breath and telling herself that the man was recovering from a major trauma, for heaven's sake, when the telephone rang. Some sixth sense told her that it was him even while experience told her to gear herself up for the inevitable disappointment.

It was a Sunday morning, and the house was utterly

peaceful. She was drinking coffee on the terrace when she heard the ringing and she put her cup down.

It won't be him, she said to herself, just as she did every time it rang.

But this time it was.

'Kiloran?'

Her heart was pounding so loudly that it seemed to deafen her voice and for a moment she could hardly speak.

'Adam!' She put just the right amount of pleased delight to hear him in her voice. Not enough to frighten him away, or to make him think that she wouldn't be able to cope with whatever he had decided.

And besides, it wasn't just his decision. She had done a lot of thinking herself. She knew that she needed to be a lot more proactive than she had been before. If Adam was offering a relationship on the same terms as before, then she was going to have to say thanks, but no, thanks. It might temporarily break her heart, but it would have to be done.

Because she was worth more than that. A relationship where you were constantly having to hide the way you felt about someone could never be a truly honest relationship, and Adam had always been a champion of honesty—surely he would understand that?

He thought how distant she sounded. 'How are you?'

'*I'm* all right—more to the question, how are *you*?'

It struck him how inadequate language could be

sometimes. 'Better. Much better. Can I come and see you?'

As if he had to ask! But he *had* asked, and rather formally too—and maybe that meant something. 'Of course you can come and see me. When?'

'Are you busy now?'

'As in right now?' Her heart began to thunder. 'I'm eating toast and honey, as it happens—but where are you calling from?'

'My mobile. I'm at the end of your drive.'

And she was still in her dressing-gown!

'Thanks for the warning!'

'I'll see you in two minutes.'

He had lost nothing of his cool imperturbability, she noted as she thumped the receiver down and ran out to the cloakroom, where she washed her face and hands and dragged a hairbrush through her hair.

She stared into the mirror. Her naked face made her appear vulnerable, but inside she *felt* vulnerable. She pulled the dressing gown closer and knotted it tightly. It was a silken affair of jade, richly embroidered with birds of paradise, and it fell to just below her knees. Far less revealing than a summer's dress, but underneath it she was naked and that made her feel even more vulnerable.

She heard his car splitting the silence and she walked slowly towards the door, opening it just as he had lifted his hand to ring the bell, and their eyes met in a long moment.

And the last, lingering memory of the man who had lain so desperately ill disappeared once and for all, because it was impossible to connect him with the man who stood before her now.

Adam was back, recovered and virile and heart-stoppingly gorgeous. He looked the same and yet he looked different, but maybe that was because he had once been hers to touch and he now seemed untouchable. She wanted desperately to kiss him, but would have no more dared to put her arms around him and do so than she would to have shut the door in his face.

'Hello, Adam,' she said softly, amazed at how calm her voice sounded when inside her thoughts were racing.

He had expected to feel displaced when he returned here and his expectation had borne fruit. She looked like some luscious piece of exotic fruit in the embroidered gown, her hair as richly golden as the sun. Through the satin which clung to her slender body, he could see the curves of breast and hip, the indentation of her waist and the slight swell of her belly.

He thought of the times he had cushioned his head on that belly—an act sometimes more intimate than sex itself—and acknowledged that it seemed as if it had happened in another life.

'Hello, Kiloran.'

'You're looking good. I mean, you're looking well—fully recovered.'

'I feel it.' He raised a dark eyebrow. 'Aren't you going to invite me inside?'

'Of course!' She opened the door wide and as he walked into the hall she thought that the fact he had had to ask spoke volumes about the distance which had grown between them. As did the fact that he hadn't touched her—and the coolly remote look on his dark face which showed no inclination to do so. She faced him awkwardly. 'Where shall we go?'

He wondered how she would react if he suggested the bedroom, but, while that wasn't quite the last thing on his mind, that wasn't the reason he had come here today. 'Is it warm enough to sit outside?'

'I think so. Shall I make us some coffee and bring it onto the terrace?'

But he didn't want social ritual. He didn't even particularly want coffee. He shook his head. 'Not unless you really want some. I'm fine.'

'So am I.'

He had forgotten how beautiful the gardens were, how at peace it was possible to feel in such a rural idyll. But he shook himself out of his reverie to meet the question in her beautiful green eyes.

'What have you been doing?' she asked.

'I got checked out by the doctor.' He smiled. 'Totally clean bill of health.'

She looked at his strong, hard physique—the black hair ruffled very slightly by the light breeze and the grey eyes gleaming. She thought that you wouldn't have needed to be a doctor to give him the green light. 'That's good.'

'Mmm. And I've made a career change, too.' He looked at her. 'I'm acting in a consultancy capacity. And doing some teaching,' he added, waiting for her reaction.

'Teaching?' Her eyes widened. 'As in times-tables?'

He smiled. 'Not quite. I've helped set up a business school for underprivileged kids—it's being funded by some of the bigger banks. They've asked me for some help in designing the curriculum and I discover that I enjoy a little hands-on work as well.' He smiled. 'I seem to work best with the highly talented people with a slight—how shall I put this?—attitude problem! No prizes for guessing why.'

'No.' She smiled at him.

'You don't seem surprised,' he observed, thinking that she still seemed a long way away from him—as though a thick wall of glass divided them.

'That's because I'm not,' she answered quietly. 'I knew you'd have to change direction—and I'm glad that you haven't chosen just another avenue for making more money.'

'How did you know, Kiloran?'

She sighed. For an intelligent man, he could be so dense sometimes. 'You didn't need an accident to see that you were driving yourself too hard for things you neither wanted nor needed. All the signs were there, Adam—it's just that you chose not to see them.'

'Yet you never said anything.' He caught her in the soft grey light from his eyes. 'Did you?'

'Say anything? To *you*?' She gave a hollow laugh. 'If I'd tried to tell you that—tell you anything—you would have hit the roof—'

'Ah, so I *was* a tyrant, after all?'

She thought about it. 'I guess you were. A little. And anyway, even if I *had* told you, you would never have listened.'

'Ouch,' he said quietly. 'If a man needs his ego boosting, then a conversation with Kiloran Lacey is ill advised.'

'You,' she said firmly, 'definitely do not need your ego boosting!'

'No. I guess I don't.'

She shifted slightly in the chair, so that the jade silk clung like honey to her thighs, and a pulse began to tap out a hungry little beat at his temple.

'Adam?'

He tried not to dwell on the fact that he was pretty sure she was naked beneath the robe. 'What?' he questioned huskily.

She saw the darkening of his eyes and knew what was on his mind. But that wasn't important. This was. A lot hinged on his reaction to this next question. 'Did you find your mother?'

His stilled and his eyes narrowed. Had he never noticed her perception before, or had she just kept it hidden away? 'I don't remember telling you that I intended to.'

'You didn't. But I knew that you would think about it.'

He gave a wry smile. 'You know me very well, Kiloran.'

But she wasn't going to take credit for a closeness he had always denied her. 'It just seemed the next, natural step and, to be honest, being you—I wasn't sure whether or not you would take it.'

'I didn't want to,' he admitted slowly. 'And in a way, it might have been easier if I hadn't.'

'You didn't find her?'

'Yes and no.' He saw her confused look. 'It wasn't easy, but I eventually traced her to Wales. She'd joined some kind of commune there. She had another child.' He paused as he heard her suck in a breath. 'I have a half-sister, Kiloran.'

She heard something in his voice. Something like pride and possession. He had a family after all, she realised. The one thing he had never had, for all his wealth and power. 'And you've met her?'

'Clever woman,' he murmured and then he allowed a smile to break over his face. 'Yes, I've met her—and my young nephew. Actually—' and his face took on an unbelievably soft expression '—he looks the image of me at the same age. He's a terror,' he added indulgently.

She digested this. 'So you've found some roots, Adam—someone to call your own?'

He nodded. 'My sister is a single parent, living in a high-rise flat in Cardiff.' He saw her face. 'Yes, I know—history repeating itself. But I want her to have more than that—and I'm in a position to be able to do something about it.'

Of course he was. 'And your mother?' she asked slowly.

There was a pause. 'She died seven years ago.' He saw her stricken expression. 'It's okay, Kiloran. I felt sad, yes, but more than that—a kind of regret, that I hadn't had the courage or the insight to seek her out before.' Because he had shut all his emotions away— locked them behind a high wall.

And Kiloran had started to tap away at that wall, chipping away at the brickwork, making him take a look at himself in a way that no one else had ever done.

Maybe he hadn't needed a knock on the head to force him to look deep within himself. It might have taken longer, but might not Kiloran have managed it all by herself?

'Life's too short for regrets,' she observed.

'I know.' His voice was very soft. 'That's why I've had to let them go.'

Her breath caught in her throat and she was alarmed at the selfishness of her next thought.

Why was he here today? What did he want? But equally importantly—what did *she* want? And she knew that without even having to stop and think about it.

She wanted a proper loving, caring and equal relationship—and if she couldn't have it with Adam, then she didn't want him. She might never find it with someone else, but no longer was she going to accept half measures. Living a life only half lived.

'Oh, Adam, why did you come here today?'

Had he thought that this was going to be easy? But nothing worth fighting for was easy. 'Because I've missed you,' he said huskily. 'Don't you know that?'

Her face did not betray her pleasure. The old Kiloran would have leapt on that with all the appetite of a starving animal, but the new Kiloran accepted it simply as a compliment, not a passport to the future. 'That's nice.'

'Nice? *Nice?*' He got to his feet, suddenly forbidding. 'Is that all you've got to say?' he demanded.

It was somewhat reassuring to see that not all of the old Adam had been replaced by the more caring, sharing version. The glitter in his grey eyes reminded her of his mastery, and a shiver ran the length of Kiloran's spine as she felt the slow, honeyed rush of desire.

'What do you want me to say, Adam? That I'm falling over myself with gratitude?'

'A little genuine pleasure would help!'

'Why have you come back? Just to tell me what you've been doing? To show me how well you look? To pick up where we left off—'

'No.'

'No?' She couldn't quite eradicate the alarm from her voice.

He shook his head. 'I don't want to pick up where we left off. I'd like to start again.'

She stared at him.

'To start again,' he repeated. 'With you. Only properly, this time. If that's what you want.'

'Why?'

The words came out—new for him, but old as time. 'Because I love you.'

She stilled, wanting to believe yet not quite daring to.

He wanted to touch her, but somehow it seemed important that he didn't. Not yet.

'Men spend their life fighting it and running away from it. Especially men like me. But I'm sick and tired of running. Somehow when I met you, the race no longer seemed important. I love you, Kiloran. You're beautiful and clever and kind and caring. You make me feel strong and yet powerless in equal measures. I'm in your thrall—I can't stop thinking about you and that much hasn't changed since the moment I first met you.'

A slow smile softened her lips. 'Oh, Adam.'

'Did I ever tell you how much I admire you for the way you've turned this place around?'

But enough was enough. She had heard his declaration, seen the evidence of it in his eyes. Now she wanted him close—as close as a man and woman could be. 'Are you going to spend the rest of the day paying me compliments?'

'If you want me to.'

'I can think of some better things I'd rather be doing.'

He raised his eyebrows in mock innocence. 'Such as?'

'Don't you think it's about time you kissed me instead?'

'Oh, honey.' He gave a low, growling laugh of anticipation. 'I've been thinking of nothing else.'

He drew her into his arms and it felt like coming home as he touched his mouth to hers, brushing his lips against hers in tantalising rhythm. It was slow and tender and Kiloran felt tears begin to prick at the back of her eyes.

'I love you, too. So just take me to bed, will you? Now,' she said shakily. 'Don't say another word. Just show me.'

EPILOGUE

KILORAN slumped onto the sofa and wiped the back of her hand across her forehead. 'If I see another cricket ball within the next five years, it will be too soon,' she said darkly.

'You've got a pretty good overarm,' Adam mused. 'For a woman!'

A cushion went flying across the sitting room and hit him in the ear. 'Ouch,' he murmured. 'You're pretty accurate as well!'

'Mess with me at your peril, Black!'

'I wouldn't dare.' He shot her an indulgent look. 'Jamie loves you, you know.'

She basked in the warm approbation in his eyes. 'Well, I love him too,' she said. 'Even if he *does* wear me out—your nephew is a very lovable child.'

'Yes,' he said thoughtfully.

Jamie and his mother had just been to spend the weekend with them at Lacey's, and they had had a perfect weekend, he reflected—this somewhat bizarre, extended family of theirs.

'Grandfather loves him, too,' remarked Kiloran. 'He loves reading him the books he used to read me when I was little.'

'Mmm.' He caught the trace of wistfulness in her voice and knew what had caused it. Her grandfather had grown noticeably frail in the last year. He suddenly looked a very old man indeed and the sands of time were running out for him. Adam put his newspaper onto the floor and frowned. Had it really been a year?

'It's been a year, you know, honey,' he observed softly.

Her mouth softened. 'I know it has. Just think, a whole year.'

A year of bliss—of living and loving together. Adam still kept a flat on in London, but these days he hardly used it and when he did—Kiloran was at his side.

The 'school' had excited a great deal of interest in the normally cynical press—it had completely smashed the stereotype for the public to discover that mercenary investment bankers really did have beating hearts beneath their hard, mercenary exteriors! These days, Adam was invited to lecture all over the world. A lot of the invitations he turned down, sending someone in his place—but some he accepted, and took Kiloran with him and they saw something of the world together.

Eddie Peterhouse had finally been run to ground in Singapore, where he had been planning an escape to some remote and beautiful island in the middle of the Indian Ocean.

'He wouldn't have survived there for a minute,' Adam had remarked drily. 'He likes his home comforts too much.'

He certainly did. He had managed to work his way

through almost all the money he had stolen from Lacey's, but Kiloran had been philosophical about it. Money was only money, after all. In the grand scheme of things it didn't matter a bit.

And they didn't miss it. The company had gone from strength to strength—which might have had something to do with the fact that Adam was now, officially, a director and a major shareholder—having bought out Aunt Jacqueline and Julia for a generous and substantial sum.

'Kiloran?'

She looked at him. 'Mmm?'

'Come over here.'

'Why?' she questioned innocently, but the darkening of his eyes told its own story.

'Come here,' he reiterated silkily.

They were equals now, in every way which counted—but he could still be the commanding lover she had first fallen head over heels in love with.

She went to him, nestling comfortably into his lap, and sighing with pleasure as she began to play with his hair.

He kissed her gently and lingeringly on the mouth. 'God, I do love you,' he sighed.

She knew he did, he never stopped telling her, and it was as though, having rejected love for all his life, then having found it, he never took it for granted. He had embraced love with the zeal of the convert!

She kissed him back. 'Want to go to bed?' she whispered.

He shook his head.

'You *don't*?'

He tapped the end of her nose with his fingertip in mock-reproachful gesture. 'Not yet, my insatiable little honey!' The fingertip strayed to her forehead, where he pushed away a stray strand of silken hair, and smiled at her tenderly.

'You never did ask me why I was on the way to see you from the airport the night of the accident, did you?'

She shook her head. 'No, I didn't.'

'Why not?'

She shrugged. 'At first I guess I thought it was just because you just wanted sex—'

'Well, there *was* that, of course,' he said gravely.

Kiloran thought how much freedom real love could give you. If he had said that to her before she had known how much he cared about her, then she would have been a blubbering mass of insecurity!

'I thought so!' She pursed her lips up like a school-marm and basked in the answering spark in his eyes. 'Then I didn't want to overload you with any more memories of that night. I didn't think it would do you any good.'

She always thought of him, he realised. Her heart was good and kind and true—the spoilt little rich girl a figment of his imagination—though Kiloran herself frequently denied that. 'You made me look around and grow up,' she'd told him once. And maybe he had. Maybe that was what the best relationships were all about—you helped each other to grow.

'So why did you?' she asked him.

'You don't seem as curious as I thought you'd be.'

'That's because I'm secure now and, even if it was a terrible reason, I could live with it!'

'But it wasn't a terrible reason,' he said seriously. 'I had missed you more than I expected to—and I'd been foul to you. I was running scared of what was happening to me and then suddenly, as I was driving out of the airport, I realised how empty my life was. How I could lose you.' He gave a short laugh. 'I wonder what would have happened if I hadn't had the accident—if things would have worked out as wonderfully as this?'

'We can't know that,' said Kiloran tenderly. 'The romantic side of me thinks that things could have been good—but never as good as this,' she added, and then nodded. 'Because things happen for a reason, Adam—I really believe that.'

'Will you marry me?' he asked suddenly, knowing that he wanted to commit to her while her grandfather was still alive.

The romantic in her had been longing for this, too—no matter how much she told herself that things were perfect as they were.

'Oh, yes, please,' she whispered, and wrapped her arms around him as tightly as if she would never let him go, until he began to gently disentangle them. 'Not right now, my love,' he said sternly. 'I have something I want to give you.'

A ring, she thought happily as he disappeared out of the room, and wondered what kind of ring it would be. Knowing Adam's exquisite taste, it could be a simple, perfect diamond—or there again, he might have gone for something rare and unusual. Emeralds and seed-pearls, say.

But when Adam returned, carrying a large, brown-paper-wrapped rectangular object, Kiloran blinked.

'Big ring!' she joked.

He gave her a lazy smile. She would get the ring later. In bed. 'Come and open it.'

But the moment she began to rip the paper away, she realised exactly what it was and sat back on her heels, dazed and exhilarated to see the familiar etching, and the erotic, economical lines of the bathing woman.

She stared up at him, tears pricking the backs of her eyes. 'Why, Adam?' she asked tremulously. 'Why did you buy it back?'

'I never let it be sold,' he admitted. 'I bought it for myself, or so I thought. It took me a long time to realise that I'd really bought it for you, Kiloran.' He held his hand out to her and she took it. 'Come on, honey,' he said softly. 'Let's go and tell your grandfather the good news.'

HER BOSS'S
MARRIAGE AGENDA

by

Jessica Steele

Jessica Steele lives in the county of Worcestershire with her super husband, Peter, and their gorgeous Staffordshire bull terrier, Florence. Any spare time is spent enjoying her three main hobbies: reading espionage novels, gardening (she has a great love of flowers) and playing golf. Any time left over is celebrated with her fourth hobby, shopping. Jessica has a sister and two brothers and they all, with their spouses, often go on golfing holidays together.

Having travelled to various places on the globe researching background for her stories, there are many countries that she would like to revisit. Her most recent trip abroad was to Portugal where she stayed in a lovely hotel, close to her all-time favourite golf course.

Jessica had no idea of being a writer until one day Peter suggested she write a book. So she did. She has now written over eighty novels.

CHAPTER ONE

ERIN was in the habit of waking early. Dawn was just breaking on that Monday when she awoke, and while knowing she would not go back to sleep again she let her thoughts drift.

She was getting used to living and working in London now, albeit that her job was only temporary. A month ago she had been living in the tiny village of Croom Babbington, with her father, in the house she had lived in all her life.

Her parents had divorced when she had been five years old, her mother declaring she'd had enough of domesticity. She had walked out of their Gloucestershire home. That her mother had soon fallen into the domesticity trap and married again shortly after her divorce was neither here nor there—two years later Nina, as she preferred Erin to call her, had walked out of that marriage too. 'Never again!' she had vowed.

Nina had stuck to it too. Though that had not precluded her from having a string of admirers. Erin thought of her with love and affection. Nina had not abandoned her entirely, but, now living in Berkshire, she would make a point of coming to see her every two or three months. Erin did not go to Berkshire to visit with her mother. For one thing, Erin's father would not allow it.

Unbelievably he was still coldly bitter, seventeen years later, that the woman he had married had walked out on him and he did not want his daughter growing up 'wild' like her mother. For another thing, while Erin knew there was a bond of love between her and Nina, her vain mother had no intention of anyone in her circle knowing that she had a daughter. Particularly when as Erin had grown up she had blossomed into a blonde-haired, violet-eyed, something of a beauty too. Erin had learned not to mind that her mother did not want her to visit, though life was never dull when Nina was around.

However, it was probably because life with her strict father was a touch repressing that she had started to think that surely there should be more to life than getting up in the morning and going to a dull going-nowhere sec-retarial job. Erin had immediately felt guilty for that thought, because he had been a wonderful father, always there to comfort and counsel.

It had been his idea some years previously that she undertake a course of business studies combined with secretarial training. He had suggested it after one Sunday when her mother had breezed in, kissed his cheek re-gardless that he froze at such contact, and blithely told him, 'I'm taking Erin out to lunch. You don't mind?' she'd asked as an afterthought.

That night he had suggested that there would always be work for personal assistants. While financially there was no need for her to work—he had inherited wealth which he added to by shrewdly dealing in stocks and shares—it would, he'd said with a smile, keep her out of mischief.

Erin had trained hard, worked well, and found her first job exceedingly boring. Six months ago she had changed jobs and gone to work for Mark Prentice.

She could not have said she found that job any more scintillating than the job she had left, but when she had been working for Mark for a couple of months life had suddenly started to pick up. Mark had asked her out. She had thought he was seeing someone else, but she had obviously got that wrong.

She'd dated before, but her father always insisted that any male friend should come to the house to call for her. Which meant that while they were given a grilling before being allowed to take her out, Erin was given a grilling when she arrived back home—her strict father wanting to know in detail everything that had gone on.

She knew that her father loved her, and that he was still afraid she might turn out 'wild'. But, while it was true she had inherited some of her mother's genes, she had also inherited some of his too. And while she might feel a healthy interest in experimenting, Erin had no intention of losing her virginity to just anybody.

Mark had been happy enough to call at the house for her, but not so happy when, returning her home, her father had been up waiting, with no intention of going to bed until her escort had departed. Nor, Mark had found out, was Erin interested in staying overnight at his place.

Her romance with Mark Prentice, Erin had discovered, was not to last long. She had still been working for Mark six weeks ago. She had not seen him the previous evening, and had been busy beavering away when Dawn Mason, an ex-girlfriend of his, had sauntered into her office with the tie he had worn the day before dangling from her fingers.

'I'll just take this through to Mark,' she'd said, adding archly, 'He left it at my place last night.'

Erin was so stunned she didn't say a word—then. She did ten minutes later, though, when, clearly having let Dawn out through his other door, Mark came in to see Erin.

'Did you stay at Dawn Mason's place last night?' Erin asked directly—fully expecting him to deny it.

'I—um—yes,' he had the decency to admit.

'You—didn't...?' She couldn't finish it.

'Well, *you* wouldn't!' he returned defensively.

And that was when Erin discovered that she was neither her father nor her mother, but a person in her own right—and not the rather quiet mouse she had sometimes suspected she might be.

Without more ado she got up from her chair, picked up her jacket and shoulder bag, and told Mark Prentice, 'Perhaps Dawn Mason would like to do your typing for you as well,' and walked out of her job.

She did not regret her decision to leave her job, and in fact felt quite proud of that spurt of spirit that had decreed she wasn't going to meekly sit there and take any sort of nonsense.

A week later, however, and she was starting to feel that life was just a tiny bit dull. She had an allowance from her father, so did not need to work, but she applied for other jobs, and could not help feeling that other young women of her age must be having a much better time than she was having.

A day after that and she was starting to believe that they probably had a much better time because they probably weren't virgins. Well, she decided, she could jolly well do something about that, and would—at the first opportunity!

And then she remembered her father. How could she? How could she possibly? He had always insisted that she be honest with him. So how could she come home and tell him what she'd been up to?

Another two gloomy days passed—and then something happened that was to change her world completely.

She met Charlotte Fisher. There were two large houses on the edge of the village. Erin and her father lived in one of them; Charlotte Fisher and her parents had at one time lived in the other. Charlotte was a few years older than Erin, but the two had liked each other and had got on well. But Charlotte and her family had left the area five or six years ago, so it was a complete surprise for Erin to bump into her at the village post office.

'Charlotte! What are you doing here?' she exclaimed.

'Erin!' Charlotte beamed, and, post office business forgotten, they were soon chatting away as though Charlotte had never left. Charlotte filled in that her parents still lived in Bristol but that she now lived in London and was shortly to be married. 'Gran still lives here, and I've brought Robin to introduce him to her. Can you come and have a coffee with us?' she invited. 'I've only popped out to get Gran some stamps she needed.'

Erin declined the invitation, guessing that Charlotte's grandmother would want Charlotte and her fiancé all to herself for the few hours they would be there. But she and Charlotte ambled to the corner of the street, catching up on each other's news.

'Did you start that business course?' Charlotte asked. 'I remember you were thinking about it around the time the removal vans turned up at our old house.'

Erin nodded. 'Started and finished. I'm between jobs at the moment, though,' she confided.

'What a pity you don't live in London.' Charlotte remarked. 'I could do with some help.'

'And I could do with a change,' Erin commented lightly.

And suddenly Charlotte was taking her up on her comment, telling her that she was in textiles, in a small-ish way, and did her own paperwork, but what with the wedding coming up she was so far behind it was a nightmare. 'It would only be temporary, to get me out of the muddle I'm in, but I'd love it if you'd come and help me out! Do say you'll come?' she urged.

And at once Erin felt a rush of excitement at the idea. That excitement mingled with a sense of relief that here was a chance to get away from the utter dullness of her present existence. 'I'd love to,' she answered. She responded enthusiastically—but even as she was speaking she was suddenly swamped by the thought that her father would frown on the notion. Charlotte, too, it seemed, had just remembered him.

'Oh! Your father!' she exclaimed. 'Will he let you come? Is he still vetting everyone you meet and everything you do?'

It came as a bit of a shock to Erin that outsiders were aware of how watchful her father was over her. But at the same time she felt instantly disloyal to him for allowing Charlotte to say such a thing unchecked. But then again this new and spirited person that had sprung to life in her ten days ago was starting to twitch again, that the whole village seemed to think that she could not take a decision unless her father agreed.

'Oh, I'm sure he won't mind,' answered she who had never spent a night anywhere when she wasn't under the same roof as him. She knew in advance that to even think of moving away to London, even if it would be only temporary, was a non-starter. 'But he wouldn't be very happy if I left home to live in a bedsit somewhere.' Erin started to retreat. 'And to rent what he'd consider a decent flat in London would cost the earth. I just couldn't let him pay.'

'I have it!' Charlotte exclaimed. 'And it would be doing us both a favour.' Hurriedly she went on to explain that when she had left her Bristol home for London her father had thought much the same as Erin's father, and so had bought her a tiny mews place. 'It's only very tiny, a small apartment, really, but I've been dithering about what to do about it. I've been unsure about selling it, and I feel a bit nervous about renting it out to someone I don't know. But, Erin, you'd be ideal!'

Erin felt another rush of excitement, the idea beginning to take root. Though she tried for calm as she began to point out, 'You'd want a London rent...'

'No, I wouldn't,' Charlotte denied. 'Just a token rent, if you insist. But you'd be more of a caretaker for me— which would give me space to decide what I want to do with it. It's only poky, compared with the room you're used to, but I fell in love with it straight away and I'm sure you will too. Do say you'll come?'

Already Erin was ninety percent of the way there— Mrs Johns, their housekeeper, had been with them for years and would continue to look after her father. 'If it's so small, will it be big enough for both of us?'

'Oh, I'm seldom there!' Charlotte replied cheerfully. 'To be honest, I spend most of my time at Robin's place. And with the wedding coming nearer and nearer, and my mother panicking we'll never be ready in time, when I'm not at Robin's I'm down in Bristol. Now, do say yes?'

'Er—may I let you know?'

Charlotte at once gave her several phone numbers. 'I know I've rather dropped it on you. It's a surprise to me too.' She grinned. 'But if I'm not at work, or you can't get me on my mobile, ring me on Robin's number—but only if the answer's yes.'

They parted company and Erin, her head full of her meeting with Charlotte, returned home to be greeted by her father, who reminded her that she had not got him the padded envelope she had gone to the post office for.

'I'll go back,' she said. 'I—er—met Charlotte Fisher.'

'Charlotte Fisher? Good heavens! Charlotte Fisher who used to live next door?'

Erin relayed how Charlotte had returned to introduce her fiancé to her grandmother—and the rest of their conversation.

'You told her you'd like to go?' he enquired, not sounding anywhere near as shocked and stern as Erin had anticipated.

'I wouldn't mind. It would only be temporary,' she added hastily. 'I—um—thought you'd be upset.'

'I admit I'm not keen on the idea, but in all truth I expected when you turned twenty that you might soon want to stretch your wings a bit and want to leave home.'

'You did?' Erin was astonished.

'I've done my best to protect you, but I accepted some while ago that I would be unlikely to keep you with me for ever.'

Again Erin was surprised, and touched. 'Oh, Dad,' she said softly.

But that shared moment of empathy was as much as Leslie Tunnicliffe would allow, and he abruptly went on to practicalities. And Erin discovered that he was not yet ready to let go his protection of her when he declared, 'Naturally I shall want to see this mews apartment you're moving into. And of course you'll pay Charlotte Fisher a proper rent—I'll take care of that side of things.'

It was not what Erin wanted. She felt on the brink of gaining her independence and wanted to be self-reliant. But, against that, he was her father and she loved him, and he must be having a hard enough time letting her go, albeit only temporarily.

So she agreed, and found that she did not have to phone Charlotte Fisher because Charlotte phoned her. Not to tell her she'd had second thoughts, as Erin at first feared, but to endorse that she really, really needed her. 'It would be such a tremendous help to me just now if you could free me from that mountain of paperwork,' she pressed.

'When would you like me to start?' Erin answered, and on Charlotte's cry of glee it was settled.

Erin had spent the following day putting together such of her belongings that she would need for what Charlotte vaguely felt would be a three-month arrangement. And, the day after, Leslie Tunnicliffe got into his car and followed his daughter's car to London.

And, as Charlotte had thought, Erin at once fell in love with the mews apartment. It was a first-floor apartment but had its own front door, the rooms being reached by a steep and narrow staircase. Part of the mews flat was over an archway that led into a large cobbled courtyard. On one side of the archway was the bedroom and bathroom, the part over the arch doing service as a dining area with a tiny kitchenette adjoining. This led into an absolutely charming, if small, sitting room. But, more to the point, her father, with the comment that she wouldn't be practising any cat-swinging skills, seemed to approve of her temporary abode too.

'You're a good girl,' he said, when she went to see him off. 'I trust you, Erin, to remember your upbringing.'

Erin, who was about to get her first taste of real freedom, had a feeling that to remember the dos and don'ts of her upbringing might be a bit restricting. But he was her father, she loved him, and did not want him to worry about her.

'I'll try to be good,' she answered lightly, straining at the leash to let go of being good. This, for her, was a big adventure. She had started to crave adventure.

He kissed her goodbye and she returned to the apartment with an involuntary smile breaking across her features as she climbed the narrow staircase. Who would have thought it? Last week life had been deadly dreary and she had been upset at Mark Prentice's behaviour. But look at how exciting life was now! And Mark Prentice? Pfff! Erin realised then that she had never cared very deeply for Mark.

For a moment she felt a touch panicky that she might be a bit more like her mother than she had realised. Her mother, having walked out on two marriages and determined not to venture into a third, had adopted the habit of 'letting them go'—just as if they were in her employ—when any of her men friends mentioned the 'M' word.

Erin grew calm again. She wasn't like her mother in that area; she just knew that she was not. But thinking of her mother made her realise that, with everything happening so fast, she hadn't informed Nina of the latest developments.

Before unpacking, Erin took out her mobile phone and thumbed out Nina's number. Unusually, she was in—and disbelieving.

'Happy Harry actually let you go!' she squealed.

'It's only temporary. For three months or so,' Erin replied. Happy Harry! Her mother was incorrigible.

Nina laughed. 'You won't want to go back after three months! I know I wouldn't! Give me your address. I'll come over and see you when I have a minute.'

Now, Erin stretched in her bed. All that had been a month ago. She had begun working for Charlotte and

had soon made inroads into the paperwork. Erin left her
bed and headed for the shower. She got ready for the
day, fearing that the three months Charlotte had said it
would take to sort out her office and get everything up
to date was an overestimate. Even if she only went in
part time, Erin considered, she would still shortly have
everything in apple-pie order.

And the trouble was that once the office was up to
date Erin knew she would have to go back home. And—
Nina had been right. She did not want to go back to
Croom Babbington to live. She had spent the weekend
there with her father, returning to London only yesterday; the weekend had seemed to go on for ever. Not that
there was a lot happening on her social scene in London.
Nina had been to see her, and Charlotte had been to
remove the remainder of her clothes. Erin had met
Robin, Charlotte's fiancé, a man in his mid-thirties, a
non-pushy kind of man whom Erin had taken to straight
away.

Robin was totally unlike Gavin Gardner, the slightly
pushy man who had the industrial unit next to
Charlotte's. Gavin had asked Erin out within the first
half an hour of meeting her. But while Erin was quite
keen to 'cut her teeth', as it were, she had discovered
that there was something inbred in her that ruled out
brash males of the Gavin Gardner type. She had refused
his invitation. That did not put him off. He continued to
ask her out—she continued to refuse.

Erin left the mews apartment to join the rest of the
commuting herd. She had soon learned the folly of driving through London in the rush hour to reach her temporary job, and then trying to find a nearby parking spot.
Public transport might be crowded, but it was the better
option.

She had Fisher Fabrics in her view when Gavin Gardner fell into step with her. 'Good weekend?' he enquired for openers.

Erin saw no reason not to answer him. 'I stayed the weekend in my old home,' she replied. 'How did your weekend go?' she asked in return.

'It would've been better if you'd featured in it,' he returned flirtatiously.

Dream on! 'Busy?' she enquired, meaning his work—he did something with plastic extrusion.

'Not so busy that I can't spare time to have coffee, lunch, dinner with you. You choose?' he offered.

She laughed. Her lovely mouth curved upwards. He was either much too obvious or she was growing a very faint coating of sophistication—she wasn't sure which. At any rate, she was glad that they had just reached Fisher Fabrics. 'Bye, Gavin,' she bade him.

'One day,' he threatened. 'One day.'

Erin was smiling when she entered the building that was more like an overlarge shed than anything else. Charlotte, the first in, looked up and saw her smiling face. 'Gavin Gardner?' she guessed.

'He'll give up eventually.'

'If you believe that you'll believe anything. How's your father?' she asked, aware that Erin returned to her old home every weekend.

'He was pleased to see me.' Her smile faded. 'I think he's missing me,' Erin added.

'He's bound to. You've been his life since your mother left,' Charlotte commented.

That did not make Erin feel any better. 'Do you think I should go back?' she asked worriedly.

'Grief, no!' Charlotte objected. 'Do you want to?'

It was a truth that, much though she loved her father,

and was grateful to him for his nurturing of her, she was loving her brief time in London. She shook her head. 'No,' she answered honestly. 'I don't. Though the way your paperwork's going,' she felt she should mention, 'it isn't going to take me all of three months to get everything running smoothly.'

Charlotte considered what she'd said for a moment, and then replied, 'Even so, even if you won't need that long, there's nothing to stop you staying on, is there?'

'In London, do you mean?' Erin asked, startled. The thought hadn't occurred to her.

'You'd have no trouble in finding another job—and I'd give you the best ever reference. And I still haven't decided what to do about whether or not to sell the mews place.'

'You're saying I could stay on there?'

'Of course. And, should I decide to sell, I'd give you ample notice so you could look around for somewhere decent. What do you say?'

What Erin wanted to say was, yes, yes, yes. But there was her father to consider. 'May I think about it?' she asked, feeling torn in two.

'Of course,' Charlotte said again, and, smiling, 'And if you're not so busy as I thought you'd be, why don't we drop everything and—shop!' Charlotte was positively beaming. 'I've worked my brain to a standstill this weekend. I'm in need of a stiff dose of retail therapy.'

Erin considered the amount of work she had been going to do that day—not colossal by anyone's standards—and decided that to shop was the best idea she'd heard in a long while. 'Lead on!' she encouraged.

Two hours later, with a satisfactory collection of carriers already starting to mount up, they were seated at the window table of a salubrious café, taking a break.

Charlotte had just commented, 'I think I'll go back for that scarf,' when they both became aware of the tall, dark and, Erin had to admit, very good-looking man who had entered and was approaching their table. 'Josh!' Charlotte exclaimed with delight, and as Erin felt a most peculiar sensation in her heart region the man glanced from Charlotte to Erin, and back to Charlotte again.

'I thought it was you,' he said, having plainly seen Charlotte from the window and come in. 'I could do with a coffee. Shall I join you?'

Charlotte was again delighted. 'Of course. Erin and I are taking a breather from the more serious work of life.' He glanced at their carriers as though quite understanding the ways of women. And while Erin was forming the opinion that he very likely *did* understand the ways of women, thoroughly, Charlotte set about making the introductions.

'This is Joshua Salsbury, Robin's best man at our wedding,' she said, and as Erin noted that the good-looking Joshua Salsbury would be about the same mid-thirties age as Robin, Charlotte was saying, 'Erin Tunnicliffe. Erin hails from the same village in Gloucestershire where I originally came from.'

Joshua Salsbury stretched out his right hand to Erin and, feeling oddly glad that she was wearing a favourite trouser suit that particularly became her, Erin shook hands with him. Then Joshua took possession of a spare chair at their table and, magically, a waitress appeared to take his order.

'You've come to London to shop, Erin? Or do you live here?' he enquired as the waitress departed.

'Erin's trained in business and secretarial work and is here answering my SOS because my Everest-high

paperwork grew out of control,' Charlotte answered
for her.

'But you decided to hit the shops instead?' he commented pleasantly.

'We're having a lovely time,' Erin said with a smile,
saw his glance stray very briefly to her curving mouth,
and felt all out of her depth suddenly. So much for the
faint coating of sophistication she had thought she might
have acquired! She was glad when the waitress returned
with his coffee. Then Charlotte was remarking that it
seemed ages since she and Robin had seen him.

Him—singular? Was there no Mrs Joshua Salsbury?
Looking at him, Erin rather thought that from his well-
cut business suit, not to mention his looks—leave alone
that the man had charm enough to sink a battleship—
there would be any number of females queuing up for
that distinction.

Joshua Salsbury answered that he had been out of the
country for a while, and asked, 'Have you been in town
long, Erin?'

'A month,' she replied pleasantly.

'With another two months to go,' Charlotte filled in.
'I've been trying to persuade Erin to stay on after she
has my paperwork up to date.'

'You have a place in town?' he turned to Erin to enquire, and Erin, not knowing if it was common knowledge that Charlotte was living at Robin's apartment, hesitated.

'Erin's caretaking my place for me until I decide what
to do with it. Sell it or rent it out,' Charlotte came in
openly.

And a short while after that Joshua Salsbury glanced
to his watch, finished the last of his coffee, wished them
more successful shopping and said that he must be on

his way. Remarking that he would be in touch with Robin, he paid for his coffee and theirs, and left them sitting there.

Erin wanted to make some comment about him, ask questions about him, but did not want Charlotte to think she was overly interested in him. In truth, though, Erin felt she had never met anyone like Joshua Salsbury. To her mind he had everything, absolutely everything. Successful, obviously. Without question sophisticated. He made the men she had dated seem mere boys.

'You were saying something about going back for that scarf you were undecided about?' she reminded Charlotte instead.

'I think I will. You know how it is. If I don't buy it now, I shall never find what I'm looking for when I want it.'

Erin returned to the mews apartment at the end of an agreeable day's shopping with a few purchases of her own. But she had to admit that her thoughts were not on the new additions to her wardrobe as she put them away, but on the tall, dark-haired, grey-eyed man, the like of whom had never crossed her path before and, sadly, was never likely to again.

Somehow, Erin just did not seem able to get thoughts of Joshua Salsbury out of her head. He would return frequently to interrupt her concentration throughout the rest of that week as she busied herself with various pieces of correspondence or accounting.

She left London on Friday evening to spend the weekend with her father, and owned to feeling mean and treacherous because she wanted to stay on in London. But the idea of finding a permanent job and staying on just would not leave her. Though it was Sunday afternoon before she was able to broach the subject to her father, and then only by recalling how he had stated over a month ago that he had expected she might want to leave home when she turned twenty.

'Would you mind very much if I didn't come back after I've finished my work for Charlotte?' she asked in a sudden rush, the time growing ever closer to when she should start back for London.

Leslie Tunnicliffe looked at her sharply. 'The grass is obviously greener on the London side,' he answered, and, as terrible as she was feeling, Erin just could not say what she knew he was hoping she would say—that it didn't matter and that she would return to Croom Babbington to live. But, 'I'm being unfair,' he relented after a moment. 'You must enjoy living in London or you wouldn't want to stay on. You'd better tell me about your plans.'

Erin drove back to London and could hardly believe she had her father's blessing to stay. She had told him of Charlotte's opinion that she'd have no trouble in finding another job, and had also told him that Charlotte would give her ample time to look for other accommodation should she ultimately decide to sell the mews apartment. Erin had also assured him that she would come home each weekend, on either Fridays or Saturdays.

Charlotte was at her most encouraging when on Monday Erin told her of her intention to look for a job in London. 'That's great!' she exclaimed, adding, 'Purely selfish of me, I know, but apart from anything else I needn't rush to make a decision about the apartment.'

'Would you mind if I started looking for another job now?'

'As long as you don't leave me straight away,'

Charlotte replied lightly. Then calculated, 'Though if you start going for interviews, say, next week, and then tell your future employer that you want to give a clear month's notice here, that would complete your three months with me. Not that I'd hold you to that if you found an absolute gem of a job,' she added swiftly.

Erin purchased an evening paper on her way back to the mews apartment that evening. She scanned it quickly as soon as she got in, but saw nothing that caused her to want at once to get out her writing materials and apply.

She decided to make her meal and then study the situations vacant more leisurely afterwards. Which in effect was what she was doing when the phone in the tiny apartment rang. Erin had been in the habit of using her mobile phone to make any calls, and had not given out Charlotte's phone number to anyone.

Aware the call would be for Charlotte, Erin went over to answer it. 'Hello,' she said pleasantly—and felt instantly all of a jumble inside when she heard who was calling.

'Hello, Erin,' said a firm, well-modulated voice. 'Josh Salsbury.'

'Oh!' she exclaimed, and wanted to die that she had exclaimed anything, and hurriedly forced herself back together again. 'I'm afraid Charlotte's not here just now.'

'Which makes it just as well that I rang hoping to speak with you.'

He wanted to speak with her! Joshua Salsbury, tall, dark, good-looking—she had never forgotten his face— wanted to speak with *her?*

She tried for even a tiny scrap of his sophistication.

'How can I help?' she asked politely—as if a man of his calibre would need help from her in any way!

'I'd like to have a meal with you,' he replied—straight out, just like that! Her legs went weak.

He was asking her for a date! He was... She collapsed onto the nearest chair. Then to her surprise found that the duplicity of the man she had last dated had affected her more than she had realised. Inasmuch as instead of jumping at the chance to go out with Joshua Salsbury— and surely by 'have a meal with you' he wasn't suggesting that they stay in and she cook it?—she first asked, 'You're not married—or anything?'

'Not married,' he replied, and, sounding amused, 'Or anything. Nor have I ever been married. Though I believe that state is quite popular and that some people actually enjoy it.' Erin felt her lips twitch. Quite clearly he was stating up front that he had positively no interest in being married. Quite clearly, too, when he followed up with, 'Dinner—Friday?' he had no time for trivialities either.

Oh, help. Her insides felt as if they belonged to anyone but her. So who was this casual-sounding person who popped out of her mouth to tell him, 'I'll look forward to it'?

'I'll call for you. Seven-thirty,' he said. 'Until then.' And rang off.

Erin sat too paralysed to move for ages afterwards. All memory of what she had been doing when the phone had rung—checking again the situations vacant column—went from her head. Had that really happened? Had Joshua Salsbury really and truly rung her to ask her out on a date? Had she really and truly accepted?

That he had in fact done just that seemed no less real the next day as she busied herself at Fisher Fabrics. She was in a way grateful that Charlotte was busy for most of the day with buyers who had come to see her work. Part of Erin wanted to tell Charlotte about Josh Salsbury's phone call, but another part of her felt too shy to do anything of the sort. Also, Erin felt she must be vastly different from the type of woman he usually escorted to dinner, and did not want Charlotte to confirm as much by so much as a raised eyebrow.

Though perhaps Charlotte knew that he had intended to phone her? He had the phone number, after all, and, since he was calling at the mews apartment on Friday, he must know Charlotte's address. Perhaps Robin had told him the phone number and the address.

All of which was rather getting away from the point of why Erin felt in such a flutter. Joshua Salsbury was an attractive man of the world and she, Erin Tunnicliffe, was drowning in feelings of insecurity. How on earth was she going to be able to eat so much as a crumb? Just thinking of Josh calling for her, of sitting beside him in his car while he drove them to whichever eating establishment he had chosen, was making her stomach churn. What would she be like on Friday?

Erin arrived home from work on Wednesday still coping with mixed emotions whenever she thought of her proposed dinner date with Josh Salsbury—which she did often. She was half inclined to find his phone number and ring and tell him she could not make it after all. Since he had phoned on Monday to make the arrangement for Friday, it wasn't as if he was exactly champing at the bit to go out with her, was it?

On the other hand he was probably a very busy man. The day he had joined her and Charlotte for coffee he had said he had been out of the country for a while. Perhaps he was frequently out of the country. Either that or she had been right first off, Erin mused agitatedly, and he was not in any way eager to see her.

That was when her pride reared up. And, conversely, she was then blessed if she would go out with the wretched man.

She found the piece of paper Charlotte had given her with her contact numbers. But before Erin could ring Robin's number to enquire about Josh Salsbury's number she was recalling how she had come to London to, as it were, get herself a life.

Hadn't she come away from Croom Babbington precisely because life was deadly dull? Hadn't she determined to be like other women? Hadn't she decided to seek a little excitement? And remembering her uneventful father-waiting-up-for-her-when-she-got-in life, a lot of excitement, actually.

So was she to fall at the first hurdle? Yes, but man-about-town, had-it-all Joshua Salsbury? Erin had an idea she would be wading in deep, deep waters way above her head if she went out with him. But then again—she gave herself a mental shake—for goodness' sake, wasn't it high time that she *did* wade into those waters? Even if she did quail a little at the thought of so much as dipping a toe in those waters with Josh Salsbury there as chief swimming instructor.

The next morning Erin told Charlotte about her date for the following evening. 'You're going out with Josh Salsbury!' Charlotte exclaimed, to Erin's relief not raising an eyebrow but smilingly adding, 'You jammy—!' She broke off. 'You *do* know that half the beauties in London are waiting for his phone call?'

'I was as surprised as you…' Erin began, but someone called to see Charlotte and Erin turned her attention back to work—but not her full attention.

Half the beauties in London... Half the *sophisticated* beauties in London, would that be? Again Erin was unsure. The last thing she wanted was that Josh Salsbury should think her stupid or naïve.

On that basis alone, when Charlotte was free Erin asked her for his phone number. Charlotte was kind enough to not ask why she wanted it, and, after checking her personal directory, wrote down both his business and his home number.

By the time Erin went home that evening, however, she had given herself a stern lecture. For goodness' sake, hadn't she wanted more adventure in her life? Buck your ideas up, do. Did she want to see Josh Salsbury again or not?

There was nothing more to think about. She very definitely did. And she would. Though how she was going to feel around seven-twenty-five tomorrow night, while she waited for his ring at the door, she did not want to think.

She decided to have her meal and check through the situations vacant of that evening's paper for a job that would have something about it and that wouldn't leave her bored to tears in a month. Then she would check her wardrobe for something smart, without being over the top, to wear on her date tomorrow.

Erin did not get as far as making a meal. For, on flattening out the paper she had bought on her way home, she was shaken rigid to see a picture of none other than the man she would be dining with the following evening! Pictured with him was an older man, but an equally good-looking man. Both wore dinner jackets, both obviously attending some function or other.

Speedily she scanned the headline. The picture, she read, was of Thomas Salsbury, chairman of Salsbury

Engineering Systems, with his son, Joshua Salsbury, chief executive of the company. The picture had been taken a month earlier, when Thomas Salsbury had been in full health. He had yesterday, unfortunately, been taken ill with a heart attack.

Still feeling somewhat shaken, Erin read it through twice. She learned little more, other than a description of Salsbury Engineering Systems being a huge company of international specialists in complex engineering projects. Globetrotting Joshua Salsbury was expected one day to take over the chairmanship of the company.

Poor Josh, Erin couldn't help thinking. The two men pictured appeared to have a special affinity with each other. As if, without having to broadcast the fact, they cared very much about each other. No way would Josh want to take over the company because of his father's illness. Erin just seemed to know that for a fact.

With all thought of checking the situations vacant columns gone from her mind, she made a cup of coffee, reflecting on her inner turmoil in considering whether or not to cancel her date with Josh, when now it was very likely that he would ring her and suggest postponing it.

Should she ring him? Ring him and say that she'd seen the paper and understood perfectly that he had more pressing matters on his mind than taking her to dinner tomorrow?

Erin did not make that call then, for two reasons. One was that she who had never particularly suffered from shyness in her life suddenly felt incredibly shy. The other reason was that she was pretty certain he was more likely to be at the hospital with his father than at either of the numbers Charlotte had written down for her.

Then her doorbell sounded and Erin went down the stairs to answer it. Only to have thoughts of Josh

Salsbury taken temporarily from her mind when she opened the door and found her mother standing there.

As usual, Nina's standards being of the highest, she looked as smart as ever. 'I was near and realised I'm early for my—appointment. Don't want to appear too eager,' she trilled. 'So I thought I'd come and spend half an hour with my dear daughter.'

'Come up,' Erin invited, wondering how long this present man-friend would last before her mother had to 'let him go'. It was without question that Nina was meeting a male of the species.

Erin led the way to the sitting room and turned, about to ask her mother if she would like some coffee, when she saw that her mother had spotted the evening paper and was staring at it, startled.

'Tommy Salsbury!' she exclaimed, picking up the paper to read what it was all about.

'You know him?' Erin questioned, feeling startled herself.

'I was out with him only last week,' Nina replied, going on in alarm as she put the paper back down, 'Good heavens, he could have had a heart attack while I was with him! Thank goodness I let him go in time!'

Feeling stunned, Erin stared at her parent. 'You—let him go?'

'Let him go. Dumped him, I believe the expression is these days. You know how men get after a while. He'd been asking leading questions about my family, the way men do when they're getting serious. I should have let him go then, at that first sign, but...'

'Serious? As in wedding bells?' Erin asked, her head all of a whirl at this development.

'Serious as in marriage. As in pipe and slippers! As in Boredom County!' At one time Erin might have been amused by Nina, but this wasn't funny. 'He asked me to marry him—I couldn't have that,' Nina stated thoughtlessly.

'You turned him down?'

'Naturally I turned him down!' Nina replied, as if doubting why her daughter should need to ask.

Erin was speechless. For heaven's sake, her mother had been out with the man only last week! Why—Nina 'letting him go' might even have contributed in some large degree to him suffering that heart attack!

'I should have recognised that the writing was on the wall when he introduced his son to me and then started to hint that he wouldn't mind meeting some of my family. But Tommy had always been such good fun that I at first missed the warning signs...'

Her mother had met Joshua Salsbury! Oh, heavens, this was a nightmare! 'You—er—told Mr Salsbury you had a daughter?' Erin asked, and knew she must be in some kind of shock to have asked such a ridiculous question.

'Are you mad?' her mother retorted. 'Of course I didn't. Nor would I consider introducing you to any of my—friends.' But, taking any sting out of those words, she smiled becomingly at her daughter and complimented her, 'You're much too pretty.' And while Erin stared at her beautiful mother, who would always be beautiful, Nina Woodward was going on to amaze her by saying, 'I've been thinking of having some cosmetic surgery.'

'You're having a face lift?' Erin asked, feeling absolutely shattered.

'Must you be so crude?' her mother complained. 'I said I was only thinking of it, so I very probably won't. I wouldn't mind the end result, but I wouldn't care for an anaesthetic—and I certainly wouldn't want it done while I was conscious.'

'Mother, you're beautiful just as you are!' Erin quickly told her, finding the idea of her vain mother going to such lengths frightening, particularly when it was so not necessary.

'You think so?' Nina responded, and appeared to be a little comforted. 'For that I shall forgive you the "Mother" word. Now, if I can just use your bathroom to freshen up, I'll be on my way.'

Erin sat for a long while after her mother had left, going over and over everything in her head. Though in actual fact she knew then, as she had more or less known at once, what she must do.

She had all along been a little trepidatious about her dinner date with Josh Salsbury tomorrow. She had also been excited and eager about it too. Many times she had thought of contacting him to cancel, but the excited and eagerness part had won over the trepidatious part. But now how could she go out with him?

He had met her mother. He in all probability knew that his father had asked her mother to marry him. Just as with that same probability Josh knew that her mother had dumped his parent the moment that proposal was aired, and how her callousness, for that was the way he would most likely see it, had contributed largely to his father being rushed into hospital yesterday. Now, was Joshua Salsbury remotely likely to want to take out to dinner the daughter of the woman who had a big part in causing his father's suffering?

Erin remembered the charming and pleasant dark-haired man who had joined her and Charlotte that morning for coffee. She remembered his firm jaw, his grey eyes which, though friendly then, she did not doubt would turn hostilely cold should she explain who she was. The question of would he want to wine and dine her did not need to be asked. She already knew the answer. He would not.

Erin felt sick inside as she accepted that there was nothing she could do other than telephone him. It was ingrained in her to tell the truth at all times, yet how could she tell him that she was Nina Woodward's daughter? While it was without question that he would be fiercely loyal to his father—it was all there in that newspaper photograph of the two standing together—Erin too felt a loyalty to her parent, no matter what she had or had not done. No way, Erin felt, would she be able to stay quiet while Joshua Salsbury gave forth with some detrimental opinion of her mother.

It was nine-thirty before Erin had herself sufficiently together to pick up the phone and make the call that had to be made. She hoped he would be in. After being in a mental stew over the last few hours, she now wanted it all over and done with. She glanced at her watch again, calculated that if Joshua Salisbury had been hospital-visiting he should be home by now—and dialled. Her call went unanswered.

She rang again a half-hour later. The phone rang out a few times, and when Erin didn't know whether to feel glad or sorry that he still wasn't in, suddenly the ringing tone stopped. 'Salsbury,' said a firm all-male voice.

'Oh, Josh—ua.' She added the last two syllables, realising that they weren't on shortened name terms. 'It's Erin Tunnicliffe.' There was a pause during which he said nothing but waited for her to continue. 'I read in the paper about your father,' she plunged in, in a rush. 'I do hope he is feeling better.'

'Thank you for your concern. He's being well looked after,' Joshua Salsbury replied evenly.

That seemed to end the conversation right there, and Erin realised that about matters close to home, as it were, Josh Salsbury was a very private man. 'The thing is,' she went on in another rush, 'I'm sorry I can't see you tomorrow after all.'

What she had expected, she rather supposed, was some polite, Thank you for letting me know, before he put the phone down. A little to her surprise, though, what she got was a querying, 'You can't?'

Oh, help. Erin thought that perhaps she did owe him some sort of explanation, but if either of them was to use the excuse of his father's illness then Josh had prior claim. She hadn't thought he would bother with wanting to know why, and just wasn't ready. She hurriedly searched round for some truthful excuse—there wasn't one. Not one she could tell him anyway.

'I've—um—there are... That is...' She took a deep breath in an effort to calm down, then continued, 'That is, I've a few complications at the—er—moment.' She felt hot all over, and hoped he would leave it there.

Thankfully, he did, his voice sounding cool and not the least tiny bit disappointed when, not deigning to press her for more, he drawled, 'Why not give me a ring when you have your complications sorted?'

Like he was desperate to see her! 'I...' she began, but he had put down the phone. Well, what had she expected? All too clearly he didn't give a tinker's cuss if he never heard from her again.

And that saddened her. She had liked him. But she didn't have to be the sharpest knife in the drawer to know that she had blown any chance of a second invitation from him. For certain Joshua Salsbury was just not used to women cancelling dinner dates with him.

Just as she knew, circumstances being what they were, that she could never ring him again, Erin also knew he would not be holding his breath waiting for her call. She seemed to know he was not the kind of man who asked twice—and she, Erin knew too, had just blown all chance of ever seeing him again.

CHAPTER TWO

LIFE seemed dull again as Erin journeyed to her place of work the next morning. She wondered about Joshua Salsbury's father and felt sad. She hoped Mr Salsbury would soon be well again. She thought of Joshua Salsbury himself and felt even more depressed. She had ended something before it had begun.

While she accepted that it was most unlikely that her date with him would have gone very far, or even have led to a second date, she didn't so much as have one date with him now.

'Good morning, Erin!' Charlotte greeted her cheerfully as she went in, and was in a chatty mood.

Erin responded as cheerfully as she could manage. After all, it wasn't Charlotte's fault that life had gone back to being as dreary as if she still lived in Croom Babbington.

Erin was amazed that just cancelling a date with a man she hardly knew should so put her spirits at basement level. She hadn't been sure about going out with him anyway, for goodness' sake!

She determined to put 'ring when you have your complications sorted' Joshua Salsbury out of her head. It was for certain he wasn't wasting a second of his day in thinking of her.

But so much for not thinking of him. She had just made some coffee, and Charlotte had joined her for a break, when Charlotte remembered, 'Oh—it's tonight you're going out with Josh Salsbury, isn't it?'

Oh, crumbs. Erin had no idea how friendly Charlotte was with Josh. But since he was to be her fiancé's best man he must be good friends with Robin, and, it was a fair bet, a friend to Charlotte too. Erin knew then that she could not be as open with Charlotte as she would prefer to be—notwithstanding that Erin felt she owed her mother her first loyalty.

'It's—um—off,' she answered, searching for some good reason.

Then Erin discovered that she did not need to search, because Charlotte had either seen the same newspaper or had heard of Thomas Salsbury's heart attack from another source. 'Oh, yes. Josh's father,' she said, and Erin went back to feeling totally fed-up again.

So much so that on her way back to Fisher Fabrics, after going out at lunchtime for something to eat, when Gavin Gardner fell into step with her and asked her to go and have a drink with him that night, she thought, why not?

'You will!' he exclaimed eagerly. 'Great!' And while Erin was already starting to have second thoughts—was her life really that dull?—he was going on, 'I've already had a few jars this lunchtime, to celebrate a business deal I clinched this morning. But we'll celebrate for real tonight. I'll call for you in a taxi. Don't want to risk my driving licence,' he laughed.

Oh, grief, he sounded three parts towards being tipsy before he had another drink. But he had the whole afternoon in which to sober up, and anyway dull was dull, and a drink with a three-quarters-inebriated Gavin, while not putting a shine on her lot, couldn't make it any duller. Live a little, for goodness' sake.

On that thought she gave him her address, and when he suggested seven-thirty she had no trouble in recalling

that Josh Salsbury had been going to call for her at
seven-thirty that night. 'Make it eight,' she told Gavin
as they reached Fisher Fabrics.

'Can't wait,' he answered, and with a too-familiar
kind of squeeze to her arm they parted.

Erin knew that she had made a mistake in agreeing to
go out with him, but had inherited part of her father's
stubborn nature. And even though she knew that what
she should do was go next door and tell Gavin Gardner
that she had changed her mind, she would not.

She had agreed to go out with him and she would.
She had come to London determined to see and experience something of life. But what life would she see or
experience if she stayed home the whole of the time—
delightful though the mews apartment was?

Erin showered when she got home, while impressing
on herself the whole time her need to see and experience
life. She selected a deep blue trouser suit from her wardrobe, but was aware that had she been going out with
Josh Salsbury she would most likely have chosen a
dress—oh, stop thinking about him do. You aren't going
out with him; you're going out with Gavin. Get a life!
See a bit of life!

Gavin arrived at seven-forty-five. Erin was glad she
was ready. Somehow, for all her self-lecture about getting a life, she did not fancy inviting Gavin up to the
close confines of the small apartment.

A decision that she knew was the right one when,
ogling her figure and her long length of leg in the deep
blue trousers, Gavin seemed even more forward than she
had thought. To her surprise, though, the pub he took
her to was more of a select kind of small hotel with a
public bar.

'What are you having?' he asked, and caused her not

to know whether to laugh or be frosty when, looking deeply into her violet eyes, he actually licked his lips.

She decided on humour. 'Just a tonic water, please,' she answered, suspecting he'd done some more celebrating since they had parted at lunchtime and musing it might be a good idea if one of them stayed sober.

So much for him asking what she wanted. 'I put a gin in it,' he informed her when he came back with a couple of glasses in his hands.

Erin could have got cross. But the mere fact he had not tried to conceal what he had done, but had so openly told her, made her feel less irritated than she might have otherwise. She raised her glass to him. 'Congratulations on the deal you made today,' she said in friendly fashion, and smiled.

She was not smiling an hour later, however. Gavin was turning out to be a pain. He had been up to the bar several times to get himself another drink. True, he had bought her one each time—she had three untouched ones lined up in front of her, and that was how they were going to stay: untouched. But he was decidedly the worse for wear.

'Drink up, Erin, you're very slow,' he urged, sounding like a man who was trying hard to pretend he hadn't been staggering the last time he'd returned from the bar.

'No, thanks.' And because this wasn't what she'd had in mind when she'd thought of getting a life, of living a little—she'd rather stay home, thank you very much—'I'll get us a taxi, shall I?' she offered. He'd be falling over his feet if she asked him to go and get one!

Gavin looked at his half-finished drink, then at the beautiful violet-eyed blonde sitting next to him, and positively, if beerily, beamed, 'Splen… good idea. Shall we go straight to your place?'

Oh, dear. He clearly had ideas that she did not have. 'Do you remember where you live?' she asked.

'You want us to go there?'

No, I want to go home and to be able to tell the taxi driver where to take you. Erin might have told him as much, but all at once she felt the grip of his hand as he familiarly decided to make his acquaintance with her thigh.

She might have laughed, but ice entered her soul. This was no laughing matter. Particularly not in a public place, where anybody watching could get totally the wrong idea.

Very firmly she picked up his hand and removed it from her person, and told him coldly, 'You do that again and I shall smack you.'

His face fell at her cross look, and, more than ever wishing she had never agreed to go out with him, Erin turned her head away—and as everything in her jangled from shock, she wished that the ground would open up and take her. For as her eyes focused on the bar so she saw a tall, dark-haired man who was half turned and was watching her and her companion. Oh, *no!* The fates just wouldn't be that unkind!

But they were! There, very obviously getting totally the wrong idea about her and the man she was with, was none other than Joshua Salsbury!

No. Oh, no, her brain screamed. She couldn't believe it. Even as her face flamed—he could not possibly have missed Gavin's familiarity with her thigh—she could not believe it, did not want to believe it. But it was true.

She wanted to look away, but felt hypnotised by a pair of grey eyes that seemed to refuse to let her look away. Oh, grief. She had given up her date with a good-looking man who was totally in charge—for the drunken specimen by her side! Oh, the ignominy of it!

She managed at last to drag her eyes away from Josh Salsbury, and her brain ran off at a tangent. She was still busy coping with her shock at seeing him there, of all places, but she vaguely remembered spotting a private clinic type of place close by. She realised then that Josh had in all likelihood stopped by for a quick drink after visiting his father.

But she had no time for further speculation because Gavin Gardner—who, having sunk the rest of his pint was now too far gone to know when his advances weren't welcome—was again showing some fascination with her thigh.

She couldn't cope, Erin realised. Without so much as a glance in Josh Salsbury's direction she got abruptly to her feet. Gavin got rockily to his feet too, and as he stood there swaying Erin knew that she just couldn't abandon the idiot, much though she would like to.

'Come on,' she said, taking a hold of his arm. He smiled inanely. She didn't think he would be much more trouble. Nor was he, particularly, though it was a shame that they had to walk near the bar, and straight in front of Joshua Salsbury. A shame too that Gavin Gardner's feet should choose that moment to do a wobbly dinky side-step—which brought him stumbling up against the man at the bar.

Josh's hand came out to firmly prop him up. Though it was not to her escort that he addressed his remark but to her when, mockingly, he commented, 'What a one you are for complications, Erin.'

She looked at him, wished that she could think up something sharp and witty with which to reply, but her sharp and witty cupboard was bare. She did the next best thing and ignored him, concentrating instead on getting Gavin out of there before he crashed into anybody else.

'Ooh!' Gavin mumbled when the fresh air hit him, but thankfully his suddenly spinning head cooled any amorous intent he might have previously set his mind on.

Taxis were like buses, Erin fretted. None at all, or three at once. Eventually one came along, and she helped Gavin inside, giving the taxi driver her address. Whereupon Gavin went sleepy and she had to prise him awake in order to extract his address from him.

As the taxi pulled up at her mews address Erin relayed to the driver where Gavin lived. Her idea to pay the driver her fare with a little extra, and then pay him to take Gavin home—while making a note never to go out with him again—became a non-starter. Because as she opened the door and got out, and handed over her fare, Gavin got out too, and the cabbie—clearly not enamoured of having a drunk aboard—closed the door and drove off!

Now what did she do? To her mind Gavin was fairly harmless, but the idea of dragging him up the stairs to the apartment and bedding him down on the sofa was one she did not wish to consider overlong. The problem was, taxis did not seem to pass by this area too often.

Erin had just decided on plan B, which was to open up the apartment, scrape Gavin off the wall he was clinging to and leave him sitting on the stairs while she went upstairs and phoned for a taxi, when to her surprise a taxi suddenly drove through the archway and into the courtyard!

What was even more surprising was that the man who stepped out, and asked the driver to wait, was none other than Joshua Salsbury! *Joshua Salsbury!* Erin did a double-take, her mouth falling wordlessly open.

She was still staring at him open-mouthed when, 'Need any help?' he drawled, flicking the briefest of glances in the direction of her sozzled escort.

This was no time to be swamped again by the utter humiliation of it. She looked from Josh to the man it seemed she had stood him up for. My stars—no contest! 'You wouldn't like to share your taxi with Gavin, I suppose?' she asked tentatively. 'I'd intended for him to go on in the taxi that brought me home, but the driver didn't wait.'

'I wonder why?' Josh muttered, but to her relief went first to have a word with his taxi driver and then to peel Gavin away from the wall. 'Come along, Gavin,' he said pleasantly. 'Time to go home.' Having been manoeuvred into the taxi, Gavin promptly settled down to quietly doze and clearly wanted no part in the proceedings. 'Where does he live?' Josh turned to ask Erin.

She gave the address Gavin had said, and designated this as the worst night of her life. She wanted nothing more than to go inside and shut the door on the world. Her thoughts were on going straight to bed, burying her head under the bedclothes and hoping this would all look better in the morning—some hope—when Josh Salsbury shut the door on the sleeping Gavin and went to talk again to the driver.

She saw money change hands, but was staring thunderstruck when Josh stood back and it suddenly dawned that the taxi was going to drive off—leaving her standing there, with him!

'T-taxis aren't too frequent around here,' she informed him witlessly.

Josh Salsbury turned and, staring down at her in the

security-lit area by her door, was silent for a moment or two. Then, very clearly, he said, 'Black, no sugar.'

She had never met anyone like him. But, getting herself together, she rather thought that by following her—and she had no idea why he had done that—and seeing Gavin on his way as he had, he was perhaps owed a cup of coffee.

'Come up,' she said, turning and unlocking her door. She felt very unsure of her ground here, and she enquired as he followed her up the stairs, 'Have you been here before?'

'Charlotte gave a small dinner party one evening,' he replied as they entered the sitting room.

In Erin's view it would have had to be a small dinner party. More than four people and it would be overcrowded. She could not help but wonder who his dinner partner had been. Probably one of the beauties whom Charlotte had once remarked were waiting for his phone call.

'Have a seat,' Erin invited, her voice calm, her insides a disaster. 'I'll just see to the coffee.'

She might have guessed he was not a man who was used to doing what he was told. He came and stood in the kitchenette doorway and watched while she deftly set the kettle to boil, got out cups and saucers and a jar of instant coffee.

'Er—why did you follow?' she asked. 'I mean, you didn't have business this way, did you?'

He shrugged. 'You didn't look as though you were enjoying being pawed.' As she had known, he had not missed Gavin clutching a too-intimate hand on her thigh. She hoped she wasn't looking as red as she felt. 'And my plans for the evening had been scuppered,' Josh added, his expression solemn as he fixed her with a steady grey-eyed gaze.

Oh, heck! She wanted to apologise, but felt hot all over at the thought of having to give him any sort of truthful explanation. 'How is your father?' she asked abruptly.

'He's mending,' Josh replied, her swift changing of the subject not lost on him, she knew.

'You went to see him this evening?' she queried, starting to feel a little desperate and wishing that the kettle would hurry up and boil.

He nodded. 'Your parents are well?' he enquired conversationally.

She wanted him to go. She was feeling uncomfortable. Parents plural meant a father and a mother. She did not want her mother anywhere near this conversation.

'Yes, thank you,' she answered primly, and with utmost relief saw that the kettle had boiled. She made coffee, loaded it on to a tray and calculated it would take five minutes, ten at the most, for him to drink his and then be on his way. Now, what the Dickens was she going to talk to him about for ten minutes that cut out family background?

Josh carried the tray into the sitting room and, as big as he was, seemed quite at home in the small room. She had opened her mouth to offer some polite piece of conversation about his work when he forestalled her by commenting, 'I assumed you were unmarried, and not "anything".' Batting back at her her own question, when he had asked her out, if he was married or 'anything'. 'Should I also assume that Gavin is your "anything"?'

'Grief, no!' she exclaimed before she had time to think. 'I—er...' To explain would be impossible. How could she explain anyway? She had given up dinner with the good-looking, non-pushy man opposite—for an evening in a hotel bar with Gavin! 'Is your coffee all right?' she asked jerkily.

'Perfect,' he replied, though she suspected he was not too well acquainted with instant coffee. 'You sound nervous?' he observed calmly.

'I'm not!' she hastened to assure him, hastily adding, 'It's just that this is a new experience for me—entertaining someone to coffee without my father there.' Oh, drat. Oh, confound it! She wanted to die. She saw Josh Salsbury still, as though arrested by what she had just said. She would have welcomed a faint.

'You've never...?'

'Forget I said that!'

'Until you moved here—what? Five weeks ago?' Almost six, actually. 'You'd lived in Gloucestershire with your parents?' Josh queried slowly.

Oh, families! She did not want to go in that direction. 'My parents are divorced. I lived with my father.'

'Who, by the sound of it, looked after you very well.'

'I'm twenty-two,' she told him, as if that had anything to do with it.

'I'm thirty-five—how do you do?' Josh responded— and she just had to laugh. She saw his glance go to her mouth, as if he liked to see her mouth curve upwards. But she was not happy with his questioning when suddenly, as if the thought had just come to him and had shaken him a little, he said, 'You're a very beautiful woman, Erin, but I'm getting a very distinct impression here that you are not altogether—worldly-wise.'

'I...' am, she wanted to say, but the lie stuck in her throat. 'I'd like to be!' she said, and *did* then go crimson. 'Oh!' she wailed. 'I wasn't hinting or anything!' Why didn't the floor open up and swallow her? Was she really having this conversation?

'You're not telling me you have never...' he paused, then resumed, 'had a boyfriend?'

'Of course I have!' she defended. 'Actually, I'm between boyfriends at the moment. Oh, heck, this is coming out all wrong!'

'What happened with the last boyfriend?' he asked evenly, charmingly, and so entirely matter-of-factly that it didn't seem at all startling to Erin.

Which was perhaps why she did not find it startling that she should honestly reply, 'I wouldn't. So Mark went to bed with a woman I'd thought was one of his *ex*-girlfriends.'

It did not take Josh but a second to sift through what she had said. 'Have you ever?' he asked, point-blank.

Been to bed with anyone? 'No, but I'm going to as soon as I can!' she replied openly—and stared at him, stunned. Had she really just said that? 'I only had one gin and tonic—my mouth seems to be running away with me.'

'It's a rather lovely mouth. Is that why you left home? Because you couldn't—mmm—indulge in extracurricular—activity—while under your father's roof?'

'You make me sound terrible.'

'Not at all. You're a healthy young woman with a young woman's natural—appetites. You're obviously finding your chaste state a touch irksome.'

'Everybody seems to be having a better time than me,' she found herself confiding.

'I'm sure they're not,' he replied kindly. Erin fell a little bit in love with him. 'Have you anyone in your sights?'

To make love with? 'I haven't met anyone yet,' she

replied, looking at one who might well be one such. 'I think I must be a little—er—fastidious!'

He could have been offended—she had, after all, in effect turned him down. A date with him anyway. But he wasn't offended. 'Is this the complication you spoke of?' he asked.

She shook her head. 'No,' she replied honestly.

Josh looked into her eyes for a second or two longer, then got to his feet. 'Don't be in too much of a hurry, Erin,' he advised quietly. 'It will be a special time for you. Choose carefully.'

'I'll come down with you and make sure the door is locked when you've gone,' was all she could think of to answer.

Then she wished she had left him to let himself out, because the problem was that there was hardly any room at the bottom of the stairs. Barely enough room for two people to stand together. They bumped into each other, and as she looked up uncertainly into Josh's eyes so he looked into her eyes for long moments. And then, unhurriedly, he took her into his arms, and gently he kissed her.

Her heart thundered as his kiss came to an end. He still had his arms loosely about her, and she stared up at him with stunned eyes. She transferred her glance to his wonderful mouth; she wanted to feel that exciting mouth over hers again.

She looked into his eyes again, and what he was reading in hers she did not know. But as he gathered her that little bit closer to him so his head came down again, and she was on the receiving end of the most sensational warm and lingering kiss. Her lips parted and his kiss deepened—and as her head spun she held on to him.

Their kiss ended, and as unhurriedly as he had taken

her in his arms Josh was releasing his hold and looking down into her slightly bemused face. 'It's time all good girls were in bed,' he stated calmly—when she was feeling a churned-up mass of she knew not what. 'Goodnight, Erin,' he bade her, and just like that he went—leaving Erin totally bewildered.

A state she was in for the week that followed. Again and again she recalled his fantastic kiss. And again and again she went through a whole range of emotions, wondering if—even though she had told Josh that she had not met anyone she wanted to make love with yet—he had thought from her response to him that she had changed her mind about that. Her face flamed because she quite honestly did not know how she would have reacted had he added 'but not alone' to his 'It's time all good girls were in bed.'

Another week went by, and gradually Erin started to adjust to what had happened. She began to be more comfortable within herself, and to not feel so flustered when each day she would recall different parts of her conversation with him. Never had she been so open with any man.

So what was so special about him? Well, just about everything, she supposed. He made all other men non-starters, at any rate.

Gavin Gardner didn't so much as figure, though he did offer his most abject apologies when they next bumped into each other. 'I well and truly blotted my copybook, didn't I?' he said, shame-faced.

'You were sloshed,' Erin replied.

'It was that deal,' he explained. 'They don't happen like that every day.' And, ever the trier, 'Are you going to let me make amends by coming out with me again?'

'There's only so much of a good time a girl can take,' Erin told him lightly.

She had half hoped that Josh Salsbury might give her a ring, even though nothing was changed and she would still be unable to go out with him. But she felt it would have made her feel better had he shown so much as a small spark of interest. But, all too plainly, whatever spark had ignited for him to invite her to have dinner with him that one time had died an instant death.

If her social life was nothing to rave over, however, work-wise everything was going splendidly. Her work for Charlotte was coming to an end, the catching up more or less completed, which left her with just the day-to-day matters to deal with. Erin had had a word with her and said that really she didn't now require her services, and Charlotte had agreed that if the right job came along she could leave in under the three months they had initially agreed on. But only if it was the right job and they absolutely needed her to start right away.

And the right job *had* come along.

Erin had seen one or two that looked interesting, but it was 'secretary with ability to adapt to changing situations' that had caught her eye. Though when she'd seen who the firm advertising was, none other then Salsbury Engineering Systems, she'd been a little hesitant. Josh and his father were at the head of that company—should she apply? It sounded a very busy office. She liked to be busy.

Erin had given the matter some long and in-depth thought. She wanted to stay in London. She wanted a job that kept her busy—no chance of boredom there. She'd read the advert again. It was in the experimental division, which was several miles away from the main offices. Very probably Joshua Salsbury never showed his face there.

She had applied, been interviewed and had liked what she saw. They had liked what they saw, too, and had been keen for her to start whenever she was available.

'I'm going to miss you!' Charlotte had lamented, when Erin had arrived back at Fisher Fabrics and said she had agreed to start her new job the following Monday. 'But you're still living at my place, so we won't lose touch. And of course you'll come to my wedding. But, oh, Erin, it's just not going to be the same without you here.'

As Erin had anticipated, she thoroughly enjoyed her work at Salsbury Engineering Systems. It was varied, often more dogsbody work than secretarial, but she did not mind a bit. She worked with a fair-sized group of super people, but in three weeks knew everyone by name and, importantly, knew what she was doing. She no longer had to ask questions, but was confident in what she was doing.

While a few of the men there were mature boffins, who treated her as they might a daughter, there was a younger element with whom she also got on with very well. In particular Stephen Dobbs, a man in his late twenties who had one day surfaced from his work and come to find her.

'If you're not busy tomorrow night, and otherwise un-attached, we could go and have something to eat some-where?' he had suggested.

Erin had looked at him, tall, fair, and bespectacled. She had wavered. She liked her own company. But, hey, she could spend time on her own back in Croom Babbington.

'That sounds very nice,' she had replied. He had beamed, and she had decided to enjoy herself.

Which she had. He was pleasant, and not pushy. They had kissed, briefly, on parting—there was no spark there.

She went out with him several times, and they kissed more warmly, but that spark just could not be conjured up, and she knew then that things between them were never going to go further than friendship. Which was what she told him on their next date. And he proved as pleasant and nice as she had thought. He accepted what she said, and asked her out again.

Erin had other offers to wine and dine too, and wouldn't have been human if she hadn't felt flattered at such attention. But she was not interested in dating more than one man at a time, even if her friendship—it could hardly be called a relationship—with Stephen was going nowhere. If her thoughts drifted too many times to Joshua Salsbury, though, then only she was going to know of it.

Life plodded on. She went home to Croom Babbington each weekend, either on a Friday or a Saturday, with nothing too earth-shattering happening. Then, on the Tuesday of her fourth week at Salsbury Engineering Systems, several things out of the ordinary occurred.

Firstly she received an invitation to the wedding of Charlotte and Robin. By then that sensation of love she had experienced for Josh Salsbury made Erin very much want to see him again. He would be at the wedding, she knew, and even if she didn't get to talk to him she would see him. The decision was made for her. The wedding was to be in Bristol. She would go.

The next thing that happened was that she was passing by the office manager's office when the door opened and

Ivan Kelly, the manager, came through. 'Ah, Erin! I was just coming to see you!' he exclaimed.

'What can I do for you?' she offered cheerfully.

'How's your shorthand for technical matter?'

'It's come on by leaps and bounds since I've worked here,' she replied with a smile. Clearly he wanted her assistance with something involving deeply technical matter.

'The Prof is holding a meeting this afternoon, and Kate's called in sick.'

The Prof, otherwise know as Professor Joseph Irving, had the sort of mind that went up corridors few others were likely to go. 'You want me to take the minutes?' she queried, it requiring little guesswork, her thoughts already on sitting up and taking notice.

'Would you?'

'I'd love to,' she obliged, hoping it would not be too complicated a meeting.

It was not. But Erin was kept alert, and only at the end of the meeting, when the Professor had finished and everyone had begun to tidy their notes, did she feel free to relax.

But then something happened that made her tense and her heart suddenly start to beat faster. For, contrary to her opinion when she had decided to apply for the job that Josh Salsbury probably never showed his face there, all at once the door opened and, tall, dark and as totally good-looking as she remembered, he came in. The head of the experimental department came in with him, but Erin barely noticed the other man.

She felt her cheeks burn, and was glad everyone was too taken up with the chief executive's unexpected arrival to be glancing her way. The last time she had seen him she had been in his arms! He had kissed her, lingeringly. It had been oh, so wonderful. She had never forgotten the feel of his mouth over hers.

She saw a very pleased Professor Joseph Irving shake hands with him, and watched as the Professor reacquainted Josh with some of the senior members of his team.

Sorely needing to get herself under control, Erin looked away. But she still felt all of a mish-mash inside when she looked back again. She was glad that her hot burn of colour had subsided, and when she noticed that some of the junior members had started to drift back to their workstations she realised that she had no business sitting there any longer.

Glad to have something to clutch on to, be it only her notepad, Erin got to her feet. The Professor was by that time well into deep and technical conversation with Joshua Salsbury, and Erin knew as she neared them that Josh would not even glance her way.

Wrong! He did glance at her, albeit that he did not appear to take his attention from what the Professor was saying. Grey eyes met violet eyes, and for all Josh Salsbury did not interrupt the Professor to say a word to her—she'd hardly expected him to; it was, after all, the Professor he was obviously there to see—Josh's glance moved briefly down to her mouth, as though he too was remembering her lips beneath his, and as though she was not the only one who had never forgotten their kiss.

As if! Impatient with herself, impatient with him, Erin went swiftly from the room. She stopped by her desk, but only to drop down her notepad before going swiftly on to shut herself away in the ladies' room. As if was right. For heaven's sake, get things in proportion. Joshua

Salsbury had probably kissed half a dozen women since then!

Well, it was for sure she didn't care—so why did she find seeing him again so totally upsetting?

CHAPTER THREE

NOTHING seemed, or was, the same after Josh Salsbury's visit. There was still a buzz about the place when Erin went into work the next day. When she learned the reason for that buzz, her emotions went haywire.

Apparently Josh seldom visited the experimental division, preferring to leave them alone to get on with what they did best. But a facility was now available within the head office of Salsbury House, and, while they would still hold the larger plant at their present site, a minor experimental section, including support staff, would be moving at short notice to Salsbury House.

'Do *we* have to go?' Erin asked Ivan Kelly, her immediate boss. She felt vulnerable somehow, all sort of shaky inside, and didn't know that she would have applied for this job had she known she would be spending her working life under the same roof as Joshua Salsbury.

'Most definitely,' Ivan answered. 'The Prof's been badgering away for ages about the shortage of space here. He's over the moon that at last his voice has been heard. You don't mind, do you?' Ivan thought to ask. 'Does working over there represent some kind of transport problem?'

'No, not at all,' Erin answered, and smiled. 'I can just as easily get there as here.'

But do I want to? she had to question. It was a fact that just seeing Josh Salsbury made her feel all funny and peculiar inside. But she consoled herself that, having detoured past Salsbury House on her way back from

Croom Babbington one Sunday, it was a large enough place for her never to ever bump into him.

Besides which, Erin discovered as the move progressed, and only two weeks later she transferred to her new working abode, that new working abode turned out to be a converted building adjacent to the rear of the main building. It had its own entrance, and apart from a need for someone to occasionally hand-deliver various figures to the statistics department, or take a note to some other department, she did not in fact, as she had supposed, work in the same building as Josh Salsbury.

Which in turn made her feel most mixed up. Because while she had shied away from the thought of perhaps daily running the risk of bumping into him in some corridor, the fact that now presented itself—that she might never see him again—was, she reluctantly admitted, a little disconcerting. Without thinking about it too deeply, she was glad she had written and accepted the invitation to Charlotte's wedding. She would see him then, anyhow.

On Thursday evening, a couple of days later, Erin rang her mother. Nina was home, but sounded so unlike her usual ebullient mother that Erin grew concerned. 'What's wrong?' she asked.

'Nothing's wrong!' Nina Woodward replied smartly. Too smartly.

Erin was not taken in, and did a rapid think. She was going out with Stephen Dobbs tomorrow, and although she would quite happily cancel the arrangement, she doubted her mother would be free on a Friday evening. 'Have lunch with me tomorrow?' she invited. And, when Nina hesitated, 'Don't worry. I won't tell anyone I'm your daughter.'

'I should think not!' her mother replied, and sounded

more like her old self when she added, 'I'm much too young to have a daughter your age!' Erin knew for a fact that her mother was forty-one, but felt pleased when she agreed to lunch. 'I'm in town anyway. But it will have to be a quick lunch. Phillipe is doing my hair at two-fifteen—a marvellous man.'

Erin's concern for her parent, which had been mollified the evening before, reared up again when over lunch her mother seemed unusually quiet and thoughtful. 'Something *is* wrong,' Erin stated.

'Don't be silly,' Nina responded, and, adept at changing the subject, 'I was surprised to hear you're working for Tommy Salsbury's outfit. How are you getting on?'

'Fine,' Erin replied. 'We've transferred over to Salsbury House, but—' She broke off as a reason for the difference in her mother came to her. 'That's it, isn't it!' she exclaimed. 'You're worried about him?'

Nina Woodward gave a start. 'Worried—about who?'

'Tommy. Mr Salsbury,' Erin pressed. 'Have you heard? Has he had a relapse or something?'

'How would I know?' Her mother sounded so totally uncaring that Erin knew she had jumped to the wrong conclusion. 'The last I heard Tommy was tearing up the laps on some rubber-belted treadmill.'

Erin was much pleased to hear that. By the sound of it, Josh's father was doing well in his recovery. 'What, then?' she insisted.

'Oh, for goodness' sake! You're just like your father! He was as stubborn as blazes once he thought he was on to something.' Erin said nothing, but sat quietly and waited. 'Well, if you must know,' Nina began a touch shortly, 'I've—um—met someone.'

'When didn't you?' Erin replied calmly.

'This one's—different.'

'Different?' Nina did not answer. 'How different?'

Her mother gave her an exasperated look. 'Well, he's younger than me, for one thing. Though not by much,' she added quickly.

'And?'

Nina smiled. 'He makes me laugh. He rings me in the morning and makes me laugh. He rings me in the afternoon and...' Her voice fell away.

'And you're in love with him?' Erin suggested gently.

'Oh, I wouldn't go that far!' Nina said sharply, but then, the edge going off her voice, 'But Richard does have that little—something extra.' She looked at her watch. 'And now I must fly. We'll do this again. Lunch. Soon.' She gathered up her belongings, genteelly air-kissed her daughter, said, 'Bye, darling,' and, as elegant as ever, her hair looking immaculate, as if she had just come from the hairdresser instead of being on her way to the salon, she was gone.

Erin paid the bill and went back to her office, hoping that things went well for her mother and Richard. She did not want either of them to end up hurt, though with her mother's track record guessed that Richard was the more likely candidate. With luck, perhaps he would keep well away from the 'marriage' word.

Erin went out with Stephen on Friday evening, and on Saturday she drove to Croom Babbington. She spent a quiet time with her father and drove back to the mews apartment on Sunday evening. And by Monday she was on a more even keel about—well, Josh Salsbury in particular. It lasted until Tuesday, when Ivan Kelly, looking enormously pleased about something, came seeking her out.

She looked at him. The cat who'd swallowed the

cream had nothing on him. 'You got all six numbers in
the Lotto?' she teased.

'Not quite as good, Erin, but certainly a feather in the
cap of this department.' She was pleased for him. They
were a clever bunch, the people she worked with, and
deserved every accolade that came their way. She was
not so pleased, though, when, clearly bursting to share
his news with her, he grinned hugely and said, 'Apparently your praises have been sung in high places.' Erin
stared at him, mystified. 'As of now, you've been seconded to work for none other than the chief executive!'

Her mouth fell open, and while there was a kind of
roaring in her ears Erin stared at him. 'Ch-chief executive?' she stammered.

'Only Mr Joshua Salsbury himself!' Ivan replied
proudly. And, while Erin just stared at him, wide-eyed,
'I'm going to be lost without you,' he went on. 'But it
will only be for two weeks—nine days, actually, while
Mr Salsbury's PA is on holiday.'

'Me?' Erin managed, if faintly. 'I'm to act as his PA
for...' Her voice trailed away.

'Oh, it won't be just you,' Ivan informed her jovially.
'It seems that the PA called in to substitute for Isabel
Hill is having a hard time coping with the volume of
work. You're to assist her.'

Erin was undecided whether to run right then—out
from the building and back to the sanctuary of the mews
apartment. But excitement was stirring in her bones.
Though she made herself appear outwardly calm, at
least, when she questioned, 'You're saying that I'm to
work in Mr Joshua Salsbury's office?'

'If not his office, then the office adjoining.' Ivan
looked at his watch. 'As of now, Miss Tunnicliffe, you
are the temporary assistant to the temporary PA to the

next chairman of this company. Hurry, now,' he urged, but smiled as he added, 'But don't forget to come back.'

Erin finished the work she had been doing and tidied up a few loose ends with the first rush of excitement fading to be replaced by questions. Her? Why her? It was all very flattering, and someone somewhere must have mentioned to Personnel that she did her job well—but still, why her? Salsbury Engineering must employ dozens of other business-trained secretary dogsbody assistants with the ability to float into any section and tackle whatever came their way. So—why her?

An hour later she stepped into the main building, heading for the top floor where Josh Salsbury had his offices, and began to worry that he might know nothing of whom Personnel had selected to assist his temporary PA. Would he be annoyed that it was her?

Erin started to feel more churned up than ever when she so easily recalled that day when she had taken the minutes of a meeting and Josh had appeared. He hadn't exactly looked through her, she recalled, remembering his glance to her mouth, the lips he had once kissed. But neither had he acknowledged her either.

Erin reached the office she was looking for, having worked herself up to anticipating that in about two minutes from now she would be making her way back the way she had come, Josh Salsbury having politely—or not—told her thanks, but no thanks.

Which was when her pride kicked in. Who did he think he was? She rapped smartly on the door and went straight in. Josh Salsbury was there, and was alone. She saw at once she had chosen his office instead of the PA's office, but that was all to the good. If he was to send her on her way, she would prefer that no one else overheard.

'I've been seconded here to assist your relief PA, but I can go back again if my face doesn't fit!' she charged hostilely—her insides belonging to anyone but her.

Josh Salsbury, tall and as good-looking as ever, rose to his feet and, even though she was across the room, appeared to look down at her. He studied her for several moments. But when she was ready to do the quickest about-turn in history—if not get thrown out for her sauce—'You must know you have a most beautiful face—that fits perfectly,' he drawled, making her heart leap about for all he hadn't made it sound like a compliment. 'But heaven alone knows from where you grew that tremendous chip on your shoulder.'

Shame me, why don't you! 'I didn't know if you knew it would be me—if you—er—w-wanted me.' Swiftly, feeling herself going red, she corrected that. 'If you wanted me working in your office.'

'Now, why shouldn't I?'

You saw fit to ignore me the other day. She almost said it, but realised in time that that would make matters between them too personal. And she was here to work. 'Er—shall I get started, then?' she asked.

'Come and meet Angela Toon,' he answered.

It was then that Erin started to learn what working in a top-notch office was all about. It had taken her a couple of days to get into the swing of things, but by Friday she could fully see and understand why Angela Toon needed someone to help her with the workload; and could only admire from afar the unknown PA, Isabel Hill, who was at present taking what Erin knew without a doubt was a well-earned holiday.

But by Friday Erin knew too, without a single, solitary question of doubt, that—she had fallen in love with Joshua Salsbury.

She tried to tell herself that it was ridiculous, that she hardly knew the man. But, while it might be ridiculous, it was also fact. She woke up thinking about him, went to bed thinking about him, and if that was not enough her dreams were filled with him.

She would have liked to believe that what she felt for him was nothing more than a passing infatuation, pure and simple. After all, there was much to admire about the man. While he could be tough if the occasion demanded it, and she had heard him, at others he was positively charming. The fact that he seemed to gobble up work like none other—the charge of nepotism could never be laid at his door—amazed her. He kept both her and Angela fully occupied. But, as well as loving him, Erin loved the work.

The days flew by. In stark contrast the evenings dragged by oh, so slowly. Even so, Erin turned down a dinner invitation from Stephen Dobbs when he rang—somehow she wanted only her own company.

Erin left work on Friday, telling herself that this was crass. She would never get Josh Salsbury out of her head this way. She resolved that the next time Stephen rang she would say yes. She might even ring him. She didn't.

She went home to Croom Babbington on Saturday, counted almost every tick of the clock, and returned to London on Sunday, eager and hardly able to wait to get to work tomorrow.

Angela Toon started with a cold on Monday, and, try though she did, she had a hard time keeping up. By Tuesday her cold was ready to break out, but by Wednesday it had arrived in full force.

Josh Salsbury came into the office after her fourth sneeze in quick succession, took one look at her runny eyes and red nose, and strode over to the coat rack and selected the coat that was hers. 'Much though we value your input, Angela, I'm afraid we're going to have to manage without you,' he informed her kindly.

'I'll be fine!' Angela protested thickly.

'After a few days' rest,' he assured her, helped her into her coat and told her not to think of returning before Monday. And, once she was gone, 'Ring Personnel,' he instructed Erin. 'You'll need an assistant.'

'Suddenly I'm promoted!'

'Less of the sauce,' he growled, and halted for a moment when Erin's lovely face lit up with laughter, then went back to his own office.

Was it any wonder that she loved him? Erin gave her attention to her work and put her hand on the telephone, ready to ring Personnel. But, recalling how it had taken her time to get the hang of the office, she changed her mind and went through to the next-door office instead.

Josh was already busy with something, but after a second or two he looked up, and Erin plunged straight in, 'I was thinking, Mr Salsbury—' She broke off, fascinated when he raised an eyebrow at her formal use of his name. So, okay, yes, they had kissed. 'Well, the thing is,' she rushed on, 'I can't see anyone Personnel find arriving here before lunch. That leaves only two and a half days to go before your permanent PA comes back.'

'Your point?'

Trust him to want to get straight to the point—it was his way; she knew that by now. 'The point is that it will take someone new a couple of days to get the hang of things up here—and by the time I've finished explaining everything I could have done whatever it is myself.'

'You're saying you don't want an assistant?'

'Well, I know I can't hope to be up to Isabel's standard. But, yes, that's what I'm saying.'

'You think you'll be able to cope on your own?'

She wanted to say a firm and confident Of course, but did not want him to think she was big-headed. 'Given I shall probably have to work late a couple of times. Yes,' she answered.

His glance slid to her gently curving mouth. Though she doubted he was recalling how their lips had met, or that he even remembered it. Then he flicked his glance back up to her lovely violet eyes. 'Go to it—Miss Tunnicliffe,' said he, who had only ever addressed her as Erin. 'Go to it.'

She laughed, and went back to her own office. She knew her work was going to seem awfully dull after she departed his office come Friday afternoon. She had thought she loved her work in Experimental, but now rather thought seeing the busy cut and thrust of business from up here had spoilt her.

Josh went out at midday and did not return until three, when she went in to see him with some queries. 'Still coping?' he asked.

'Having a lovely time,' she answered, and smiled.

His gaze stayed on her. 'I suppose you must be. Weren't you only going to be in London for a short while?'

It was the first time while working in his office that he had referred to the fact they had known each other outside of the office. 'I came, liked what I saw—' she smiled '—and decided to stay awhile.'

'Away from your father's parental protection!' Josh commented, and Erin felt all churned-up inside suddenly.

'I—er...'

'I've embarrassed you?'

You care? 'I go and stay with him every weekend.

Talking of fathers,' she said in a rush, 'how is your father?' And, having rushed in without thinking, felt obliged to go on, 'It must have been something of a shock when he had a heart attack.'

'He's doing well, and should, if he heeds medical advice, make a good recovery.'

'Oh, I'm so glad!' Erin said fervently, and caught Joshua-never-miss-a-thing-Salsbury's sharp look.

'You know my father?' he demanded abruptly.

'No, no,' she denied, and, fearful that she might give something away, placed the folder in her hands on his desk and spoke of work.

Back at her desk, she half wished she had used what she now saw as a tailor-made opportunity to tell Josh that, while she herself did not know his father, her mother had known him. Erin admitted that she wanted to tell him; it just did not feel right to *not* tell him.

But she had not missed that tough strand of protectiveness in his abrupt tone when he'd asked 'You know my father?', and on reflection she thought it better that she had stayed silent. She would have to put up with that feeling of guilt that niggled away at her, she realised. Because it seemed pretty plain to her that Josh was aware that Nina Woodward had had a hand in stressing his father into heart attack country. Josh would just love it, wouldn't he, if he knew that that woman's daughter was working in his own office?

She would just have to put up with feeling guilty. How could she tell him? She hadn't asked to work for him, but had loved every minute of it. And to tell him would, she knew without doubt, see her back in Experimental quicker than that. Worse, Josh would probably refuse to countenance her working anywhere at all in Salsbury Engineering Systems. She'd be thrown out, her feet never touching the ground. No, she couldn't tell him. Quite definitely, she could not. While she was working for the company she might chance to occasionally see him, remote though the chance was. And, who knew? He might want cover again one day, should his PA be away again, and Personnel might call on her services once more.

Erin sighed. She loved him. Weak, feeble she might be, but she did not want to close the door on the chance to see him again—however remote that possibility might be.

But Erin did not like what falling in love had done to her. She did not enjoy the thought that she was being weak and feeble. So she determinedly ousted Josh Salsbury from her thoughts and got on with what she was good at: her job.

Even so, even having put in a good day's work, she still had to work late that night. She did not mind a bit. Josh had left his office around four on some business or other. He had not returned by the time she was ready to leave.

She tidied her desk, realising that she must guard against him seeing anything of her feelings for him. Going smartly from the building, she recalled how easily he could make her laugh, and Erin resolved then that there was no way he was ever going to know what he had done to her.

'What time did you work until last night?' he asked when she went in the next morning.

'Did you want me for something when you got back?' she asked in reply.

He shook his head. 'I was just impressed by the amount of work you cleared while I was out.'

He must be referring to the typing she had locked

away in his drawer prior to going home. 'Some have genius thrust upon them,' she cheerfully misquoted—and loved it when *he* laughed.

The day went well. They worked hard and in splendid harmony together. Erin feared Experimental was going to be only half as stimulating after this.

'Have you much more to do?' he asked, coming into her office some time shortly after six.

'Not so much,' she answered. And, noting that he appeared to be about to leave, 'Just off?'

'I've a dinner engagement. I'd prefer not to be late.'

Ferocious green spears of cruel jealousy slammed into her. He was going home to shower and change and get ready to call for some luscious lovely! Momentarily Erin felt she hated him. But it was an emotion of the moment and then she was swiftly recalling how she had resolved that there was no way he was going to see how it was with her. So, even while she was feeling totally devastated—ridiculous, she owned, but who said love was reasonable?—she looked down to tidy the papers in front of her.

'Either you've got it or you haven't,' she trotted out with a flick of a glance up at him.

He held her glance, making her unable to look away. 'True,' he agreed, and added, 'And you're a lippy little trollop.'

And she had to laugh. In spite of herself she had to laugh. 'Lippy, maybe. But trollop? I'm working on that.'

'Still?' He seemed interested that she had not yet carried out her stated intention to 'whatever' as soon as she could.

'I'll get there,' she assured him. And, feeling all hot and bothered inside at this personal turn, she looked from him, picked up her pen and, without the least idea of what she had been doing, said, 'Goodnight,' and leafed unseeingly through a few sheets of typewritten matter.

'Goodnight, Erin,' he answered quietly. She did not look up again until she heard the door close behind him.

She did not sleep at all well that night. For one thing what fractured sleep she did find was interspersed with dreams of Josh Salsbury dancing the night away with some sylph in his arms.

Erin journeyed to work on Friday with her stomach all knotted up, because this was her last day of working with him. Isabel Hill would be back in harness come Monday, and that would be that.

Erin had just crossed the road to Salsbury House when, to set her heart fluttering, Josh Salsbury stepped up to the building with her. 'Where did you park your car?' he enquired in friendly fashion as, reaching the door, he opened it and waited for her to precede him.

'I don't use my car for work. It's easier to use public transport to get here,' she replied, and as they walked over to the lifts she fought to get herself together, green barbs doing their nasty work again—he was always, but *always* in first! Always early! All too obviously he'd had one very late night!

Others joined them in the lift, which gave Erin a chance to get herself in more of one piece. But the lift emptied before it reached the top floor and she was very conscious of Josh standing next to her. 'Good meal?' she heard herself say, when she was sure she was not the tiniest bit interested. He didn't look as though he'd spent the whole night on the tiles, but what did she know?

'Not bad,' he replied. 'Went on a bit, as these things are prone to do.'

He sounded bored! Good! Erin hoped she had bored

him senseless, whoever she was. 'The meal?' Shut up, Erin. Shut up, do. You just don't need to hear any more.

'The evening,' he replied, to gladden her heart. 'You know what these business dinners are like.'

She didn't, actually, but as they entered their offices she could not deny that she was suddenly on cloud nine. He hadn't been wining and dining some lovely! Erin only just managed to prevent herself from breaking into a few choruses of 'Oh, what a beautiful morning'.

Matters took a downturn around ten-forty-five when, with the door between the two offices open, her phone rang and a male voice she had forgotten she knew said, 'Hello, is that Erin?'

'Speaking.'

'Mark Prentice,' he announced himself.

Mark Prentice? Mark Prentice? Click. Grief—and she had at one time thought him her boyfriend! 'Hello, Mark,' she replied, perhaps more warmly than she'd meant—probably because it didn't hurt a bit. If anything, he had done her a favour. But for him and that episode she might still be working for him in a nothing kind of job, might still be living in dear but—let's face it—dull as ditchwater Croom Babbington. 'How are you?' she followed up brightly, glancing through to the other office to see that Josh had looked up from what he was doing, as though suspecting the call might be for him. She placed her hand over the mouthpiece and told her employer, 'It's for me—personal,' and gave her attention back to Mark.

Apparently he was in London for the day and would like to take her to lunch. 'I know it's short notice, but you weren't answering your mobile yesterday and I didn't manage to get your office number until last night.'

From her father, obviously, who—equally obviously—would have insisted on knowing why he wanted it.

Erin kept her mobile switched off in the office, and realised she had not switched it on when she got home. But—lunch? In truth she didn't have time to take a full hour for lunch. Against that though, she didn't want Mark Prentice forming an impression that she had been so enamoured of him that she was still too hurt to see him.

'I'd love to have lunch with you,' she assured him brightly, made the arrangements, and put down the phone.

She went into the other office a few minutes later, but before she could carry out her intention to check a detail on the work she was engaged on her employer bluntly questioned, 'You have a lunch date?'

Had he asked nicely she might have replied in the vein that she didn't know how to contact her lunchee, but that if Josh had something urgent he wanted doing she would contact the restaurant and leave a message for Mark. But Josh had not asked nicely. In actual fact his tone had been quite antagonistic. And if he was anti because she had taken a personal call in his time, then, after the way she had slaved for him, not to mention the extra hours she had put in, could *he* go and take a running jump!

So, instead of being the good little temporary PA, Erin fired straight back, 'Why should you have all the fun!'

A grunt was her answer. She went back to her desk. She would sort out her query when he was in a better humour. Honestly! He might be the big noise around here but, having come to realise that she was neither her mother nor her father but a person in her own right, Erin knew she did not have to put up with such treatment. Nor did she intend to!

Her annoyance with Josh Salsbury did not last long. In fact, loving him as she did, it amazed her that she could be angry with him at all. Love was making a nonsense of her, and she almost went and asked him if there was something in particular that he required actioning in the lunch-hour.

She did not do anything of the sort. Pride, another part of unrequited love, roused its stiff back and decreed she made herself a doormat for no man. If he felt he could speak to her like that, then he could suffer the consequences.

On the stroke of one she picked up her bag and left the office. A pity his door was by then closed—he wouldn't even notice!

Mark was waiting for her and kissed her cheek in greeting. He might have kissed her mouth, but she turned her head when her radar antennae went into action.

'You're as lovely as ever,' he said, holding on to both her hands.

How trite when he said it—how spine-melting it would have been had Josh Salsbury said it. 'You're looking well,' she replied, retrieving her hands.

They made their way to their reserved table and Erin sat opposite Mark Prentice and wondered—What on earth did I see in this man? She tried to be fair—he had seemed quite something back in Croom Babbington. But she had left Croom Babbington three months ago. And she had since met many different men, men at work, Stephen Dobbs. Nice men all. Even Gavin Gardner. So perhaps she had grown a little since leaving her home village. True, she had also met Joshua Salsbury who, without even knowing it, made all other men fade into the background. But, whatever had happened to her since she had left her home, Erin knew that were Mark Prentice to ask her on a date tonight—and it had little to do with the fact that he had taken his 'pleasures' elsewhere—she would not have accepted.

Which was a pity, because that was more or less what he did ask, barely into their starters. 'I've missed you, Erin,' he said soulfully across the table.

Perhaps she should have felt guilty that *she* hadn't missed *him*, not in the slightest. 'I'm sure your new secretary is very good at her job.' She chose to tactfully misunderstand him.

'I wasn't talking about work.'

So much for tact! She didn't believe he'd missed her anyway. It had taken him three months to find out he'd missed her! 'How *is* work? I expect business is as good as ever?'

'I was wrong to do what I did,' he pressed on, and Erin began to wish that she had never agreed to lunch with him.

'Well, it can't be helped now,' she answered lightly, and was a little shaken when he leaned across the table and caught a hold of her left hand.

'I was a fool, Erin. If only I could turn back the clock,' he said earnestly.

She quickly pulled her hand out of his grip. 'We all do things we—er—regret a little,' she said brightly, but felt dreadfully embarrassed.

'I regret what I did so much—so very, very much!' Mark declared ardently.

Oh, crumbs. 'You've no need to apologise,' was the best she could come up with.

'You mean you've forgiven me? You'll let us start all over again? You'll—'

'That's not what I'm saying at all,' Erin butted in quickly. And, with more tact than he deserved, 'It just isn't on, Mark. I live and work here now. We'd never see each other.'

'You come home every weekend,' he came back speedily, encouraged rather than discouraged, as she'd intended. 'Your father said you did when he told me to call around and see you when you came home tomorrow if it was so urgent.'

She stopped him right there. 'I'm sorry, Mark.' There was no way to dress it up. 'I don't think our getting back together is a very good idea.'

He took some convincing, but at last he appeared to accept that he didn't stand a chance. The restaurant was crowded, the service slow and, too late realising that to meet Mark at all had been a mistake, all Erin wanted to do was to get back to the office with all speed. The lunchtime seemed to go on for ever.

'Perhaps we'll bump into each other at the weekend?' Mark suggested hopefully as they parted.

'We may well do,' she said smilingly, and suffered another kiss to her cheek, knowing she was going to take jolly good care not to 'bump' into him.

She was late getting back to the office. The dividing door now stood open and she was in full receipt of Josh Salsbury's baleful glare when she went in. But when she knew she would work late to make up for any time lost—perhaps because she owed him the courtesy, or perhaps because she couldn't bear to be bad friends with him, or maybe a mixture of both—she went through to apologise.

'Sorry to be late back,' she trotted out prettily. 'The waiters were rushed off their feet. You know how it is.'

What she was expecting she had no idea, probably

some kind of, Now you're here, shall we get on? So she was more than a little taken aback when, tersely, he questioned, 'Mark's the one you left home over?'

Startled, Erin stared at her employer, more surprised that he had remembered her telling him about Mark than anything. 'I—er—don't actually recollect Mark having too much to do with my decision,' she replied, while trying to recall if he had figured in her decision at all.

'He's the one who bedded an ex-girlfriend when you declined the offer,' Josh documented. And, while Erin was still staring at him, but unable to deny it, 'You're surely not thinking of going back to him?' he bit shortly.

What was this? She'd only come in to apologise! 'That's another offer I declined,' she answered stiffly, and was halfway to the door when Josh's voice stopped her.

'He wants you back?' Erin was not happy with this conversation. It didn't seem quite right, somehow, to be discussing someone else's emotions. But Josh had his answer anyway. 'You dumped him,' he detailed. 'In effect, you dumped him.'

She opened her mouth to say it was none of his business, but then to her horror heard herself say something she had never, ever thought that she would say. 'I felt obliged to let him go,' she answered shortly, and went swiftly back to her desk, having to accept that while for sure she was her own person, there was without question something of her mother in her too somewhere!

Erin crashed into her work and put in a good hour on some complicated material, her mood lightening because when she went in to see Josh with a query he had lost his short edge with her.

It did not last. They had a lot to get through, and he was a work-oriented man, and did not care for interruption when the phone rang and it was another personal call for her.

'Oh, hello, Stephen,' she answered with a smile when she recognised his voice.

'Are you doing anything tonight?' he asked, and followed up with, 'How's your bowling arm?'

She laughed. 'I don't have one.' And as for going out that night, the pace they were going she'd be ready to flop at the end of her working day—always supposing she finished work before midnight. 'Tonight's a bit difficult,' she said, and, aware just then of Josh's impatient movement when he must have realised she was dallying in his time, 'I'll see you on Monday.' She closed the call, knowing that she'd be returning to Experimental come Monday.

'See you then,' he accepted happily enough, and they said goodbye.

It was not a figment of her imagination that J. Salsbury Esquire had gone crotchety again. 'It sounds as if you've moved on!' he snarled the moment she'd put down the phone.

'You know how it is, I'm sure,' she coldly bit back.

They worked in stony silence, managing, just, to be civil when business decreed they talk to each other. They worked without a break. She supposed she could have gone and got him a cup of tea, but she was feeling stubborn.

What a way to end what had started out as a fantastic nine days, she mourned when, gone seven that evening, she finished the last of her tasks.

She prepared her desk, ready for Isabel Hill to take over on Monday, left appropriate notes in Isabel's desk drawer regarding pending matters, and went in to say goodnight to the man she still loved—even if he was being a pig of the first water. Erin felt certain then that she would never again be called on to work for him. And since the only time she had ever bumped into him was that morning—using an entrance that she would not use when working in Experimental—she knew that, apart from Charlotte's wedding, she was unlikely to see him again.

He looked up just as Erin opened her mouth to tell him she was off home. 'You look tired!' he grunted.

'What every girl just aches to hear!' some snappy part of her she was not too familiar with erupted.

He gave her an icy look, then glanced at his watch, saw they had been hard at it for the past five hours and capped his pen. 'I'd better take you for something to eat,' he declared.

Don't force yourself, she fumed as he rose to his feet. 'I had a big meal at lunchtime, thanks all the same!' she retorted, her stubborn hat well and truly in place as she denied herself the chance to sit at a table with him.

Nothing more to be said, she went quickly back into the other office, picked up her bag and smartly got out of there. Thank you so much for all the hard work you've put in! Erin fumed. I so appreciate it! Eat with him? She'd sooner *starve!*

She calmed down a little as she walked along. She was heading in the direction of the tube station when she suddenly became aware of a long sleek dark car purring beside her. She stopped. The passenger door opened.

'Get in!' Josh Salsbury commanded. It was not a request, but an order.

About to tell him to get lost, Erin hesitated, and *she* was lost. She got in. The car picked up speed, and when he headed in the direction of the mews apartment she knew that he had accepted that she did not want anything to eat but that he was making it his business to see that she arrived home safely.

They drove in silence, but she didn't mind. He had said she looked tired. Tired was how she felt, and, given that she had been stubborn about not eating with him, she was glad she had given in about taking a lift home.

Though he must be tired too. Her heart started to warm towards him. The work he got through was phenomenal. He'd be glad to get home too.

Suddenly—belatedly, she admitted—she realised that he must be starving. He had been at his desk when she'd gone to lunch, and still there when she'd got back. Had he eaten anything at all?

By the time he drew his car to a stop at the mews apartment Erin was feeling mortified that she hadn't so much as fetched him a cup of tea. It made no difference that he was quite capable of fetching his own tea. She loved him; she should have looked out for him.

Impulsively she turned in her seat to look at him. 'I'll feed you if you like,' she blurted out, apropos of absolutely nothing. But, immediately recalling the last time he'd been in the apartment, she felt herself going a touch pink. And, at pains to let him know that this was no come-on, she rapidly followed up with a gulped, 'But I don't want any of that kissing business!'

He turned his head to stare hostilely at her. Oh, my word—kissing? He gave her a *killing* look. 'I'm hungry for neither!' he informed her curtly. And, if that wasn't enough to put her in her place, 'Some men might want to bed you, Erin Tunnicliffe—I'm not one of them.'

Open-mouthed, she stared at him. Then fury with him rocketed in. If he had anything more to say in the same acid vein, then she was not waiting around to hear it. She shot out of the car, jet propelled. The swine! The utter, unspeakable pig! In her view she had heard more than enough!

CHAPTER FOUR

AS ERIN had supposed, work in the upper echelons of Salsbury Engineering Systems had rather spoiled her for the experimental division. She missed the buzz, the excitement. She gave serious thought to leaving. But couldn't do it.

Two weeks went by and she gradually adjusted to being back in her own section. But her thoughts that she would never again be called upon to work directly for Josh Salsbury seemed to be underlined when, half anticipating that Isabel Hill might ask her up to the top floor to help sort out some query left behind, Isabel did not ring. She had sent her a note of thanks for managing so well in her absence—a note that included the information that a bonus would be paid into her bank at the end of the month.

Erin started to sleep badly. Josh was constantly in her head and she tried to get angry with him that when he could have just as easily written a 'thank you for managing' note he had not.

Which, she owned, wasn't quite fair to him. She'd seen the work he got through. Was he supposed to take time out of his busy day to write her a note? Get real. That was what PA's were for.

And why would he write her a note anyway? And if he did, which he wouldn't, would she read it and feel happy? She remembered the way they had parted and her pride reared up again. 'Some men might want to bed you, Erin Tunnicliffe—I'm not one of them'—as if she wouldn't tear any note he wrote into a dozen pieces!

Pride did not make it hurt any the less, though. He'd be lucky to get the chance! she fumed indignantly. Then she would recall his lingering kiss that time, and she knew his were the only kisses she ever wanted.

She was glad of her uncomplicated friendship with Stephen Dobbs. They went bowling together, and she met a few of his friends, and occasionally they went out in a small group—and she never once caught so much as a glimpse of Joshua Salsbury.

The logical part of her head demanded that she cut Josh totally out of her life. That she leave her job and remove even the remote possibilities of bumping into him. That would, of course, include writing a 'Sorry I can't come to your wedding after all' kind of note to Charlotte. But Erin could not do it. Instead she found she was scouring the shops for something 'a bit special' to wear on the day.

She found it two days before she was to drive to Bristol for the wedding. It was a pale violet shade, more of a deep lavender, that brought out the violet shade of her eyes to perfection. It was a sleeveless sheath of a dress made of silk, but with a chiffon overdress that had long sleeves. She felt she looked good in it

It was to be an afternoon wedding, and as she drove to Bristol on Saturday Erin was beset by a whole gamut of emotions because she would see Josh today. She had a tremendous need to know that she looked good.

Her confidence was given a boost in that when she reached the church several of the ushers made a beeline to direct her to her seat. She was escorted down the aisle by two men who introduced themselves as Greg Williams and Archie Nevitt.

She spotted Josh seated at the front, to the side of Robin, and her heart flipped over. Josh had his back to her but, to do her heart good, both Greg and Archie had decided to stay awhile and chat when Josh glanced back and across.

Their eyes met but, outwardly cool, even if her insides were all of a tremble, Erin looked from him and smiled up at Greg, in answer to something to do with him becoming better acquainted when his duties were over. Josh Salsbury might not 'fancy' her, but it was a salve to her pride that he should witness two men who clearly did.

'That makes two of us.' Archie was quick to stake his own claim. She smiled at him too.

But, their usher duties calling them away, Erin settled in her seat and studied the Order of Service she had been handed. When she thought she had herself under control she casually, pleasantly, glanced around, taking in with the sweep of her glance the man at the front to the right of the aisle.

Josh was no longer looking her way, had only glanced over for the briefest of moments anyway, and was now facing the front. Which gave Erin all the time in the world to feast her eyes on him. He looked particularly handsome in his morning suit. Looked both sharp and relaxed, sophisticated yet friendly. She loved the way his hair, kept short, wanted to bend into the back of his neck.

She wished things had been different. Wished she could have told him about her mother. But, then again, how could she? The last time she had seen him he had accused her of dumping Mark. More than ever now she could not tell him that her mother had known his father quite well, reveal that her mother was Nina Woodward, the woman who, a week before Thomas Salsbury had suffered a heart attack, had dumped him. No way did Erin want to see outrage in Josh's eyes as he noted, like dumping mother, like dumping daughter.

'Shall I sit with you?'

There were others in the pew, but not only did Greg Williams move into the pew to keep her company, Archie Nevitt squeezed in too. The fact that two of the ushers had for the moment completed their duties was a fair indication that the bride had arrived.

She had, and Charlotte looked absolutely gorgeous when, on her father's arm, with bridesmaids following, she came down the aisle in a cloud of white.

Erin felt quite emotional as Charlotte and Robin exchanged their vows, but during other parts of the service Erin's eyes would stray to Josh.

She had herself under control from then on, though. When the bride and bridegroom walked back up the aisle, followed in procession by their parents, and then the best man with the chief bridesmaid on his arm, Erin was intent on eye-to-eye contact with Greg Williams.

When she too walked from the church door she was still determined not to be caught with her eyes on the best man. That was not to say, however, that she wasn't aware of where he was most of the time.

And most of the time it seemed to her, as that green-eyed alien appeared again, to be paying more attention to the rather lovely chief bridesmaid than, in Erin's view, was strictly necessary. Erin gave her attention to Greg and Archie.

Because so many people had been invited the reception was being held at a hotel just outside Bristol, and not in the bride's home. Both Greg and Archie offered to drive her to the reception, but, their offers declined, they soon found her when in her own transport she arrived at the hotel.

Somehow or other, to the chagrin of Archie, Greg Williams managed to arrange it so that he sat next to her for the wedding meal. And, in truth, Erin was glad that he did. Greg was good-looking and attentive, and since she and Greg were seated facing the bridal table it was an aid to her pride that Josh Salsbury should not think her some unwanted wallflower.

Not that he appeared to have noticed that she was in the room, or was there at all, Erin considered, feeling inwardly an emotional mess as she outwardly smiled at Greg and kept up a pleasant line of banter with him. She'd like to know what Josh had just said to the bridesmaid that had sent her off into peals of laughter!

No, she wouldn't, Erin denied. She didn't care a bit. Which was why she laughed lightly when Greg said anything amusing, and why she kept her eyes mainly on him.

Speeches were made, toasts were drunk, people started to move around, mingle. Erin had a few words with Charlotte and Robin, and felt misty-eyed again when dancing began and the two executed the first waltz together. They looked a couple, a pair, a match, and she felt good inside that they had found each other.

Erin danced with both Greg and Archie, and with other men too, but saw no sign of Josh Salsbury wanting to dance with her.

Time started to drag, and when at eight o'clock Charlotte went to change out of her wedding dress Erin was wondering how much longer she could bear to stay. Josh was dancing with the bridesmaid—Erin had to admit they looked good together on the dance floor.

'I think I'll make tracks too,' Erin told Greg, who was

sticking close to her side when they later went outside to wave the bride and groom off to their secret honeymoon location.

'You can't go yet!' Greg protested. 'You haven't told me nearly enough about yourself. Besides...' he smiled down into her violet eyes '...we're getting on together so famously!' His smile became an arch look. 'Surely we should get to know each other—better still?'

Erin wasn't sure she felt too comfortable with that remark, but just then, as everyone started to wander back inside the hotel, she brushed heavily against someone. She looked up to automatically apologise, but as her heart started to pound so her voice dried in her throat.

'You're sure you know what you're getting into?' Josh Salsbury questioned coldly.

She heard him; no one else did. But she was more interested in showing him that she didn't give a light than in comprehending what he was talking about. 'Perfectly,' she answered loftily, and stuck her head in the air—and instead of going to her car, as she had intended, she turned to tell Greg, 'You're right, of course, Greg,' with small idea, until she caught his lecherous look of delight, what he was 'right' about.

They were on the dance floor, and he was holding her much too tightly, when it dawned on her that she had just agreed to get to know Greg Williams better. Couple that with Josh Salsbury's 'You're sure you know what you're getting into?' and warning bells started to ring in her head.

Those warning bells did not merely ring but started to clang out a tremendous clamour when the dance ended and Greg escorted her back to a table. He grabbed up a couple of glasses of champagne from a hovering waiter *en route*, and grinned as he said, 'Word has it that the hotel's full. But sit here while I go and sweet-talk the receptionist into finding us somewhere to lay our heads.'

She stared at him.

'I won't be long,' he promised confidently.

And while she was feeling too stunned by this turn of events to so much as squeak out a protest, Erin took a grip on the champagne glass in front of her. She knew then that, whatever erroneous signals Greg had been picking up, the time had come to tell him, and to tell him quickly, that wherever he was laying his head that night she wouldn't be there to share his pillow.

Agitatedly she played with the stem of the champagne glass, realising that some of the fault for those erroneous signals was well and truly hers—and Josh Salsbury's! It was only because Josh was there that she had been much more forward, flirtatious, even, than she would normally dream of being. It was only because she was trying to cover up what seeing him with 'the laughing bridesmaid' was doing to her, while at the same time hiding that she loved the over-confident, over-everything swine that...

'Bolstering up your courage, Erin?' A silky-toned voice she would rather not hear just then broke into her thoughts.

She looked up sharply. Just what she didn't need! Josh Salsbury, having seen what was going on before she had recognised Greg Williams's intent herself, had come to mock her. Her eyes followed Josh's glance to the table, where her long dainty fingers were still in contact with the stem of the champagne glass.

'For your information, I've limited myself to only one glass of champagne!' she snapped.

He ignored her reply, hellbent, it seemed, on following his own line of thought. 'And I quote—"No, but I'm going to as soon as I can."' And as she just sat and stared at him, recalling how she had once more or less told him she was going to go to bed with someone as soon as she could, he went on to challenge, 'Do I take it you're about to embark on your ''soonest'' endeavour?'

Stunned, it took her a second to let what he had just said sink in. But a moment after that fury rushed in, and she was absolutely outraged. Of all the nerve! Of all the... 'And the reason I've limited my champagne consumption,' she flew, too incensed all at once to stop and wonder why she was explaining anything at all to him, 'is because I have every intention of driving myself back to London—alone!'

She was angry with herself then too, that she was actually *explaining* anything! And in a rush of further fury with him, and with the whole male population— Greg Williams included, that he should toddle off without so much as a by-your-leave to go and find them a bed for the night—she stormed to her feet, sparks positively flying from her eyes that Josh Salsbury should think what he so obviously did think.

'And for your further information,' she charged, her violet eyes on fire, 'to go to bed with some man could not be further from my mind. And if you see Greg Williams you can jolly well tell him that from me. The only place I'm going,' she hurled, incensed, 'is home!'

And, having delivered that outraged tirade, she spun furiously about. And though Josh moved fast, it was not fast enough; she went crashing into a marble pillar that she had known was there but had been too enraged to give thought to. She saw stars—then nothing.

She slowly became aware of voices, hers and—she was having a conversation with someone. That was to say someone was talking to her, asking her questions and making her answer. She wished they would shut up—she wanted to go to sleep. Hang it all, she had been sleeping so badly, and now—now that she had the chance to get some rest, now that she was ready to get some sleep—somebody was badgering away at her.

'How many fingers am I holding up?'

She opened her eyes—light screamed in—she quickly closed them again. The light hurt her eyes. 'If I tell you three will you shut up and go away?' she answered.

'She'll do,' said the voice.

Then she had funny dreams of Josh being there. But then, he was always in her dreams, so what was new? 'How are you feeling now?' he asked.

'How do I look?'

'Enchanting,' he answered.

She sighed. It was a lovely dream. She wanted to tell him she loved him, but some strand of modesty, even in her dream, held her back. 'Do you like me?' she asked instead.

'Who could help but like you?' he replied.

'Suitably non-committal,' she mumbled, and sighed again. 'Goodnight, darling,' she said softly.

'Goodnight, sweetheart,' he said in the same quiet tone.

'Would you kiss me?' she requested. 'Just a gentle kiss, like before.' There was a bit of a pause. But then she felt his lips gently touch her brow. 'Thank you, Josh,' she whispered.

'You know it's me?'

She felt so tired, so dreadfully tired. 'Who else would I let into my dreams?' she answered sleepily. 'Goodnight,' she bade him again. And, her dream closing down, she went to sleep again.

Erin awoke and didn't quite know where she was. She

was in bed, but it wasn't her bed. She was in a strange room and, while it was otherwise dark, there was a small bedside lamp on somewhere. It was not to the left of the bed, where she had been sleeping, but on the other side of the bed where—Josh Salsbury, his face turned towards her, was sleeping.

She smiled. 'I'm still dreaming,' she said out loud. But at the sound of her voice the man beside her opened his eyes and, bare-chested, sat up. And as he looked over to her so the knowledge stampeded in to Erin—*that she was neither dreaming nor asleep!*

'What...?' she gasped, amazed, her eyes hypnotised by his all-male naked chest for moments before she gained her second wind. 'Wh-wh...? *Get out!*' she screamed. Then, urgently countermanding that, 'No! Don't!' she squeaked, having no idea how naked the rest of him might be. 'I didn't...?' she questioned hoarsely, as she fought for a memory that just wasn't there. 'Oh, my head!' she groaned, as the mother and father of all headaches made its presence felt.

She abruptly and tightly shut her eyes. And the next time she opened them it was to see that Josh had moved quickly to grab up a light robe from somewhere, had it about him and was coming round to her side of the bed. 'Here, take these,' he said quietly, handing her a couple of tablets and reaching to the bedside table for a glass of water. 'The doctor left them. He said you might need them when you woke up.'

Hearing Josh speak for the first time made it certain for Erin that this wasn't any dream. Josh was here, truly here! And he was real!

But various other matters were jostling for precedence in her head. Though first she sat up and swallowed down the painkillers. As Josh took the glass from her, and took a seat on the side of the bed, 'Doctor?' she asked.

'You knocked yourself out,' Josh enlightened her.

'At the risk of sounding like some B movie actress—where am I?' she asked.

'In a hotel just outside of Bristol.'

'Did I ask you to kiss me?' she found she was asking inconsequentially.

Josh grinned. 'You remember?' He seemed relieved. 'It wasn't such a difficult task.'

She made an effort to remember more. 'I've been to Charlotte's wedding, right?'

'Right,' he answered. 'You were encouraging Greg Williams to do his worst. Remember him?'

'Oh, grief, yes. You were accusing me of—um—trolloping,' she dragged from the painful reaches of her aching head.

Josh smiled at her description, but went on to explain, 'You had a crack at denting a marble pillar with your head—and came off second best.'

'I—fainted—um—knocked myself out, you said?'

'You went down like a sack of coal.'

'Thanks!' Very descriptive! But, growing more awake by the minute—not to mention aware—she began to feel a little panicky, and suddenly erupted, 'What the devil was I doing in bed with you?'

'Calm down, calm down!' He shushed her. 'There was a doctor in the wedding party. He needed somewhere to check you over, and since I had a room booked here, and I was the first one to you, I naturally offered my room.'

'That doesn't explain why we—we're sharing the same bed!' she inserted pithily.

'I knew you'd be grateful!' he retorted.

'What for?' she challenged suspiciously.

'You should be so lucky!' he rapped. 'I like my women responsive.'

'I bet you do!' she snorted. But did calm down a fraction to push forward. 'So, you had me brought to your room?'

'You were a dead weight.'

'You carried me?' she asked in surprise.

He shrugged. 'Somebody had to do it. Anyhow, you started to come round, and the doctor gave you the once-over and said you'd be okay, but to try to keep you awake for a few hours.'

'That was what all that talking was about in my dream?'

Josh nodded. 'Anyway, round about midnight the doctor looked in again and said you were fine, but that it might be an idea to see that you weren't left on your own for a while.'

'So you stayed?'

'There was nowhere else to go. The hotel's full and—come two o'clock—there are you, sleeping like a baby.'

'You watched me in my sleep?' she questioned, grateful—but embarrassed.

'It wasn't such a hardship. You're extraordinarily beautiful, Erin.'

Her heartbeats fluttered. She opened her mouth, but as it sank in that Josh thought her extraordinarily beautiful she couldn't think of a thing to say. 'Um—so…?' she murmured.

'So there are you, two in the morning, sleeping soundly and in no danger, and there am I, by then admitting that I wouldn't mind a bit of shut-eye myself. You were sleeping well over to one side. There was more than half a bed going to waste.'

'So, just like that—you got in?'

He glanced humorously at her. 'I disposed of most of my clothing first,' he commented dryly.

'It's a relief to know you've got something on under there!' she snapped hostilely.

'Be it only my socks,' he tormented.

But she did not think it funny. Especially as, with talk of disposing of clothes, she had just then alarmingly realised that she was wearing next to nothing herself! She looked down to where most of her lacy bra was on view, and hurriedly felt beneath the covers to discover, with relief, that the other item of clothing she was left with was her briefs.

'Who undressed me?' she asked faintly, trying desperately hard to recall a friendly female face amongst the gathering. 'Charlotte's mother?'

'There were many offers,' Josh replied nicely. But, to shake her to the core, 'I thought you'd prefer that I did it.'

'You did it!' she echoed croakily, blushing crimson. She didn't doubt that he was no stranger to undressing the female form, but—honestly! But having been rocked at the revelation that he must have unzipped her dress and seen her semi-naked, there awoke in Erin a need to shake him for his trouble. Now what...? Got it! 'We've shared a bed, you and I,' she stated, and in no uncertain terms went on to stress, 'Contrary to anything—er—improper I may have been considering when I came to London, I'm still a good girl,' she informed him. 'Which means, I'm afraid, Josh Salsbury, that you're going to have to marry me.' How she said it with a straight face she never knew, but his look of total startlement was all the reward that she needed. She burst out laughing. 'Relax, I didn't mean it,' she confessed. 'I just wanted to see the whites of your eyes.'

His face creased with laughter. 'Cheeky baggage! I think we can safely say you're not suffering from concussion. Now, lie down and go to sleep.'

Erin loved to see him laugh, but that wasn't why she stared at him. 'With you here?' she objected.

'It's four in the morning,' he informed her.

Meaning, she supposed, that she'd have to be the most heartless of creatures to turn him out of *his* room in a fully occupied hotel at four in the morning. She thought of how especially good he had been in carrying her here anyway. But when the alternative to borrowing his bed for a few hours more was for her to get up and drive back to London, with her head still throbbing away, she just didn't feel up to it.

'Goodnight—morning,' she said, and lay fragilely down.

Josh got up and bent over her—her heart picked up its beat. But whether she hoped or feared he might kiss her brow again, he did not, merely reached down and pulled the covers up over her shoulders.

She supposed that there were a couple of chairs in the room he could stretch out in. 'Will you be warm enough?' she asked softly. Perhaps there was an extra blanket in the wardrobe. There were sometimes in hotels, she knew.

'Oh, I should think so,' he answered quietly. But shook her rigid by—obviously at the other side of the bed now—switching off the bedside lamp—and getting into bed with her!

Instinctively, and with more speed than thought, she jerked upright, and was already halfway out of the bed when he stretched out a long arm and caught a grip of

her wrist. 'Oh, my head!' she cried, the fact that Josh
was holding her there inconsequential as her sore head
let her know she was not yet up to charging around.

'You'll feel much better with your head on a pillow,'
Josh coaxed soothingly. Erin stilled. Oh, help her, somebody—what was she supposed to do? To rest her head
on a pillow sounded the best suggestion she'd heard in
a long while. 'You won't try to come the—er—old soldier?'

'Old soldier?' He laughed softly in the darkness.
'That's one you pulled out of your grandmother's cupboard,' he commented, but said no more, and she knew
that he was leaving it up to her to decide whether nor
not she could trust him.

Gingerly she lay down, and he was right; her head did
feel better resting on a nice soft pillow. 'What happened
to the bridesmaid?' she asked as the thought all at once
jumped into her head.

He didn't ask what she was talking about, but answered quietly in the darkness. 'You put the kibosh on
any plans I might have been nurturing in that direction.'

'Good!' Erin said, because she was glad, so glad, and
not a bit remorseful. 'Goodnight—er—morning again,'
she added, and turned on her side, away from him.

Josh let go of her wrist and likewise turned his back
on her. And, this being something she knew she could
never tell her father about, or anyone else for that matter—who would believe she could trust Josh so?—Erin
closed her eyes. Could she tell her mother? Erin pon-
dered, half-asleep, half-awake.

She came a little more awake, feeling agitated when
the impulse came over her to tell Josh who her mother
was. Erin turned over to face his back. 'Josh,' she said.

'Go to sleep, Erin,' he said sternly.

Her eyes became accustomed to the darkness. She was able to make out shapes in the room. She looked at Josh. He had an arm on top of the covers and she felt an almost undeniable urge to touch his shoulder.

She wouldn't, of course. This was a pretty electric situation. She had as good as told Josh that time that she thought it was about time that she made love with someone. And she knew now that she did not want to make love with anyone else ever; she knew that the only man she wanted to make love with was him. What would she do if just by touching him it triggered off a chain reaction?

Get yourself together, do, Erin, she scolded. Chain reaction nothing. Josh was tired. The poor man was more interested in getting some sleep than in reacting to her. Idiot! He wasn't the slightest bit interested in her.

Eventually she fell asleep, and after some sound rest she gradually started to surface. She felt snug and warm, and as if everything was just as it should be. She snuggled delicately against the source of warmth, her limbs moving. Her left foot came up against something. She explored to find what it was with her foot. It was a leg!

'When you've quite finished kicking me!' Josh Salsbury commented humorously.

Erin's eyes opened wide. She was in bed with Josh. Strangely, though, the fact that she had slept with him did not alarm her, nor the fact that it was broad daylight and Josh was lying on his back and she had an arm across him, his bare chest warm against the skin of her arm. She pulled her arm back under the covers.

'What time is it?' she asked, somewhat dreamily, she rather supposed.

'Time that one of us got up.'

'You can have the bathroom first,' she offered nicely.

'Too kind. How's the head?'

He turned his head to look at her, and she found herself staring into his warm grey eyes. Oh, she loved him so. She lifted her head from her pillow a fraction, and back down again, beaming her delight. 'Clear as a bell,' she answered.

'No pain? No muzziness?'

'As good as new,' she promised. But while knowing that one of them would have to move soon, yet knowing that this situation would never arise again, she wanted to stay there with him for as long as she could. 'It was a lovely wedding, wasn't it?' she offered conversationally.

'Do you always wake up talkative—or do we have that bash on the head to thank for it?' he teased.

Oh, Josh, Josh, Josh. 'I wouldn't know,' Erin answered. 'I mean, this is the first time I've woken up with anyone there *for* me to talk to.'

'What a sad life you've led,' he mocked.

And she loved every facet of him. 'What does one usually do when one wakes up with a—a...' What the Dickens were they? '...a friend?' she asked, and loved it when he seemed amused by her.

He sat up, and, looking down at her, with her tousled blonde hair spread over her pillow, he appeared ready to depart their 'friendship' bed. 'It varies. Sometimes this,' he said, and bent over to touch his lips to hers. Abruptly he drew back. 'Sorry, I shouldn't have done that—but you did ask.'

Her heart was hammering. 'If I asked again, would you do it again?' she questioned, someone she did not recognise seeming to be in charge of her.

Josh looked down at her. He shook his head. 'Not a good idea, Erin,' he said, and suddenly she felt dreadful.

'I'm sorry,' she mumbled, and turned her head away, too embarrassed suddenly to be able to look him in the eye any longer.

'Oh, Erin,' he said gravely, and, stretching out a hand to the side of her face, he turned her to look at him. 'It isn't because—' He broke off, then began again. 'Erin, I don't think you fully appreciate the vulnerability of your situation.'

She did. She knew perfectly well what the situation was. From her point of view soon, within a very short space of time, they would be going their separate ways. He would go back to being the chief executive of the firm she worked for, and she might never ever see him again. She loved him; she wanted these few minutes to go on for ever. More, she wanted something—a kiss, maybe, perhaps the feel of his touch—to remember.

'I'm never going to get to—um—experiment,' she complained sniffily.

And Josh looked down at her and smiled, brushing her face with the back of his fingers. 'You're just asking for trouble, issuing open invitations like that,' he said softly, but to her delight didn't follow through what had seemed his intention, to get out of bed and take up her offer of the first shower.

And then all at once that new person she had only just met was in charge of her again, was urging her on— that new person who perhaps might never have been aroused from slumber had she not fallen in love with him. And suddenly she heard this new person tease, with a smile in her voice, 'One kiss wouldn't hurt, surely?'

Josh looked at her, seemed a touch gently amused. 'I need a shave,' he refused politely.

I don't care—I love you. She stretched up a hand and touched his shoulder, a thrill shooting through her on contact with his skin. She looked from his shoulder and into his eyes, and saw him glance down to her inviting lips. Then to her great joy, and just as if he could not stop himself, his head started to come down.

'This isn't very clever,' he murmured—but at last his mouth touched down on hers. Gently he kissed her—and she loved it. He raised his head. 'Satisfied?' he asked, humour about him.

She smiled up at him. She felt shy, yet at the same time a little forward. 'You're joking?' she laughed.

He smiled down at her. 'Well, that's all you're going to get,' he told her.

But she wasn't having that. She had tasted his lips, and besides, instinct was telling her that he would not mind too much to kiss her again. She sat up, moved in close to him. 'Just one more,' she suggested. 'Um—a proper kiss.'

He raised a quizzical eyebrow—she loved him more than ever. 'You mean—like the grown-ups do?'

Oh, help. He'd barely touched her and she felt on fire for him. 'Please,' the brazen female in charge of her requested, and, fearing that he might withdraw his offer, she moved yet closer to him, her bra-covered breasts coming into contact with his broad chest.

'Erin,' he murmured on a groan of sound. And the next moment he had taken her in his arms, and she was on the receiving end of a very grown-up kiss. And it was like none other she had ever known.

His lips tempted hers apart as he drew the very soul from her. She responded by clinging on to him, holding him tightly when his tongue tormented and played with her lips, making her tingle all over when the tips of their tongues met.

She pulled back when something akin to an electric shock shot through her. 'Josh.' She gasped his name.

'Shocked?' he queried, and she knew that she only had to agree that she was shocked and she would be sitting in the bed on her own.

For answer she smiled a mischievous smile. 'Delighted,' she gurgled, and, the time for requests gone— she no longer had to ask him to kiss her—she moved that small distance forwards and placed her lips against his.

It was an invitation for him to break down all her barriers, although in truth Erin didn't think she had erected any. She loved him so much it seemed only right and natural to be held and kissed by him.

She cared not that a few moments later Josh took charge of the kissing, their mouths meeting in such a prelude of passion that she felt dizzy from it. Nor was it only her lips that he pleasured. Erin felt his hands whispering over the silken skin of her back.

She knew yet more delight when he kissed her face and behind her ears, moving to kiss the arch of her throat. So enraptured was she by what he was entrancing her with that she almost told him of her love for him. But just as her lips parted he again claimed them, his mouth over hers while caressing fingers undid the fastening of her bra.

Erin started to grow a little shaky at this new ground she was on. But she feared that any objection she might make when he proceeded to remove her bra altogether would cause him to stop. And she did not want him to stop. She had been bereft in her love for him—she wanted solace. If there was a shyness barrier to get through she would get through it.

She held up her arms, the closer to get to him, and

felt the heat of his chest sear against her naked breasts. 'Oh, Josh!' broke from her before she could stop it.

'You're all right?' he queried, his eyes holding hers.

'Oh, yes, yes,' she told him hurriedly, dreadfully afraid he would take a non-reply as a negative answer and would make her bereft again by letting her out of his hold.

He smiled, and kissed her again, causing her breathing to temporarily halt when he pulled back and away from her—just as if nothing would do but that he must savour and see her breasts. 'You're exquisite,' he breathed, his eyes caressing the silken globes with their hardened pink tips.

But she was not feeling so very brave—or brazen—just then, so she moved in close to him, so to hide her breasts from his view. But he seemed to understand, and gently he kissed her. The next time his caressing hands came to the front of her she had herself under control, given that she swallowed hard when his warm sensitive fingers teased at those firm pink tips, and he moulded her breasts in his palms. 'Oh, Josh,' she cried involuntarily.

'Want me to stop?' he asked, sounding as if she only had to say the word and he would.

'Don't you dare!' she protested with a shy laugh, and loved it when he briefly laughed too.

Then he was tracing kisses over her nakedness, his lips finally reaching her breasts. He kissed first one and then the other, creating great swathes of wanting within her when he took the hardened pink peak of her right breast in her mouth, and tenderly toyed with the hardened tip of her left breast.

Josh's mouth took more of her breast as gently he moved her until they were both lying down. Transferring his mouth to her lips, he moved and came to cover her body with his, her briefs and his shorts the only covering between them—and Erin was in a frenzy of wanting.

'J-Josh,' she murmured shakily, but owned to a slight feeling of apprehension to feel his male hardness against her. That apprehension mingled with her by then quite desperate need of him as, their legs somehow entwined, she found she had effortlessly made room for him, and he appeared to as effortlessly have come to be captured between the silken unknown territory of her thighs. 'Josh,' she cried, and hated that hint of panic to be heard in the sound.

Especially did she hate it when Josh suddenly stilled, as though he had heard her panic too, and stopped dead. She knew it was so when, with a swiftness she found totally bewildering, he broke away from her.

'What?' she asked, wanting him back where he had been. 'I'm sorry,' she quickly apologised, it rapidly dawning on her that he thought her moment of panic meant no. 'I didn't mean...'

'You're not sure,' he cut in gruffly, going on, 'You need to be very sure, Erin.'

'I am sure!' she protested. 'I...'

'My getting into bed with you was not the brightest notion I've ever had,' he abruptly decided, cutting through what she was saying, his back to her. And as, stunned, she watched, she saw him grabbing up his trousers and begin to get into them.

Disbelieving, she stared at him. Disbelieving but, as it started to sink in that she had to believe it, she had to accept it. Erin could only be grateful for pride, that chose that moment to storm in. While wanting to desperately beg him to come back to her, she thanked heaven for pride that won the day and stated she would see him in hell before she would beg.

'Well, pardon me for being undesirable!' Pride alone pushed the huffy words out between her teeth.

'Even with your small experience, you know better than that,' Josh clipped, his shirt on, buttoning it up as he went. 'Get dressed and go home,' he ordered—and gave her the solitude to do just that.

Erin was too upset to think of hurling something at the door after him. How could he leave her like this? After awakening her body the way he had—how could he possibly leave her?

CHAPTER FIVE

ERIN arrived at her place of work on Monday fully intending to resign from her job. She got as far as going to see Ivan Kelly. 'Ivan...' she began, but found that the words to sever even the most remote possibility of seeing Josh again just would not leave her lips. 'About that Pickering query...' she went on, and on the spot asked him about a problem that she had already dealt with.

With the memory of how she had been with Josh beginning to haunt her, Erin drove to Croom Babbington on Friday evening wondering if she would ever stop feeling hot all over with embarrassment about that particular subject. Talk about giving him the green light to go, go, go! For goodness' sake, the 'Take me, I'm yours' sign must have been flashing in brilliant neon!

She felt quite shocked whenever she thought of her behaviour, her reactions. No, not even *re*actions. Because she'd been the one pushing for his kisses—all the way. Trollop? Forward? My stars, she had given the poor man little alternative but to kiss her. He had probably only kissed her anyway because he couldn't shut her up any other way.

Erin tried to get angry—against him. That didn't work either. She tried to tell herself he should never have got into bed with her in the first place. What sort of thing was that to do? Even if he *had* been sitting talking to her for a couple of hours to keep her awake—and then spent another couple of hours watching her sleep. Prior to that, no doubt yawning and bored to death, he had looked at that larger portion of free space on that bed and had thought—hang it. The fact, though, that he had carried her to that room and had so diligently watched over her weakened any anger she tried to drum up. No wonder he had given in to the notion to share what in any case had been his bed to start with!

Erin sighed heavily, knowing that, aside from what she considered was her wanton behaviour, what was really the most humiliating thing of all was that Josh Salsbury should so easily reject her—um—charms. Oh, he had desired her; she knew that well enough. But she recalled how he had curtly informed her that time he'd driven her home from the office, 'Some men might want to bed you, Erin Tunnicliffe—I'm not one of them.' His actions in the early hours of Sunday had clearly borne that out. It was without question that he certainly hadn't desired her enough to want to 'bed' her last Sunday.

She had hoped that a weekend spent in quiet and un-eventful Croom Babbington might give her some peace of mind. It did not. 'See you next weekend,' she said cheerfully when on Sunday, with every appearance of being light-hearted, she bade her father goodbye.

'Drive carefully,' he instructed, which she did, auto-matically, her head once more filled with thoughts of Josh Salsbury.

With Josh dominating her thoughts so much, however, she arrived in London and took a phone call from her mother that gave her pause to consider that perhaps she was not the only member of her family going through, as it were, 'the emotional mill'.

'Have a good weekend?' Nina enquired.

'I went to stay with Dad.'

'What you'll do for laughs!' her mother offered sar-castically.

Erin did not want to get into the sort of conversation where her mother maligned her father and left her feeling she had to defend him. 'How did your weekend go?' she asked.

'Well...' Nina began, but hesitated.

'Anything the matter?' Erin queried, realising suddenly that her mother's tone was a touch subdued.

'Nothing. Nothing at all!' her parent answered briskly. 'I just thought I'd ring and suggest we meet somewhere for lunch tomorrow.'

There *was* something troubling her! Erin just knew it. 'Fine,' she answered, wanting to press to find out what the problem was but knowing from her mother's 'Nothing' reply that she would have to wait until tomorrow to find out what it was. 'Same place as last time?'

'It's as good as anywhere,' Nina agreed. 'I've nothing else pressing tomorrow. I'll come and pick you up.'

'I'm working, Mother.'

'I know! I know!' Nina plainly objected to any hidden suggestion that she had forgotten. 'And less of the "Mother". I meant I'll come and pick you up from your office.'

Erin was not at all happy with that. 'You do know I work for Thomas Salsbury's company?' she dared to further remind her.

'Well, I'm not likely to run into him, am I? The last I heard he wasn't even in London but abroad somewhere, convalescing in some place sunny. Not that I'd mind running into Tommy; he was always good company. Up until he proposed, anyway.'

'It wasn't him I was thinking of,' Erin had to confess.

'Oh—you think his son might be around and attempt to give me a talking to for daring to turn his father down?'

Erin wasn't sure what she thought, other than, Murphy's law being what it was, and even knowing the likelihood of bumping into Josh was highly unlikely, if she *were* to bump into him then for sure Murphy would arrange it for tomorrow.

'He wouldn't dare,' she answered lightly. 'But I think it would be more tactful if I meet you there.'

Her parent did not mind either way. But with their arrangements made she rang off, leaving Erin to wonder what tomorrow's lunch was all about, but glad she was going to meet her away from her place of work. Unlikely though it was that Josh would be around at lunchtime tomorrow, Erin was sure he'd be bound to have something to say should he see her mother.

The next morning, bearing in mind that the lunch she'd shared with Mark Prentice had overrun into her office time, and with her mother having 'nothing else pressing' that she had to hurry for and knowing she would not see any urgency to have lunch over and done with in an hour, Erin went to see Ivan Kelly.

'Any problem if I extend my lunch hour today?' she asked.

'Lucky man,' Ivan fished.

'My mother,' Erin obliged. 'A half-hour extra should do it.'

'Consider it granted.' They exchanged cheerful smiles and Erin went back to her desk.

With something else to think about, albeit Josh was never very far away from her thoughts, Erin started to believe that she was getting over the humiliation of the wedding weekend.

Her mother was at the restaurant first, a clear sign she must have something on her mind, Erin mused as she joined her.

'Darling, you're much too pretty to have to work for a living,' Nina greeted her. 'Get your father to increase your allowance.' She instantly countermanded that. 'Though since you're much too soft to get what is only rightfully yours from him, I'll speak to him on the subject myself.'

'Honestly M—Nina, you're the end,' Erin commented, but had to laugh. 'I don't need Dad's money. My bank balance is more than healthy.'

'Is it?' Her mother seemed surprised, then, her tone sharpening, 'You're not getting miserly like him, I hope?'

Whatever her father was, he was not miserly. He had always been generous where money was concerned. And Erin knew for a fact that Nina had walked away from her marriage to him with a settlement that would make most men's eyes water.

So she glanced across at her mother, looking absolutely as lovely as ever, and began to realise that all this was a smokescreen to hide something that must be troubling her greatly.

She became more and more certain of it when her parent kept up a lively light-hearted chatter all the way through their first course. But when their second course arrived, and her mother appeared to have nothing more deep to talk about than her latest shopping exploits, Erin guessed that there was a man involved somewhere.

'How's—Richard?' Erin asked, bringing to the surface the name of her mother's last beau—the one Nina had declared was 'different'.

'Ah!' she exclaimed, and Erin knew she had struck a nerve.

'He's—still making you laugh?' she probed gently.

Nina gave a heartfelt sigh. 'He's gone all serious—

you know the way they do,' she complained. 'He's ruined everything!'

'You've finished with him?' Erin asked, unsure whom to feel more sorry for—Richard or her scared-of-commitment mother.

'I'm... He proposed. Honestly, I've avoided proposals like the plague for years, and then two—one on top of the other! Anyhow, Richard has asked me to marry him. Can you believe that? When I'm sure I made it perfectly plain to him that marriage and me don't agree!'

'But—I thought you—cared for him?'

Nina gave her an unsmiling look. 'I do,' she admitted. 'But I've tried being married. Twice!' Her tone lightened. 'I'm just not ready for it,' she said, her unsmiling expression giving way to such an endearing impish grin that Erin could quite see why so many men fell for her. Nina's grin had disappeared, though, when she went on to casually enquire, 'I suppose you're going to stay with your father this coming weekend?'

'He likes me to go home when I can.'

'He's a selfish old devil,' Nina announced crossly. 'Tell him you've got your own life to lead.'

'I didn't go down to Croom Babbington the other weekend...' Erin began to defend, then, as light shone through, 'You want me to go somewhere with you this coming weekend?' she guessed. But even as the words left her lips she was realising the absurdity of that. Her mother loved her, but had never craved her company for a whole weekend—ever.

But, to her astonishment, 'Funny you should ask,' Nina replied. 'But I wouldn't mind if you paid me a visit on Saturday—and stayed overnight.'

'What sort of trouble are you in?' Erin quickly asked,

certain that only in the direst of consequences would her
mother need her under her pantiles.

'Not trouble, exactly.' Nina shrugged prettily. 'The
thing is, I need space—space to think, to decide...'

'And you haven't got that?'

Nina shook her head. 'Some weeks ago I arranged for
Richard to join me for this coming weekend so he should
take part in some charity swimathon in Norman and
Letty Ashmore's pool. Can you image it?' she broke off
to insert. 'Half of them are heart attacks waiting to happen.' Erin inwardly winced. That was the fate Josh's
father had suffered. But her mother went unthinkingly
on, 'Anyhow, some bright spark suggested a six a.m.
dive-in, and with more wine than judgement we all
agreed.'

'You're swimming too?' Erin asked—foolishly, she
realised the moment the words were out. Her bandbox
fresh mother was averse to water on her face, and that
was without so much as dwelling on what chlorinated
water might do to her hair.

'No, darling,' her mother reproved mildly. 'What I am
doing, or did when everyone said they'd meet at the
Ashmores' for five-thirty—which would mean Richard
getting up at some unearthly hour to drive down and be
in Berkshire in time—was to offer him a bed at my place
for Saturday night.'

'Which he accepted?'

'And which I can't now take back or he'll think the
worst of me, not to mention the spoilsport I shall look
in front of the others. Oh, why did he have to go and
ruin everything yesterday by asking me to marry him?'

'You said—no?' Erin asked, trying to keep up.

'Richard could see I was about to, and quickly suggested I thought deeply about it before I gave him my answer.'

'And you agreed to do that?'

'Weak of me, but I said I would.'

'Only, until you've made your decision you don't want to be too much alone with him this coming weekend?'

'I think I've half decided.'

'You're going to turn him down?'

'I think Richard has to be the first to know my decision,' Nina replied, showing the delicacy of nature that Erin had known she possessed.

'You're sure you want me there?'

'It's essential! You'll come?'

'Of course,' Erin answered unhesitatingly. But, half to herself, 'I only hope I don't slip up and call you Mother.'

'Richard knows I have a daughter.'

Erin looked at her parent in amazement. 'You told him!'

'He caught me at a weak moment,' Nina confessed, but went on briskly, 'No one else need know—you needn't come to this charity thing. Richard can go on his own as it's so early. I can drive over to the Ashmores' later.' Neatly avoiding spending time solely in Richard's company, Erin gathered. But her mother's tone was altering again when she went on, a touch despondently, 'Though, come to think of it, I don't think I particularly care so much now who knows that I've a grown daughter.'

Erin recognised that her mother must be in something of the same emotional turmoil that she herself was in. Which then brought to Erin's mind the reason why she was having such an emotional time, and, having thought of Josh, Erin was back in her own emotional purgatory.

It also reminded her of her place of work. She glanced at her watch. 'It's half past two already!' she exclaimed disbelievingly. 'I'd better try and get a taxi back to the office. Do you mind if I skip dessert?'

'I won't bother either,' Nina replied.

It was two forty-five when they stood on the pavement, waiting to flag down a seemingly non-existent taxi. Erin suggested that her mother leave her to wait alone, but perhaps because Erin had so willingly accepted and answered her SOS she declined the suggestion. But, having seldom waited for anything, Nina was soon impatient.

'This is ridiculous!' she announced abruptly. 'I haven't done anything wrong!' And, in a tone that said there was no arguing about it, 'Come on, I'll drive you back.'

Erin went with her to where Nina had parked her car, supposing that in Nina's eyes she had *not* done anything wrong with regard to Thomas Salsbury. Nor did Erin have any idea of what had gone on between her mother and Josh's father. But something had triggered his heart attack, and it was for certain that not many men would walk away from the rejection of a sincere proposal of marriage without feeling a little stressed about it.

'What time shall I arrive on Saturday?' Erin asked as her mother confidently threaded her smart car through traffic.

'Early afternoon, I should think. I'll get Richard to pick you up. He lives only about a mile from you. It's senseless to take two cars when he lives so near.'

From that Erin gleaned that her mother had it all worked out. By asking Richard to call for her daughter it did away with him arriving early at Nina's Berkshire home. And, since Erin would need transport home, Nina would not be left alone with him after she had gone.

All of which made Erin realise what a dreadfully unhappy time her mother must be going through just now. She supposed that following a refusal it would normally be something along the lines of Perhaps it would be better if we did not meet again. Only this time it seemed her mother was fond enough of Richard not to want to cut off all links with him. Yet at the same time she was afraid of being alone with him in case she weakened from her resolve to never marry again—to actually be persuaded by Richard to say yes.

By the time they were pulling up outside the large imposing building of Salsbury Engineering Systems Erin's feelings were so wrapped up with what her mother must be going through at the moment that she even forgot about the unwritten Murphy's law. The law that said if you really, really didn't want something to happen then you could bet your life that it would. And suddenly—while her mother halted the car and was confirming that she would expect her with Richard on Saturday—Erin froze. Because there, briefcase in hand, strode Josh Salsbury, out through the plate glass doors of the Salsbury building, his long legs making short work of the steps.

Perhaps he won't see me, Erin prayed as joy entered her heart to see him again and mortification jumped on it when, with the speed of light, she simultaneously recalled how totally his for the taking she had been the last time she had seen him.

Not see her! Small hope. Thanks, Murphy! The car was facing him, and Josh looked straight at her. Oddly, for the briefest moment, she thought as he paused and looked at her that he appeared pleased to see her so unexpectedly. He even seemed as if he might come over to speak to her. Then he glanced to the driver's side of the car and an instant look of disbelief swiped away any pleased look. His expression darkened, and was followed by a look so instantly furious, instantly murderous, that Erin knew he had recognised Nina—the woman who had played some part in his father's close brush with death.

Luckily her mother was half turned to her and had not spotted him. 'Bye, darling,' she was saying with a smile, while leaning a little towards her to air-kiss her cheek.

Unable to live with Josh looking as though he would like to do the pair of them the greatest harm, Erin, feeling utterly numb, her brain seized up, turned helplessly towards her mother. When she turned to the front again it was to know that Josh had strode straight on past.

'Until Saturday,' she said to Nina, and with Josh's look of pure murderous outrage burned into her memory she stepped from the car, waved goodbye to her mother, and took a shortcut through the main building and out through the other side to the building where she had her office.

But so upset was she by that murderous look she would have forgotten to apologise to Ivan Kelly for the extension she'd taken on her already extended lunch hour had he not come looking for her, saying, 'Good, you're back.'

'I'm sorry. I lost all track of time,' she apologised.

'Not to worry. Though I've a report I need typing. It will probably take you some time.'

'I don't mind working late,' she offered, but when he had gone started to wonder if she would still have a job at Salsbury Engineering Systems at the end of the day in which to work late at. Somehow, effortlessly recalling

Josh's look of sheer fury on recognising her mother, Erin had a feeling that he had been much too incensed to merely shrug away the fact that his bed companion of just over a week ago was cohorting with a woman he had reason to detest. Somehow Erin had a feeling that Josh striding furiously on was not the end of the matter.

She tried to lose the feeling by scolding—don't be ridiculous, as if he'd bother! For heaven's sake, he'd had a briefcase with him; clearly he had other things on his mind. Other more important things. What on earth did she think a man as busy as Josh would do? Call her up to his office when he got back in order to let forth about whom she should and should not exchange air-kisses with? Wake up!

Nevertheless, Erin was on edge all the rest of the afternoon, and totally apprehensive when, as happened frequently, she was called upon to answer the internal phone.

She worked until just gone six, when the report was finished and ready for a meeting Ivan was conducting at nine-fifteen the following day. She went home and made herself some tea, and wondered why it was that when the threat of her being summoned up to the top floor hadn't happened she should still feel all uptight and tense—as if still expecting something to happen.

She knew why when, as she was standing at the sink rinsing through the dishes she had used, she saw from the kitchen window a car enter the courtyard. It was still light enough for her to recognise it. Oh, help!

Pulling back from the window, she swiftly dried her hands. With her mind in a whirl she dodged into her sitting room and for quite a minute was a complete emotional riot. She had still not got herself together when in the next minute someone, probably with an angry stride to have got there so quickly, was ringing her doorbell.

She would have quite liked not to answer it. But some things had to be faced. Erin took a shaky breath, and after some seconds went down the narrow staircase to open the door to Josh Salsbury.

Hot colour surged to her cheeks the moment she saw him. Mortification and embarrassment were again there to haunt her at how his for the taking she had been the last time she had seen him—and at how he had declined the offer.

But, as she had suspected, he was still angry about seeing her and the companion she'd been with after lunch, still murderously furious. She could see it in the fire of his eyes. She was not mistaken, she soon discovered. His hostility was rife as unspeakingly he eyed her for about two seconds before, it becoming plain he was in no mood to bother with pleasantries, he snarled harshly, 'I don't think much of the company you keep!'

On that instant her embarrassment fled. She had spent an apprehensive afternoon knowing somehow that she would be hearing something from him—most likely dismissal from the firm—without doubt he would find some good business reason for throwing her out. But the fact that he had come to her home, and was all too obviously dead set on insulting her mother, was more than flesh and blood could stand.

Erin was glad to feel angry, but did not care to trade insults on her doorstep. Without a word she turned from him and marched back up the stairs to the sitting room.

Josh Salsbury did not wait for an invitation. She heard the outer door close none too gently, and heard his footsteps as he followed her up the stairs. It was but a few seconds after that that he was in the room with her and they were angrily facing each other. Erin didn't know how she could be so angry with him when she loved him so much—but perhaps that was all part and parcel of loving someone—it made you sensitive to the smallest slight. Only this wasn't some small slight. This was her mother he was talking about.

'You seem very friendly with her!' Josh bit, when Erin had not yet said a word. No doubt he was referring to their air-kisses on parting. Still she wasn't saying a word. That was until, his jaw jutting, 'How do you know *that* woman?' he demanded.

That woman! That woman was her mother! Erin raised her head a proud fraction, and then fairly hurled at him, 'Since you're obviously desperate to know—that woman...' Erin paused to take an indignant breath '...is *my mother!*'

That shook him; she could see that it had. Whatever he had been expecting it certainly hadn't been that. Erin saw his brow shoot back as, speechless for a moment, he stared at her. But he was not speechless for long.

'She doesn't have any children!' he contradicted harshly.

Sorry, Mother, I forgot. 'Correction. She has a daughter!'

'She has a different last name from you.'

My stars, he was intent on digging and digging, by the sound of it. 'My mother remarried after she and my father divorced,' Erin stayed civil to inform him coldly.

'And became Woodward,' he documented, clearly having her name seared into his memory. 'Or was Woodward husband three or four?' he questioned with cutting sarcasm.

'Two. My mother now has an aversion to the married state.'

'She should have told my father that before she proceeded to make a fool of him!' he barked.

'She probably did tell him,' Erin defended.

'So how come he was so completely floored by her rejection?' Josh demanded grimly. 'How come he was so flattened by her turning him down—not what he'd been led to expect at all—that he made himself ill?' And, not waiting for an answer, but becoming more incensed than ever, *'You knew!'* he accused. 'All this while you've known about it!' Her anger with him began to fade, guilt banishing it. 'You've lied to me!' he charged hostilely.

'No, I haven't!' she denied, glad of a small flurry of anger.

'I specifically asked you if you knew my father,' he carried on antagonistically, as if she had not spoken. 'You told me no.'

'I don't know him!' she protested.

'You lied by omission. You know of him. You knew he'd asked that woman to marry him. That she so heartlessly spurned him. You've known all along!'

'It wasn't…'

'What a terrific time you and your tramp of a mother must have had. A whole barrel full of laughs at the expense of my father!' he fired, outraged, more outraged still as he added, 'And of me.'

'I've never laughed at you!' Erin denied hotly. 'And don't you *dare* call my mother a tramp!'

'Why not? She doesn't care whose heart she breaks!' He broke off, looked racked for a moment—Erin guessed he was thinking of his dear father—but then came roaring back to life, hurling at her, 'Like mother, like daughter! Hell's teeth, was I taken in by you!'

'What do you mean?' Erin questioned faintly.

'What *would* I mean? All that virtuous talk of never having been to bed with a man! All that play-acting,' he jibed. 'The innocence, the shyness, the nervousness. It didn't last long, though, did it—once I got you between the sheets?'

'Are you being deliberately offensive?' she challenged, angry but with no defence, and she knew it. Shyness had played only a very small part once Josh had started to kiss her.

'Offensive?' he mocked. 'You were so willing. Had my tastes not run in other directions I could have had you any time I liked.' And, his words and tone deliberately insulting, 'I still could. You, like your mother, are anybody's!'

Erin sucked in her breath. His words were meant to wound, and wound they had. He had desired her, she knew that he had, but his tastes, as he'd just said, lay in other—probably more sophisticated—areas.

'My mother's not like that!' she defended as best she could. But in all honesty didn't know what her mother was like in that direction. 'And you're wrong about me!' Erin informed him heatedly, raising her head proudly. Love him she might, but she did not have to take this.

Though as a glint of something she did not quite understand came into his eyes, she was soon to know that her words and the proud look of her had been received by him as a challenge. 'Wrong, am I?' he thundered angrily.

'You know you are,' she insisted.

'Joke of the day!' he sneered. 'You're denying you were so all fired up in that bed that you told me not to dare to stop?'

'You're—um—taking it out of context!' she protested, a familiar feeling of humiliation about her behaviour that early morning getting to her again.

Josh shook his head and came nearer. 'It doesn't take much to turn you on, does it, little Miss-butter-wouldn't-melt-Tunnicliffe?' he drawled, his anger still there, his control hanging by a thread.

He took another step closer—Erin started to get worried. 'I think it's time you left!' she ordered crisply.

'Oh, you do?' he mocked.

'Right now!' she demanded, taking a step back as he came another step nearer.

'When I'm ready,' he retorted ominously.

'N-now would be a good time.' She was by then seriously worried, and took another step back. And another. It was a small room, and as Josh continued to come relentlessly forward so suddenly Erin's retreat was halted when her back came abruptly up against a solid wall.

'Go!' she ordered hoarsely. He smiled. It was a smile that had no humour in it. Oh, heavens.

He came closer. 'Wrong, am I?' His tone was silky, and suddenly there was no doubt in Erin's mind that, while he might prefer a more sophisticated woman in his bed, he was angry enough in his belief that she had played him for a fool, furious enough on his father's behalf and his own, to take up her challenge and prove that she would be his any time he cared to take her.

'I shall fight you!' she stated, her violet eyes worried, huge in her face as she strove for courage.

But apparently he welcomed a fight. 'Good,' he replied. 'That should make it more interesting.'

She looked wildly about, wondering if she could make it out of the room and down the stairs and outside before he caught her.

He read her mind to answer. 'No chance.'

She tried to bolt anyway. He caught her before she had taken two steps. 'No!' she yelled, but he was strong, much stronger than her, and he was pulling her back, pulling her into his arms.

'You'll soon be saying yes,' he assured her confidently, pinning her flailing arms at her sides as his head started to come nearer.

His mouth fastened over hers. *'No!'* she screeched, dragging her mouth away from his.

He smiled. 'This must be a new role for you, sweetie—playing hard to get. Especially when you know and I know that that's all it is, play-acting.'

'Get lost!' she snorted, and aimed a kick at his shin which, as she heard him grunt, connected. But she gained only small satisfaction from that because, more incensed, he made his arms rigid around her, making it impossible for her to free herself.

His head came down again and his mouth was over her mouth, forcing her lips apart. She wriggled, she struggled, she kicked at his shin again, more viciously this time. It connected. 'I'll soon settle you!' he grunted, obviously believing he had taken enough of that because, while she was still struggling furiously, he did no more than take her kicking feet from under her by picking her up in his arms.

'What...?' she gasped as he began to carry her from the room.

'I think I know somewhere we'll both be more comfortable,' he informed her, staring malevolently down into her bewildered face.

But she was not bewildered for long, because suddenly she knew what he was about. Stunned, she stopped fighting—for about two seconds. Then, one arm free as he carried her to the bedroom, she was punching and pummelling at him and generally fighting like a tigress to be free.

And was free—briefly. That was because Josh allowed her to be free when he tossed her down on the bed. Winded, she struggled to rapidly get up. But, as swiftly as she had moved, he was not wasting a moment either. And before she could leap from the bed he had found the perfect way to keep her where he wanted her.

'Get off me!' she shrieked when he lay down on top of her, using his body to pin her down.

'Trying to pretend you don't like it?' he mocked.

'Go to hell!'

He smiled an insincere smile. 'Don't be like that,' he coaxed.

'I hate you!' she spat.

'Preferable to your love, sweetheart,' he retorted, entirely unmoved, and aimed a kiss at her mouth, which met her cheek when she jerked her head away. He then proceeded to kiss her throat, one hand free as he unbuttoned her shirt and kissed her throat.

Infuriated, Erin used her body to try and jerk free, her lower torso coming into solid contact with his hard male body. 'Will you get off…?' she demanded.

He mockingly cut her off. 'Oh, sweetie, do that some more and we'll have a fine time.' And then his mouth was over hers again, seeking, taking—and Erin, in love with him still, while hating him for what he was putting her through, did not want these sort of kisses. When before they had lain on a bed together his lips, while seeking, had been giving and not all taking. Had been tender and sensitive to her, not punishing and so totally insensitive.

She wrenched her mouth away from his. 'Don't…'

was all she could manage before he claimed her mouth again in another angry kiss.

And that was when it suddenly came to Erin that to fight him was not the way to go about it. Josh wanted her opposing him, fighting him—it fuelled his anger. But if she lay passive, unresisting, would he then leave her? She knew a little of him by then, had socialised with him—if you could call it that—had worked for him, and thought that she knew a little of his sensitivity.

She stopped moving. Stopped writhing beneath him. By then she was fully aware that he wanted her, that his body desired her body—but she did not want him—not like this—in hate.

The next time his mouth clamped on hers she let him kiss her. When he forced her lips apart she let him. He raised his head, his expression saying What's this? Unsmiling, she met his gaze. He caught on. 'You think passive resistance will stop me?' he demanded harshly.

She shrugged her shoulders. 'I don't expect you to change your mind about what you intend to do to me,' she answered quietly. 'I'm just a bit surprised, that's all.'

He looked for a moment as if he would resume his onslaught of her regardless, but then hesitated. 'Surprised?' he questioned.

She smiled up at him, her voice taking on a taunting note. 'Correct me if I'm wrong, but aren't you the man who once told me, and I quote, "Some men might want to bed you—I'm not one of them"'? She could still feel the pressure of his maleness against her, and further taunted, 'Surely you haven't changed your mind and now want to bed me after all?'

Josh Salsbury raised himself away from her, an inscrutable kind of look in his grey eyes. Somehow she managed to stay perfectly still, just doing that taking all of her will power. And then, to her relief, Josh at long last rolled away from her.

Unmoving, she eyed him, but could tell he was still hating her. Or the person he still thought was her. Because his tone was cutting when he coldly reminded her of something *she* had once said, his arrogant tone beating her taunting one hollow when he loftily told her, 'I sure as hell don't want to marry you, sweetheart!' With that he got up from the bed.

She could, she supposed, have attempted to retaliate with some kind of acid remark. But as she watched him leave, for all she had won, she felt too beaten to try.

CHAPTER SIX

THAT night, the night after he had gone, seemed endless. Erin was still going over and over Josh's visit at three the next morning. No wonder she had decided not to tell him that the woman who had broken his father's heart—in more ways than one—was her mother. Look what had happened when Josh had found out!

Feeling mentally bruised and battered, Erin turned restlessly over yet again in her bed. She had known he would be angry, furious even, but in all honesty had she deserved such treatment?

Dawn eventually came into being and she left her bed knowing that deep down she would always love him—unfortunately love could not be turned off just like that, no matter how one might desire it. She was glad, though, to find as she went to shower that her pride had surfaced and come to her aid. She had spent a good deal of last week in mortified embarrassment at how eager to be his she had been. But no more!

She hoped she had last night shown Josh Salsbury that it was untrue and that she was not, as he had accused, anybody's. She refused to dwell on the fact that had he kissed her in any way tenderly, as if he did not hate her, the outcome might well have been different. But while acknowledging that she loved him she hated him too, that he could treat her the way he had, no matter what the provocation. And she was just not going to put up with it.

And, being of that mind, as soon as she arrived at her

office Erin went and sought out Ivan Kelly. She handed in her resignation. From choice she would have preferred to leave straight away. But there was always masses of paperwork in the experimental division, and she liked everyone there, and loyalty to her particular group meant that she was honour-bound to give them a month in which to find her replacement.

'You can't leave!' Ivan protested. And, as intelligent as she knew him to be, 'Was that where you were yesterday? At a job interview?'

'I had lunch with my mother, as I said. I haven't got another job lined up yet.'

'Then stay until you have. Or—is there something you're unhappy with here? Tell me what it is,' he urged. 'Whatever it is, I'm sure I can put it right.'

If only he could. She shook her head. She was unhappy, in fact had never felt so down, so beaten, but there was nothing Ivan or anybody else could do about that. 'It's a domestic matter,' she told Ivan, and liked him more than ever when he respected her privacy and did not press her further.

Domestic? Erin went home that night having spent the day hiding her inner unhappiness and feelings of near despair. And once inside the walls of the small mews apartment she almost gave way to tears. But she would not give way. Pride kicked in once more; no man was worth it.

Her pride was still riding high, indignation joining it that any man should push her to this pitch, when suddenly her phone rang. She did not feel like answering it, but if it were her father it would be a chance to let him know that she would not be paying Croom Babbington a visit at the weekend.

It was not her father but—astonishingly—Josh Salsbury!

'I...' he began, and, oddly for him, seemed at a loss for words. But to give that weird notion a hiding he was going on to inform her, 'I'm in New York.'

Erin was too winded for the moment to be able to answer. Then her pride surged anew and she was suddenly furiously angry that he thought he could ring her and verbally insult her over the phone into the bargain.

'I'll see you when I get back...' he was saying.

It was as far as she allowed him to get. 'Not if I see you first, you won't!' she hurled at him, and slammed the phone violently down—wishing it had been on his head.

Tears sprang to her eyes then. No! No! No! She would *not* cry! How *dared* he phone her? Who the devil did he think he was? The fact that he'd rung her home number decreed it was nothing to do with work. And if it was personal—as in 'You, like your mother, are anybody's'—then she'd put up with more than enough of that, thank you very much.

Erin went to bed unhappy and got up unhappy, and went to work determining that she was just not going to let Josh Salsbury do this to her. So when Stephen Dobbs stopped by her office and asked her to go out with him that evening, she pinned a bright smile on her face and said she'd love to.

She slept badly that night, and was not any happier when that evening's paper, purchased so she should look at the Situations Vacant column, showed a picture of a dinner-jacketed Joshua Salsbury squiring some New York lovely around.

She hated him, hated her—the woman with him—but that did not prevent her from cutting the picture out of the paper. The male half of it anyway. She placed it in her bedside table, telling herself she'd buy a set of darts tomorrow and use the picture for target practice. She forgot all about scrutinising the Situations Vacant column.

Erin had a difficult telephone conversation with her father the next evening. It was just acceptable to him that she would not be driving to see him this coming weekend, but totally unacceptable that she should be driving to stay the weekend with her mother. Erin thought it politic not to tell him that, to be more precise, her mother's friend Richard would be doing the driving. Not that Nina would give a hoot what she told him.

When around nine that evening her phone, which seldom rang, again let her know that there was someone waiting to speak to her, Erin owned to feeling nervous to answer it.

Thanks to pride, and a determination that no man was going to reduce her to this, she picked up the offending instrument and managed what would pass for a civilised, if curt, 'Yes?' down the phone.

'Erin?'

'Yes,' she answered, more affably this time. It was not Josh Salsbury—she began to wonder why she'd thought it might be.

'Greg Williams,' her caller announced himself.

Just what she did not need! 'Hello, Greg. How are you?'

'Better now I've reached you. How are you now? Apparently you went out like a light when you connected with that pillar.'

'I'm fine, thank you,' she replied, hoping that if he had rung to ask after her health then he would now go. Too much to hope for! 'I've only just this minute managed to track down your phone number.' She waited politely for him to say why he wanted her phone number, and he went on, 'Our plans for the other Saturday went up in smoke, didn't they? But I'd like to see you again.'

Erin went hot all over when she recalled how his plans for the other Saturday had not coincided with her plans, and how Josh Salsbury—more experienced than she—had so much sooner than her clearly seen what had been in Greg's mind. It suddenly struck her that perhaps the way, in her ignorance, she had been with Greg had gone some way to concrete in Josh's mind that she was, indeed, anybody's.

'I'm sorry, Greg,' she said abruptly—she'd had enough of this. 'I knocked myself out before I had a chance to tell you, but I never had any intention of being more than just friends with you.' And, in case he still hadn't got the message, 'I just don't—do not—sleep around.'

Something of a lengthy pause followed her terse statement. But she came close to liking him again when at last he gave a dramatic sigh and commented, 'Win some, lose some,' which made her laugh, and went on to state, 'I sometimes come up to London; perhaps I could ring you one weekend?' He made her laugh again when he said, rather tongue in cheek, she thought, 'We could go to the zoo or something.'

As if! She couldn't see him spending any time strolling round a zoo. But he had lightened her mood and she was glad of that. 'Ring me then,' she invited, though doubted, since she spent the weekends out of London, that she would be there if he rang.

Inside minutes of that phone call ending Josh Salsbury was back in her head. Though this time, while still out of sorts over him, Erin found she did not hate him so much as she had.

Erin had an overnight bag packed and was ready when Richard Percival arrived to drive her to her mother's Berkshire home on Saturday. He was a good-looking man, perhaps two or three years older than Joshua Salsbury—stop thinking about him, do—and Erin liked him on sight.

'Nina tells me you work for Salsbury Engineering,' he commented as they drove along.

So much for putting a block on Salsbury-type thoughts! 'Do you know the firm?' she asked politely.

'Only by reputation—which, as you know, is first class.'

It pleased her that Josh's firm had a first-class reputation, but this wasn't helping her to forget him. 'What sort of work do you do?' she asked Richard, eager to get away from anything to do with the Salsbury name.

Having liked Richard on sight, she grew to really warm to him during the next twenty-four hours. While it was true that he did not wear his heart on his sleeve, so to speak, Erin saw the way his eyes followed Nina around the room, and it was clear to Erin that he was deeply in love with her mother.

Just as it was equally clear that her mother was most anxious not to be left alone with him. Which in turn caused Erin some small embarrassment, because while Nina's manners were as ever perfect, and she treated Richard as a much wanted guest in her home, if Erin slipped out of the room for any reason she would find that within half a minute her mother had made some excuse and had slipped out of the room too.

'You're going to have to have a private conversation with Richard at some time,' Erin said when, returning a tea tray with cups and saucers to the kitchen, her mother had followed to help.

'Stay close,' Nina said sharply—and then Richard was there too.

'Anyone fancy a walk?' he enquired.

Erin, while quite liking the idea of stretching her legs, was aware the invitation was meant for her mother, and was about to decline the suggestion when she caught the frantic signals her mother was making.

'Lovely idea.' Erin took up Richard's suggestion and, certain that he was nobody's fool and knew exactly what was going on, felt sure that she was the more embarrassed of the three of them.

Knowing that Richard had only suggested a walk in order to spend some time alone with the woman he had given his heart to, Erin was even more embarrassed when her mother declined to accompany them.

'We don't have to go far,' Erin remarked, feeling quite awkward about it as she and Richard started out.

'Nonsense. It will do us good. I've been desk-bound too this week,' he answered cheerfully. His cheerful tone had departed five minutes later, however, when he enquired, 'Has Nina mentioned that I've asked her to marry me?'

Oh, grief. A proposal of marriage should be private, between two people, particularly if, as might be in this case, the suitor got turned down. 'Er...' she faltered.

'Sorry. That wasn't fair,' Richard apologised, and Erin warmed to him some more for his sensitivity. 'New question,' he went on. 'How would you feel were I lucky enough to become your stepfather?' Oh, Richard, please don't count your chickens, Erin fretted. 'You wouldn't be averse to the idea?' he pressed.

No, she wouldn't. He was a nice man, a good man, and, having seen the way he regarded her parent, Erin felt they would do well together. 'I just want my mother to be happy,' she answered, and hoped that Richard would know that, had she been averse to the idea, she would not have encouraged his suit to her mother by accepting this build-up to any step-relationship by taking a walk with him.

'And would you say your mother is happy with me?' he continued to press.

Nina *was* happy with him; Erin knew that she was. She also knew that her mother was scared stiff of entering a third marriage which she might or might not want to get out of in a few years' time. Erin searched for something positive to reply, and found it in, 'Nina says you make her laugh.'

'Well, that's encouraging,' he replied. Then he smiled and promised, 'I give you my word, I won't say another word on the subject.'

Erin stayed home the next morning, though she was aware that Richard was up and about early. She was no lie-abed either, and had showered and dressed and had joined her equally early rising mother downstairs by seven.

'I suppose I'd better get myself over to the Ashmores',' was her mother's greeting. And, getting straight to what she wanted to know, 'What did you and Richard talk about on your walk yesterday?'

'You should have come with us,' Erin answered.

'Are you being cheeky?'

'Am I being reprimanded?' They both laughed, and Erin revealed, while feeling a tinge disloyal to Richard, 'We spoke of marriage proposals. One in particular.'

'He still has this notion he wants to marry me?' Nina asked sharply.

'You know he has.'

'Oh, Lord!' Erin feared the worst. Her mother did not

look very happy about it. 'I'd better go. I shall never hear the last of it if I'm not there for the mutual back-slapping.' And, back to being her more usually effervescent parent, 'Thank heavens they'll all be out of the water and dressed. I've seen their skinny, varicosed, knobbly-kneed legs before—not a pretty sight.' She laughed, and a short while later was leaving to drive the small distance to her friends the Ashmores.

Erin's thoughts were soon centred back on the man whom on Tuesday she had hated and whom today she wished she still did. 'I'll see you when I get back,' he had said, and her heart gave a little flutter at the thought. It steadied down again when she recalled her furious, 'Not if I see you first, you won't.' She doubted she would see him after that. Though that did not stop her wondering why he had phoned—from North America, no less—to tell her that. From what she knew of him, wasn't it more likely that he would just turn up if he felt like doing so? And—her ridiculous heart just did not know when it was beaten and fluttered again—why would he want to see her again anyway? If it was merely to give a repeat performance of his last visit, then, thank you, but no thanks.

And if he had no intention of calling at the mews apartment ever again, but was stating his intention of seeing her at her place of work, then he'd better get himself back here from New York within the next three weeks. She had already served one week of her month's notice.

Her mother and Richard were having something to eat over at the Ashmores' house, so Erin made herself some lunch with her thoughts still on Joshua Salsbury and his phone call from New York. She guessed that he made phone calls from abroad like most people made local telephone calls, so saw no special significance in the fact that he had bothered to call her from so far away.

But why would he bother to make even a local call to her? she had to wonder. Was he intending to make contact to further insult her? She recalled his voice had sounded more sort of carefully even than anything.

Had he tried hard for that even tone? Had he been afraid that he might lose control and lambast her from New York with whatever it was he had rung up to castigate her about?

Thoughts on the fact that the only things he could censure her about was her mother's behaviour in relation to his father and what Josh believed to be her own loose-moralled behaviour kept Erin fully occupied.

Shortly after three, earlier than she had anticipated, her mother drove up, closely followed by Richard in his car. Her mother did not wait for him, but entered the house straight away.

'How did the swimming go?' Erin asked Richard when he came in.

'To the devil with modesty,' he said with a smile. 'You're looking at a champion.'

Erin beamed a smile back at him as she congratulated him. But she sensed a slight tension in the air and was sure she wasn't imagining it. Particularly when he declined her mother's offer of some tea.

Sensitive to atmosphere, even if both her mother and Richard were too well-mannered to be anything but pleasant to each other with a third person there, Erin sensed that now would be a good time to leave.

'Any time you want to make tracks back to London?' she suggested.

'I do have some important work I should be doing,' Richard answered. 'We could go now, if you're ready.'

Within half an hour they were on the road. Richard regaled her with an amusing account of the swimathon as they drove along. But the nearer they got to London the more he seemed unable to keep up the pretence that all was well with his world.

There was sometimes difficulty in the mews courtyard if other mews-dwellers were entertaining Sunday visitors, as was the case when Richard went to drive through the archway. At once assessing the situation, he reversed out from the archway and found a nearby parking spot.

Erin would have collected her overnight bag and said goodbye to him there, but he insisted on carrying her bag to her door. 'Would you like some tea?' She felt courtesy demanded it after his drive—besides, she liked him.

He shook his head, dropping her bag down by her door. 'I'll get off.' He smiled then as he looked at her. 'I should have been proud had I been allowed to claim you as my stepdaughter,' he said quietly, pain in his eyes that he could not totally disguise.

'Oh, Richard,' Erin said softly. 'Did my mother…?'

'The lady said no.'

'I'm so sorry,' Erin said sadly, a hand going to his arm in genuine sympathy.

He took a step back. 'I doubt our paths will cross again,' he commented. On impulse he came forward again, and this time put his arms round her and gave her a hug in parting.

'Bye, Richard,' she said, and, aware that no words of hers were going to ease his pain, stretched up and kissed his cheek.

'Bye,' he answered.

Erin felt quite choked as she watched him walk away. Poor Richard. He must have managed to get her mother on her own at some time after all. She felt sorry for her mother too, because if her mother followed her usual pattern she would now, whatever her feelings for Richard, refuse to see him ever again. He knew it too. It had all been there in that 'I doubt our paths will cross again.'

Erin turned to the door, inserted her key in the lock and turned it. But with the door open she was startled almost out of her skin when from nowhere an all-masculine hand was there, picking up her overnight bag and tossing it indoors. And as he straightened, looking none too friendly, Erin stared at him stupefied. *Josh!*

'Who was he?' he snarled before she had her breath back.

Where had he sprung from? 'The wanderer returns!' she snapped, remembering that last time she had seen him and not feeling very friendly either. She would not be pleased to see him; she would *not!*

'Who?' Josh demanded.

She ignored his question, but took quite some pleasure in being able to tell him, 'If you've made a special journey especially to dismiss me, then you can't! I've already handed in my resignation and leave in three weeks' time.'

He did not look impressed. 'This has nothing to do with business!' he rapped. That being the case, Erin stepped over her threshold. So too did Josh. Deliberately—and with more force than was required, in her opinion—he slammed the door shut and in something of a fury again demanded, 'Who was he?'

By then, although starting to come away from the shock of seeing Josh—an angry Josh—so unexpectedly, Erin was still stunned enough to be on the way to forgetting that someone by the name of Richard had driven her home.

'Who?' she questioned snappily back.

'Don't play smart with me!' Josh Salsbury gritted.

Who did he think he was? She looked up into grey eyes that were threatening and her heart started to pound. He was close, too close. There just wasn't room for two angry people in this space at the bottom of the stairs that could not in anyone's wildest imaginings be termed a hallway.

Erin turned away, needing some space, and started up the stairs. 'You know your way out!' she lobbed arrogantly at him over her shoulder.

A mistake!

Josh was right there with her when she reached the top of the stairs, a hand descending on her shoulder spinning her round to face him. 'Don't you turn your back on me!' he ordered her furiously.

Oh, my word! Erin knew she was in trouble. But she discovered she had too much spirit to do what she knew she ought to do—perhaps apologise and answer anything he wanted to know. 'Correct me if I'm wrong, but haven't we been here before?' The murderous look in his eyes made her quail, but still her tongue wouldn't shut up. 'Isn't this the part where you pick me up and throw me on the bed?'

As if burnt, he thrust her away from him, pushing past her to go to the sitting room. She knew, she supposed, that if she decided to go back down those stairs and out of the apartment this time she would probably make it. But she still loved the bad-tempered swine—and love, and a need to be with him, no matter what the consequences, was in charge of her.

She did what her head said was wrong. She followed

him to the sitting room. Josh had his back to her, but although she had entered without making a noise he must either have sensed she was there or have heard some small sound. He turned to face her, saying nothing, just looking his fill.

He took what seemed a steadying breath, and, with his glance fixed determinedly on the stubborn look of her, he asked, 'Who was he?' with no let-up on his insistence to know.

'It doesn't matter who he was. I shan't be seeing him again.'

Josh took that on board. 'That was one very tender parting of the ways!' he sneered.

'What?' She'd lost him somewhere.

'Have you been with him all weekend?' Josh demanded, his tone more quiet than it had been—Erin felt it to be more ominous.

She could, she supposed, have told him that both she and Richard had been staying with her mother. That Richard had been her mother's man-friend. But a sensitivity to Josh's father rose up just then and prevented Erin from telling Josh where she had been—and that her mother had just dumped another one. His father apart, Josh's opinion of her mother was already low—she did not want it going any lower.

'Well?' Josh demanded, obviously believing he had been waiting long enough.

'Yes,' she answered, her chin tilting even as she saw his jaw clench at her affirmative answer. 'I've been with him ever since he called for me yesterday.'

'So you've finally done it!' Josh grated, his quiet tone straining at the leash.

Erin did not mistake his meaning. 'I thought you regarded me as some kind of tramp!' she reminded him hostilely. 'But it has nothing to do with you, anyway, whether I did or didn't!' she snapped, going red in spite of herself. And wanting to get away from the subject, she found she was repeating, 'I won't be seeing him again.'

'So either you did, and didn't care very much for the experience, or you didn't and he got upset that his hopes for the weekend got ruined. Which was it?'

Erin was starting to get angry again. Honestly! This man! This man—he thought he could barge his way in and be privy to the most intimate details of her life!

'It's none of your—'

'*Did* you bed him?' he cut in.

'I've seriously had enough of you!' Erin tossed at him shortly.

'You did!'

'As if I'd kiss and tell!' Erin jibed, close to hating one Joshua Salsbury once more. 'What's it to you anyway?'

'Not one damn thing!' he roared, not taking kindly to her attitude. And, coming close enough for her to be able to see flecks of amber in his grey eyes, 'I'm just the idiot who declined to take what you were so clearly offering when you clung on to me in my bed!'

She hit him. She didn't mean to. She didn't even know that she was going to. She just did. Saw red and her right hand flew through the air and caught him a furious blow. *Crack!* His head jerked to one side and she was on the instant totally appalled and ashamed. Violence was just not part of her nature. Or—she hadn't thought it was. Being in love was making a nonsense of everything she had thought she knew about herself.

'I'm sorry!' She rushed to apologise at once, her voice hoarse with emotion. 'I didn't mean to... You just...'

She turned her back on him. Regardless that he did not care for her turning her back on him she turned away, unable to bear the look of utter fury in his face.

Half expecting to receive some similar kind of retribution, she just stood there waiting—nowhere to run to. But then, to her complete surprise, two hands came to her arms. Not harsh and biting, as she would have expected, but gentle, almost tender.

'You're trembling,' Josh said somewhere above her bent head.

'I used to be a perfectly sane, rational person before I met you,' she said, entirely without thinking. Then, realising what she had said was much too revealing, 'You barge your way in here—' strictly speaking that wasn't true '—make aspersions about my friendship with Richard—' She broke off when she felt herself being gradually turned about.

'Richard being the one you've just denied visiting rights?' Dumbly she nodded, fearing to raise her head for what, in this weak moment for her, Josh might see in her eyes. 'So if you're friends do I take it you're not lovers?'

She was back in love with Josh in this gentle, more tender mood. She felt she could hold back nothing from him. 'I'm truly sorry I hit you,' she apologised again.

'And you and the surplus-to-requirements Richard were never lovers?' Josh placed a hand under her chin and began tilting her face upward so he could see into her eyes.

But only when she felt she had control of herself did Erin allow herself to look straight into his eyes.

'We never were,' she admitted.

Josh smiled. 'And Stephen?' he enquired. 'Did you make Stephen redundant too?'

Stephen? Oh, Stephen Dobbs. Erin vaguely recalled
that time she had been working directly for Josh and
Stephen Dobbs had rung through and she'd said she
would see him the following Monday or something.
'I'm—er—still seeing Stephen,' she answered truthfully,
but oddly didn't think her answer had gone down well.
Perhaps Josh did not care for staff fraternising after
work. But she didn't want Josh going back to the brute
he had been. 'Forgive me,' she said softly, and stretched
up and kissed the spot where her furious hand had connected. 'If it's any consolation, I think I've broken my
hand.'

Josh groaned. 'What am I going to do with you?' He
caught hold of her right hand and laid his lips on the
palm. Then, looking at her, he smiled. 'That's both of
us kissed better,' he murmured—and for ageless seconds
they just looked at each other.

It was without haste then, giving her all the time in
the world to pull away, should she so desire, that Josh
took her into his arms. And Erin had not the smallest
desire to resist. It seemed light years since she had last
seen him. She wanted his arms around her. She did what
she wanted to do—she rested her head against his chest.
And Josh seemed strangely content to hold her tenderly
to him, one arm moving, his hand coming to her shining
blonde head.

Gently he stroked her hair, and she wanted to stay
like this for ever. But that age-old fear that Josh might
catch a glimpse of her very deep feelings for him began
to stir, and although it took a deal of effort of will she
pulled away from him.

His hold on her slackened, just that alone telling her
that she was free, that he would not hold her against her
will. She fell in love with him all over again. 'I—er...'

She tried for sense, but the most sensible thing she could think to say was, 'I'd better ring my father. I told him I'd ring when I got back.'

Josh looked a touch amused. 'You want to do that right now?'

Well, as a matter of fact, no. Perhaps her eyes gave away that sentiment; she hoped not. But, as gently as before, Josh began drawing her to him again. This time she did not rest her head on his chest, but was ready and waiting when Josh gently kissed her.

'Oh,' she said on a breath of sound as their kiss broke and she looked up at him.

He laughed lightly. 'Oh—more? Or, oh—that's enough?'

She laughed too. This was totally ridiculous. 'Perhaps just one more—er—purely to make up for my dreadful temper when I hit you.'

'I earned it,' he absolved her. But grinned spine-meltingly when he added, 'Though perhaps one kiss would make it less painful.'

'Does it still hurt?' she asked in alarm.

'Not at all,' he replied, and if he was lying she never found out, because his head was coming nearer and once more he was claiming her lips.

And they shared more than just one kiss, his kisses absolving him too in her eyes for those other kisses taken, not given, the last time they had been together.

Her heart was drumming wildly and she neither knew nor cared where their kisses were leading. She enjoyed, adored his gentle caresses, his kisses to her throat. He unfastened her shirt and placed tender kisses on her silken skin, moving her shirt and bra straps aside as he tasted the sweetness of her shoulders.

Oh, Josh, Josh, Josh! His touch was magic. Her arms

were around him, joy taking her just to hold him. They kissed again, a kiss that hinted that soon there would be no going back. Erin did not care—she was on fire for him. She wanted to make love with him—she rather supposed that he knew that too. She pressed her scantily covered breasts against him, and was enthralled when his hands on her hips drew her to him.

'Josh, I…' she choked.

'Scared?' he asked, his eyes serious on her eyes.

'No,' she answered honestly. But laughed shyly as she confessed, 'Adventurous.'

He smiled at her. 'It's quite something of an adventure.'

'I—er—um…' She swallowed hard. 'I—think—I'm ready for it.'

He kissed her in delight. 'You have to be sure you are, not think you are, little darling,' he suggested softly—but she was too enamoured of him to be able to think logically. 'It's a big step.'

She knew that it was. But he was her one and only—and she wanted his lovemaking to remember when he had gone. But she hesitated. Was she being too forward? She wanted to die from the shame of it. 'I'm too eager?' she questioned.

He smiled. 'No, love. You've just waited for a long time—and one of us has to be sure that the time is now.'

'You're not sure—about you?' Oh, grief! The moment the words were out Erin realised that they sounded as if she was asking for some kind of commitment from him. Without thinking further, she pulled out of his arms and, taking a step or two away from him, felt herself colour when she saw the disarray of her clothes. Hurriedly she buttoned herself up. 'You'd better go,' she mumbled.

'Is this nerves speaking?' Josh asked, not coming after

her but giving her all the space she seemed to need just then.

'How would I know?' she answered, more snappily than she'd meant to—had Josh no idea of what he had been, and was still doing to her? 'I've never b-been this—um—far before with any man...' her voice faded, the 'but you' never said.

'Oh, Erin,' Josh said softly. 'Come back to me.'

She looked at him and was undecided. He must not know of her love for him, but oh, how she ached to be back in his arms. 'You're asking?' she questioned guardedly.

He did not hesitate. 'I'm asking,' he replied, and smiled a welcome.

'In that case,' she murmured, and went to him, loving him, exchanging kisses with him again, her emotions once more out of control, her body soon on fire for him again.

Josh took her to the sofa, their bodies pressed closely together when suddenly the phone started to shrill for attention. They both tried to ignore it—it declined to be ignored. Josh put some daylight between their two bodies. 'This is impossible,' he grunted. They both sat up.

Erin could not agree with him more. 'It might be my father,' she guessed. 'He'll ring and ring. I'd better answer it. Oh, grief.' She went a pretty shade of pink.

'Oh, grief, as in...?'

'As in, What were you doing that it took you so long to come to the phone?'

Josh grinned wickedly, and Erin, her emotions all over the place, hurried from the sofa, straightening her clothing as she went. It was not her father—but Greg Williams! Oh, heck.

'Oh, hello, Greg.' She answered his greeting, watched

Josh's grin disappear, saw his mouth tighten as he got up from the sofa and went to stare out of the window. 'Er—how are you?'

'Glad that at last I've managed to find you in. I've been ringing your number since yesterday afternoon!'

'I'm sorry.' She apologised nicely for not being there, though in fact her thoughts were more with Josh than the man she was speaking with. Which made it a total nonsense that, when she had been at pains to make no reference to her mother in Josh's presence, she should go headlong into explaining to Greg, 'I've been staying overnight at my mother's place.'

She looked hastily at Josh—his shoulders were rigid, and Erin knew right then that she could forget any thought of sharing more kisses with him. He turned, and there was that in his eyes that said he had remembered his father and what her mother had done to him. Erin looked away. Without doubt Josh was not too happy to realise that his lovemaking with Nina Woodward's daughter could be construed as disloyalty to his father.

Erin tried to focus on what Greg was saying—something to the effect that he had wangled a day off work next Thursday and how was she fixed to see him if he came to London?

She had not the smallest wish to see Greg Williams again. Against that, however, she was quickly realising that she was someone who had bedroom experience only with Josh—that experience indisputably unfulfilled— and Josh must, with his experience of women, have gained some clue that she cared more for him than any man she knew. Hadn't she only just told him that she had never been 'this far' with any man? It was time, she realised, to let Josh know that she was not enamoured of him to the exclusion of all men.

'... shall I?' Greg Williams was asking.

'I'd love to see you Thursday,' she answered. Josh's jaw jutted. She did not care—he must not know that the sun rose and set for her in him. 'I'll see if I can get some time off too. Let me have your phone number. I'll give you a call and we can finalise details.'

'Great!' Greg exclaimed enthusiastically, gave her his phone number and would have gone on talking at length had not Erin, trying not to show she was affected in any way by Josh's glowering expression, told Greg that she had company and now was not a good time to chat. 'I'll look forward to your call,' he told her, and eventually rang off.

Erin put the phone down, her heart aching. She could tell from the icy expression on Josh's face that they were going precisely nowhere. She supposed, despite those rapturous moments of mutual ardour, that she had always known that. They never had been.

'Impossible, did I say?' Josh questioned curtly. 'Totally bloody impossible, I should have said,' he gritted, and added icily, 'You shouldn't have terminated your call on my account—your company's leaving!'

Again Erin had cause to be thankful for her pride. Her heart might be bruised, sore and bleeding—but she still had her pride. 'Do allow me to show you out,' she offered sweetly. But could have done without his look of utter disgust as he passed and, denying her the pleasure of closing the door after him, strode angrily out, down the stairs and closed the outer door behind him with a quite dreadful thud of finality.

CHAPTER SEVEN

ERIN wished she could get thoughts of Josh out of her head. But thoughts of him haunted her after he had gone. She tried to think of something else, something other than him, and succeeded for about two seconds. Then Josh was back again.

She ejected him once more and decided to ring her father, as she had promised she would. But found she was in such an agitated stew over Josh Salsbury that she was just not yet ready to speak to anyone.

A half-hour later her father rang her. 'Been back long?' he enquired.

'Not too long. I intended to ring you.'

'Did you have a good stay with your mother?'

Erin was sensitive to her father's feelings, but felt that it was all right to truthfully tell him, 'We had a very pleasant time.'

'Who's she going around with now?'

Difficult territory. Erin wondered for all her parents' regularly exchanged insults if her father still felt something for his ex-wife. 'Mother isn't seeing anyone at the moment,' Erin glad to once more be truthful, was able to tell him.

'My God, the sky will fall in!' he exclaimed sarcastically.

'How was your weekend?' Erin changed the subject matter.

'Hmm…' Her father hesitating? Erin was intrigued. And even more so when he revealed, 'Actually, the woman who moved into the old Raven place about a month ago invited a few neighbours in for a drink last night.'

Erin could not believe that he had accepted. From what she knew of her father she would have said, if asked, that he would run a mile away from such invitations. 'You—went?' she asked.

'I thought I would.'

Just that! Erin decided it was time to use a daughter's prying privileges. 'What's her husband like?' she asked casually.

'Brenda's a widow.' Brenda! First-name terms! Not Mrs So-and-so, as with his other neighbours—but Brenda! 'Actually,' Leslie Tunnicliffe was going on, 'it occurred to me that as she's new to the area it might—um—well, perhaps we should invite her to dinner one Saturday.'

Grief! This was a sensational departure! It even put Josh Salsbury to the back of Erin's mind for longer than a few seconds. 'I'll be home this Friday,' she replied quickly, sensing her father was feeling a bit off-footed with this conversation. 'Would this Saturday be too soon?'

'I'll think about it,' he replied, but Erin did not miss that there was a smile in his voice.

While that phone call had given her something else to think about, Josh was soon dominant in her head after her father's call was ended. Josh had called her 'little darling', he had called her 'love', and she wanted him back with her—but the finality in the way he had closed the door clearly showed that he would never call again.

She escaped that harsh reality by dreamily recalling those lost moments in his arms. She thought of his wonderful kisses, his gentleness, his tenderness with her—and wanted that time back again.

But rushing in came the memory of how Greg Williams's phone call had changed all that. She had mentioned her mother and that was all he had needed. Josh had turned icy. Impossible, he'd said—he was right there.

By nine that night all Erin wanted to do was to go to bed, pull the covers up over her head and hope for oblivion until morning.

No chance! Logic told her she must have slept at some time, but it did not feel like it. She was up early on Monday, having spent half the night going over every word, look and nuance that had passed between her and Josh Salsbury from the moment she had first met him that morning when he had joined her and Charlotte for a cup of coffee.

Erin showered and dressed with Josh refusing to budge from her head. In the end she admitted defeat and let him stay, and tried to dull the incessant ache by being angry. What right had he to come knocking on her door anyway? Not that he'd bothered ringing her doorbell yesterday. He had simply been there and had taken the liberty not to wait for an invitation to come in. Though, come to think of it, he had probably realised after the previous episode that he'd have had a long wait for that sort of an invitation.

But why come at all? And had he just arrived at the same time as she and Richard, or had he been there waiting for her to come home? Huh! She scoffed at the notion that he might have been waiting for her—they didn't have that sort of relationship, or any other sort of relationship, for that matter.

While she accepted that she and Josh were more personal than employer and employee—my stars, were they—Erin recalled her state of undress yesterday and went hot all over. Too much had gone on between them. She had slept with him—albeit in the purest sense— albeit not from her choice—so very definitely they were positively more personal than employer and employee should ever be.

All the same, in her view they still did not have the sort of 'thing' going where Josh Salsbury could just pop over to the mews apartment any time he felt like it. And she'd jolly well tell him that the next time he... Her thoughts faltered. She remembered his icy parting words, the way he had looked just before he had left. That awful thud of finality as he'd shut the door on his way out— and she knew indelibly then that she would not see him again.

She felt defeated, and the hour being early, no need to rush around prior to leaving for the office, she went over to the sofa. She sat there for quite some while and hoped never to be this unhappy again as she came to terms with love and life, and the fact that she could not go on like this.

Then the phone rang. And she jumped. And she thought of Josh, her pulses racing for all she knew that it would not be him. Was this how it was going to be? That she would think it was Josh on the other end of the phone every time it rang?

It was not him; it was her mother. 'Good morning, darling!' Nina greeted her brightly. 'I thought I'd get you before you left for the office. I wonder if you're free for lunch today?'

'Of course,' Erin answered equally brightly. 'Same place?'

'If you like,' Nina trilled, and rang off. And Erin went

back to her contemplation, knowing that she was not going to have to ask Ivan for an extended lunch hour—because she was going to ring him shortly and terminate her last link with Joshua Salsbury.

She would find it not an easy task. But she knew that it was the only thing she could do. She must cut Josh completely out of her life. He wouldn't give a tuppenny damn about it, of course. In all probability he wouldn't even know that she no longer worked for him. But while she was anywhere near that building Erin just knew that she would be constantly, and fruitlessly, hoping to catch some glimpse of him.

A little after nine, while she was still of the same mind, Erin picked up the phone and dialled. She did not think she would weaken, but she felt in such an emotional turmoil that she did not trust herself not to have second thoughts.

'Oh, Erin, you can't leave just like that!' Ivan Kelly protested when she had explained that due to unforeseen domestic complications she was unable to work out her notice as she had hoped. 'Perhaps our human resources department can help?' he suggested. 'They're very good, and extremely discreet if—'

Feeling worse than ever, Erin hurriedly cut him off. 'No, no. Thank you all the same. I've so enjoyed working with you, Ivan, but…'

Ivan had lived long enough to understand that some matters just could not be put right with the help of outside agencies, no matter how good those agencies were. And they ended their business relationship with Ivan asking her to promise to be in touch should her present difficulties be resolved, when he would be happy to re-employ her.

Erin came away from the phone, glad that she had

done what she had done, but not feeling the slightest bit better for it. Ivan had been a love about her leaving him in the lurch like that, and she felt dreadful and ashamed. But what else could she have done? She did not want to go to an office so close to where Josh worked. Was she to spend the next three weeks sitting at her desk hoping he might have business in her section? Was she to wander the corridors of the main building hoping to catch a glimpse of him? No. It had to end now. And she had ended it. So why did she feel so miserable and so at rock bottom?

Erin pinned a smile on her face when she went to meet her mother. And as lunch progressed she began to realise that her mother's own bright smile was hiding that Nina was not feeling so very full of the joys of spring either.

'I've—er—finished with Richard,' she mentioned casually. 'Pass the tartare.'

Erin passed her mother the sauce to go with the fish she had ordered. 'So Richard mentioned.'

'He told you?' Nina asked sharply, the tartare sauce forgotten. 'What did he say?'

'Just that he would have been proud to have me as his stepdaughter, but that you'd said no.'

'Was he upset?'

'Oh, Mother, of course he was upset.' That he was not the only one who was upset was evidenced for Erin in that her parent let the 'Mother' go by without rebuke. 'You're going to miss him, aren't you?' she asked gently.

Her mother gave a long sigh. 'I am already,' she admitted. 'And it's not twenty-four hours yet! He didn't ring last night, or this morning.'

'Um—did you expect him to?'

Nina sighed again. 'I suppose not. And I'd have been very cross if he had,' she bridled, though was sounding quite fed-up when she added, 'But I'm going to miss those telephone calls.'

It seemed to Erin, who was enduring a love problem of her own—one that could not be resolved—that all her mother had to do to make it right was to pick up the phone and call Richard. She dared to say as much.

'I know I haven't been married, and can't possibly know how horrid it must be when a marriage fails, but— would it be such a terrible thing for you to marry Richard?'

'Make a third marriage, you mean?'

At least her mother wasn't biting her head off. Erin grew a little bolder. 'Well, to be honest, it seems potty to me that when you care for Richard, and he cares for you, you should both be so unhappy to be apart when there's something you can do about it.'

'But—marriage? I've tried it twice, remember?'

'Yes, but with the experience you have surely…?'

'I couldn't possibly go through another divorce!'

'You're looking at it from the wrong end!' Erin protested. 'Would you, right now, prefer never to see Richard again?'

Her mother didn't answer that question, though Erin noticed she did not look very cheerful at the prospect of never seeing him again. 'Men get so dull once you're married to them,' she complained. Then smiled, the old Nina not submerged for long. 'I'm just not ready to settle for a life of "What's on TV tonight, dear", and some man being king of the remote!'

Erin laughed; her mother was impossible. 'From what I've seen of Richard, I'd say he'd very likely give you your own remote as a wedding present.'

'See what I mean—hum-drum city.'

All Erin saw was that she was losing the argument and that her attempts to make her mother see that she could feel happier were failing miserably. 'Have you told Richard how you feel? How, for all you don't show it, you're still carrying mental scars, baggage, from your previous failed marriages?'

'It's nothing to do with him!' Nina bridled again. And, looking at her lovely daughter, advised her sharply, 'And you're much too observant for your own good!'

What I am, Mother, is in love as well, and finding it extremely emotionally battering. 'I don't want you to be unhappy,' she said gently. 'Why not ring Richard? Open up to him. Tell him—'

'I'll tell him what I think fit to tell him!' Nina broke in to retort sniffily. But Erin was pleased to note that she had not declined outright to ring him.

By the time she and her mother parted company they were friends again. And Erin went back to the mews apartment with much to think over. Josh was in her head again, of course—he seemed to go everywhere with her. But when she was able to concentrate on her mother Erin only hoped she was not feeling so downcast as she was feeling. Erin did so hope not, particularly when she knew that there was every chance her mother could do something about it. All she had to do was to ring Richard, start talking and…

Josh was back in Erin's head. He had not been away long. Were it Josh, Erin knew she would ring him. Though Richard loved her mother, and Josh…

Fat chance. Erin knew Josh had desired her on a couple of occasions, but he was a virile male—and desire wasn't love.

She made a pot of tea around seven. But, unable to

settle with a book, decided, sternly, to get her act together. She was still sitting there at eight, her thoughts
having darted all over the place. Firstly she had started
off by determining what to do with her future—but had
lost some time when Josh, her mother, Richard, her father and the unknown Brenda had claimed a helping of
her thoughts, Josh taking the lion's portion. Then she'd
thought about work and how she would get another job.
Then Josh and her family had intruded again, until all
at once it had dawned on her that there was not the
smallest need for her to stay on in London. She could
work anywhere, for that matter.

Erin gave brief thought to returning to Croom
Babbington to live. She loved her father, and she knew
he would welcome her back, but somehow, having left
home, having tasted something different these past
months, Erin knew, with no disrespect to her father, that
she did not want to return to Croom Babbington. What
she wanted to do was to stay in London.

She was just about to analyse that when her phone
rang. Josh? Ridiculous! As was proved when, with her
heart pounding, she answered it.

'Are you all right, Erin?' It was Stephen Dobbs,
sounding most concerned. 'I've only just got in—one of
those Mondays! Ivan mentioned just as I was leaving
that you'd rung in to say you wouldn't be coming back.
He wouldn't say why. Is it anything...?'

'It's—er—a domestic matter.' She fell back on that
excuse. Stephen was now more friend than work colleague, but still the same Erin did not feel able to confide
about her inner emotions to him.

'Anything I can help you with?' he offered at once,
like the good soul he was.

'No. I can cope,' she declined.

'Are you able to come for a drink one night this week? We could grab a bite to eat somewhere if you like?' he suggested.

Erin was about to ask him if he'd mind leaving it until next week, then flashing into her head came that newspaper picture of Josh, living it up in New York, and her pride once more surfaced. 'I'd like that,' she replied, and arranged to see him on Wednesday.

She had barely ended her call from Stephen, though, when her phone rang again. She knew in advance this time it would not be Josh—that wasn't his way. Present himself in person and then invite himself in—that was his way. Not that that would ever happen again.

So her heart was only moderately pounding when she picked up the phone and said, 'Hello.'

'Your line was engaged,' said a voice guaranteed to have the blood rushing wildly through her veins.

'St-Stephen,' she answered witlessly.

'Stephen?' Josh queried, as she struggled to gather a modicum of composure.

'I'm seeing Stephen Wednesday,' she replied, proof there if proof was needed that her brain matter had taken a hike. 'Er—what...?' She didn't get to finish.

'You're seeing Greg Williams on Thursday,' Josh documented, his voice strangely even. She wondered at that. It was almost as if he were holding himself in check about something.

Ridiculous! This love business was causing her to have the most absurd notions. 'You know how it is,' she said off the top of her head. 'No date for ages then two come along at once.'

There was a pause, but again his voice was even when Josh reminded her, 'You *have* remembered that

Williams's idea of a fun date might not necessarily be the same as your idea of a fun date?'

Oh, Josh. Erin sank down onto the sofa, fearing she might fall. 'Greg—er—knows I'm not—er—like that.'

'Those weren't the messages I was reading the one and only time I saw the two of you together,' Josh stated bluntly, his even tone gone. 'When did you tell him?'

'What?' she answered, not sure she cared for this line of questioning.

'When did you tell him that he was wasting his time— um—coming the—old soldier?'

Erin burst out laughing. In spite of herself, in spite of that feeling of starting to get a tiny bit niggled with Josh, she just had to laugh. Fancy him remembering! 'I told him when he rang previously.'

'You obviously gave him your phone number at Robin and Charlotte's wedding?'

'I didn't, actually,' Erin replied, a smile back in her heart just to be talking with the man she loved. 'I expect he rang Charlotte's parents or something.'

'Just how many would-be lovers do you have?' Josh enquired, to Erin's ears with a kind of tough edge in his voice.

'I don't think—'

'I can think of five straight off,' he stated sharply.

'You know more than me, then!'

'Gavin, Mark…'

'Gavin? Who he?'

'Gavin—the thigh-crusher.'

Gavin Gardner! 'Ah, yes.'

'Richard, Stephen,' Josh went on. 'And, most irrefutably, Greg Williams.'

'I've told you,' Erin began, and then started to get really annoyed. Love him she might—but what was this?

'Just why have you rung, Josh Salsbury?' she demanded crisply.

There was a brief pause, a sort of hesitation, as if her question had come before he was ready for it. Rot, said her head. 'I thought you might like to know—I've got a black eye.'

Her breath sucked in. From where she had hit him? 'You haven't!' she denied, distressed. 'Oh, tell me you haven't!'

There was a pause, and she had to wait an agonising second or two before he agreed, 'No, I haven't.' And, with a smile there somewhere, 'I was just after your sympathy.'

She didn't believe that for a moment. She wished then that she didn't love him, but she did. And, even though she wanted to stay talking with him for as long as he liked, there was a proud part of her that made her question, 'That wasn't why you rang?' knowing full well that once he had told her the reason for his call he would then end it.

'You weren't in work today.'

How had he found that out? 'I—don't work for you any longer,' she told him jerkily.

'So I heard,' he replied quietly. 'May I enquire why?' He needed to ask? 'I thought you said you'd some weeks to go before you left?'

Erin did not wish to invite some third degree, even though she had no idea why he would bother. She had been good at her job, but did not doubt she would soon be replaced with someone equally efficient. Yet she shied away from telling Josh that she had some domestic problem, knowing she would only end up tying herself in knots if, unlike Ivan Kelly, Josh pressed to know more.

'I've—had enough,' she answered at last.

More moments of silence followed while Josh considered her answer. Then, his tone even once more, 'My fault?' he enquired.

Too true it was his fault. 'You said it!' she retorted sharply, seeing no reason to hide that, after his visit yesterday, she had decided she'd had enough.

Though she was totally unprepared for him to dissect her answer and to then come back with a quiet, 'I have that much effect on you, Erin?'

'I—er... I—er...' Totally stumped for an answer, she did the only thing she could do—she came out fighting. 'Look here, Salsbury, I didn't invite you here yesterday. And I didn't invite this phone call either. So you can either state now why you've phoned, so I can get back to what I was doing—' which was precisely nothing '—or I'm going to put this phone down and get myself an ex-directory number!' She felt near to tears. Pig, pig, pig!

Quite a lengthy pause followed, and she thought he must have gone. But still the same she just could not put the phone down—not until she was sure he had gone. Then suddenly, quietly, Josh was saying, 'I grew impatient of waiting.'

'Waiting?'

'You didn't phone.'

She wasn't with him. She wasn't surprised that she hadn't a clue what he was talking about—she was completely all over the place. 'Me?' she questioned.

'You said you would ring me.'

'No, I didn't!' she denied. Lying hound! 'When did I?'

'Don't you remember? Surely you do. We had a date,

you and I, but the day before—a Thursday, I think it was—you rang to say you couldn't make it.'

Oh, yes, of course she remembered. 'It—er—was a Thursday,' she confirmed witlessly. Would she ever forget it? There had been a report in the paper that night about his father suffering a heart attack. Her mother had called and...

'If you remember that, you'll also remember that you had to cancel our date because you were having problems—"a few complications at the moment" I believe you said.' Erin was silent, struck dumb, and Josh waited a few seconds and then further reminded her, 'I suggested that you give me a ring when you had your complications sorted.' He paused. 'Only you haven't rung. And, since that was months ago, I felt sure you must have resolved those complications by now.'

Erin was stunned—and stumped. Was Joshua Salsbury—asking her out? Her heart began to thunder and, quite idiotically, having no answer for him, she put the phone back on its cradle—and terminated the call.

She regretted doing so at once, but then began to wonder if it had been so idiotic after all. Because, while starting to grow certain that Josh had *not* been asking her out, she was also starting to realise that those complications he had reminded her of would never be resolved.

It was a fact that his father had been serious about her mother and that her mother must have encouraged and then rejected him, dropped him, and that Josh's father had shortly afterwards suffered a heart attack. Wasn't that complication enough for anyone?

Yes, but, argued Erin's heart, while she had not then felt able to tell Josh the truth and had hid behind 'complications', he had found out anyway. Yet still he was asking her out? So did that mean that there were no complications? And was he, in fact, asking her out?

She remembered how icy he had gone yesterday when her mother was mentioned. No *way*, Erin decided, was Josh asking her if she was ready yet to go out with him.

Anyhow, she didn't want to go out with him—even if he was offering, which he wasn't. She would never get over him that way.

Feeling too agitated to sit still, Erin got up and went to take a shower. She got into her night things and went back to the sitting room, and was still chewing away at every word of that phone call. Why? Why had he rung? Why? Why? Why?

Was he asking her out? Her heart started to race. She couldn't believe it. But if he *were* asking her out—why? Would Josh ask her out because, well, because he—liked her? Could it be that he did? Oh, she knew well enough that physically they struck sparks off each other, sparks that ignited into a passion of wanting. But she had been his for the taking. He had declined, thank you very much. So why would he bother…?

Was it just that he liked her? Or was it maybe that he was out for some kind of revenge? Did he have some kind of scheme in mind to make her pay for what her mother had done to his father?

Somehow Erin did not want to believe that. But, whether that had anything to do with it or not, she told herself she did not care. She just didn't want to go out with him. He hadn't been asking anyway.

It was far safer to ignore his call, she determined. Safer and, prodded a voice she just did not want to listen to, duller. She went and made herself a cup of coffee. It might keep her awake but she wasn't going to sleep anyway.

Safer and duller dogged her heels as she walked back from the kitchen. She sipped her coffee, finished it, and padded back to the kitchen. She rinsed her cup and saucer and returned to the sitting room, and was then overcome by such a longing to see Josh that she looked over to the phone.

Ridiculous, said her head. He might have said he had grown impatient waiting for her to call him, but he didn't really mean it.

So why had he rung her anyway? The Josh she knew was more likely to present himself at her door, and without waiting to be asked come straight in, before he'd phone.

Erin knew that she would not call him back. But such a feeling of restlessness came over her just then that she got up and started wandering about. In the process she found the telephone numbers Charlotte had given her—Josh's telephone numbers.

Erin went back to the sofa, restless still, safe and dull again bombarding her. She glanced at the clock—close to midnight. She wouldn't ring him. But—why shouldn't she? He was waiting for her call; he'd said so.

She started to feel all hot and bothered, and recalled how only that day she had urged her mother to ring the man she loved. Yes, but this was different.

Erin got up and paced around, the phone seeming to hypnotise her. She couldn't ring him. Yet what was the alternative—to go over and over again on the same treadmill? Safer not to ring him. And duller, prodded the person inside her who had started to decide that if she left it any longer she would have to wait until morning to ring Josh. When who knew where he would be? He was probably always up early and off somewhere. He might even have plans to be at some airport, taking an early flight somewhere.

Her hand hovered near the phone. He might be in bed. So? If he was flying off somewhere at first light was she to wait until he came back—which could be a minimum of a week—to contact him?

But did she want to contact him? Erin sat in deep thought for the next three minutes and then faced that, in all honesty, safer and duller just did not come into it. She wanted to hear his voice, wanted to know why he had phoned. She somehow did not think a man like Josh would just ring to pass the time of day.

And anyway, whether he was in bed by now or whether he wasn't, it was not his sole prerogative to ring people up and disturb them. Not allowing herself to think further, Erin picked up the phone and pressed out his telephone number.

The phone was answered straight away—almost as if Josh was sitting there waiting for her call. Get real! 'Salsbury,' he said evenly, and she couldn't think of a thing to say.

'Er...' was about as much as she could manage.

'I'm glad you rang,' Josh encouraged.

How did he know it was her? Did he know it was her? Perhaps he was glad it was somebody else calling. 'It's Erin,' she said in a rush.

'I know.'

Oh! 'Er—how d-did you know I wasn't in work to-day?' She had no idea why she had asked him that. She had not intended to.

'I had reason to go to the experimental division,' he answered.

'You never go to the experimental division.' Well, he

never had, not the new place anyway, while she had been there.

'I went today,' he replied, his tone even still, and not impatient as she would have imagined it would be at this nothing kind of conversation.

That word 'impatient' reminded her that he had said he had grown impatient waiting for her to ring. And without further thought she grabbed at what courage she could find, and hurtled headlong in with, 'About our date...' and promptly ran out of steam.

There was an utter deafening silence. Then, 'I'll come over,' Josh said quietly, and, as she had earlier, he put down the phone and terminated the call.

For totally stunned seconds Erin stared at the unresponsive phone in her hand before she placed it back down. 'I'll come over,' Josh had said. When? Tomorrow? She began to feel thoroughly agitated. Tomorrow was Tuesday. He knew that she had arrangements for Wednesday. She was seeing Greg on Thursday. Perhaps Josh would come over on Friday. They had arranged to go out on a Friday before, she remembered—and then suddenly a most astonishing thought just then hit! He didn't mean—*now*, did he? As in, I'll come over—*now?* Erin was on her feet, all at once too stewed up to know what she was doing.

He couldn't have meant that! Surely he couldn't have? Why, it would be about one o'clock before he got here! She was being ridiculous to think such a thing.

Ridiculous or not, and knowing for certain that she was being the biggest fool of all time, Erin went to her bedroom, found fresh underwear, her best trousers and a fine cashmere sweater, and exchanged them for the nightdress and wrap she was wearing.

Grateful that she was the only one who would ever

know what a complete idiot she was being, Erin still the same could not settle or return to the sitting room to wait to have her idiocy proven.

She went to the kitchen but did not turn on the kitchen light. Her view of the courtyard was much better in the dark. Minutes ticked by. After five she went and brushed her hair, only to race to the kitchen window when she thought she heard a car.

There was no car. She waited another ten minutes. She tried to laugh at how ridiculous she was being. Even if Josh had left straight away, which he hadn't, he still wouldn't be here in under...

She caught her breath, almost choked on it, as just then car headlights fanned over her window and a car drove into the courtyard. She recovered, knowing full well that it must be one of the other residents in the mews returning from an evening out.

The car drew to a stop and her breath caught again. It was dark, but she thought she knew the car. A man got out. A tall man. A man of Josh's height.

There was a thundering in her ears as the man walked from the parking area and the security lights came on and caught him fully in their beam as he approached her door. Josh!

Her heart was pounding so hard she thought she might faint. 'I'll come over,' he had said. Not tomorrow, not Friday, but, 'I'll come over—*now*.' And he was here, and she was shaking like a leaf, with no idea of how her legs were going to carry her down the stairs to let him in.

CHAPTER EIGHT

ERIN had still not moved. In fact she felt frozen to the spot when Josh rang the doorbell. She moved then, her head a riot of half-thoughts as she went down the stairs to let him in.

He did not ring a second time, but gave her the moments she sorely needed to get herself under control. Wasted moments. She was still a quivering mass inside as she pulled back the door.

She tried for calm, tried for casual, but he looked—and was—so devastating that all she could do was stare at him. She took a step back. He did not move, but seemed content to just stand there, drinking in his fill of her from where he stood.

That was the moment, that moment of total nonsensical thought, when Erin's brain gave her a prod. 'You don't normally wait to be invited up,' she opened for starters.

Josh stared at her a moment longer before politely informing her, 'It seems to me, Erin Tunnicliffe, that normal flew out of the window on the day I met you.'

She didn't know if that was some kind of joke or what it was. She could find no answer anyway, so settled for a cool, 'You'd better come in.'

Cool—ye gods! She inwardly felt a complete and utter jumble of emotions as she led the way upstairs. They reached the sitting room and she turned to face him, finding it a joy just to have him there. But—why had he come?

'Would you like coffee?' she enquired, like any well brought up hostess would.

'Your father would approve?'

'At close to one in the morning? Probably not,' she replied. 'But let's keep our…' she faltered '…my family out of this. Though…' Abruptly she changed her mind. 'Though that is what this is about, isn't it—m-my mother and your…?' Heavens, she was inviting all-out war! She knew it! 'Do you want to take a seat?'

'Thank you,' Josh answered levelly, but waited until Erin had perched on the one easy chair before taking a seat on the sofa.

'You're being unusually polite,' she said warily, distrustfully, and plunged, 'This visit, you being here, it's all about revenge, isn't it?'

'Revenge?' He looked surprised.

But she wasn't fooled. 'It's the only answer that fits,' she said, as that answer came to her. 'No normal person comes calling at close to one in the morning on account of a—er—an outstanding date.'

Josh looked back at her. 'I may have mentioned that nothing is normal for me any more,' he informed her levelly. But then, as if fearing he had said too much, 'Revenge? What are you talking about?'

She barely knew! He had made it sound as though it was her fault that nothing was normal for him any more. Erin attempted to quieten her racing heartbeats by reminding herself that of course nothing was normal for Josh any more. How could it be? His meeting with her had coincided with his father suffering that heart attack. And although it would have to be his father's lifestyle, work-style, that would probably have to be dramatically adjusted, that adjustment was bound to affect Josh too—hence not normal any more.

'You know what I'm talking about.' Erin pulled herself together to answer Josh's question. 'You believe, rightly or wrongly, that my mother is responsible for your father being ill, and you want me to pay for it.'

Josh looked at her in disbelief. 'You're amazing!' he muttered, and went on to bluntly deny any such notion. 'Complete and utter rot!' he disclaimed.

'Is it?' she challenged.

'Incredible,' he commented. 'To think when you worked in my office for that short time I was so impressed by your quick grasp of matters!'

She tried not to be flattered, and stiffened her backbone. 'Huh!' she scoffed. 'You positively glower whenever my mother's name is mentioned. You—'

'At first, maybe,' he cut in to agree.

'Maybe! Pfff! That wasn't the way I saw it!' She stood her ground.

'So I was furious. Outraged, if you like. But only to start with.'

Erin would like to have done another huff and puff. She had not forgotten how in this very room, only the previous evening, he had changed totally from being a warm and gentle lover to being curt and icy the moment she had made reference to her mother.

She decided to give him more rope. 'Go on,' she invited, 'hang yourself.'

'It's true.' Josh took up the option. 'I was at first infuriated when I saw you in that car with her. Close to exploding when I witnessed you all affectionate to her. This was a woman whose callousness had all but killed my father. I feared for my actions if I was not able to walk on...'

'So you did walk on, and instead you came here. That

night you came here, and—and...' Her voice faded. She could not go on.

'Oh, my dear, dear Erin,' Josh said softly, his tone as much as his words ruining the backbone-stiffening she had thought she had found. 'I've tried to get that dark night out of my head, but cannot. I was so out of control when you told me that Nina Woodward was your mother...' He shook his head. 'Even now I can't believe I tried to force myself on you.'

He seemed much upset at the memory, and despite herself Erin found she loved him enough to not want him upset. 'Y-you thought I was anybody's,' she reminded him.

'As if that excused what I was about!' he said angrily. 'Not that I ever believed that anyway.'

Well, if he could be angry then so could she—she wished she hadn't tried to ease things for him. 'You could have fooled me!' she retorted snappily.

Josh stared at her for some moments, and then confessed, 'I realise now, have known for some time, that the person I was trying to fool the most was me.'

Erin looked back into his dear face. But she was not about to go soft on him a second time. 'Intriguing—if more than a touch totally bewildering,' she retorted sniffily. 'Are you sure you won't have that coffee before you leave?'

He laughed. He actually laughed at her broad hint that he should go. 'Oh, Erin Tunnicliffe, have you a lot to learn about me,' he said, and, his tone mellowing, softening, 'I've built myself up for this moment,' he stated. 'There are—things I need to say to you. Apologies I need to make. Answers that I shan't rest until I know. No way am I leaving until some, most, hopefully all of them have been resolved to my and—hmm—I hope your satisfaction.'

Her throat went dry. Oh, help, she was wilting already! Things to say, apologies to make, answers to his satisfaction—and *hers*, don't forget. 'I—er—I'll—um—take that as a no, then, shall I? Um—about the coffee?'

'Oh, Erin, Erin,' he said. 'Is it any wonder you drive me quite demented?'

Her eyes widened in astonishment. 'Me?' she checked.

He smiled. 'Since you're not running a mile, I'll take courage and explain that I've—' He broke off, as if uncertain if he should go on—how to go on. Then, manfully, he resumed. 'I've been affected by you from the very start, Erin Tunnicliffe, and that's the truth.'

To hear him say such a thing stopped her dead in her tracks, her brain appearing to seize up for seconds on end, until, her lovely violet eyes wider than ever, 'Ph-physically—you mean?' she ventured. 'I mean, I know…'

'Physically, of course,' he agreed. 'That's undeniable. But…' He hesitated, as if selecting his next words. 'It's more than that.'

More than that! Oh, heavens, she was shaking inside, and pushed her hands to her sides down the chair, in case their trembling should give her away. 'I—um—find that statement a bit, well, actually more than a bit, confusing.'

'Open your mind and listen to me,' Josh urged.

Oh, she was listening. Was she ever? 'I'm all ears,' she invited. She could hardly believe he was here, yet he was. Regardless of the hour, Josh, the man she loved, was here, and had stated that he was not going to leave until whatever it was was resolved. 'It has nothing to do with revenge, you said?' she questioned, that to her being about the only clear motive for him being there at all. He surely hadn't left his home at this time of night to come and discuss some proposed date!

'I give you my word, nothing. My father was gravely ill, but is almost back to full health now. I was, as I've agreed, outraged when I knew that Nina Woodward was—is—your mother. But within a very short space of time…'

'When you'd cooled down?' Erin suggested.

He grinned nicely, apologetically. 'I did rather lose it, didn't I?' And, not waiting for an answer, 'I knew full well when I'd cooled down that you were blameless, and that I owed you one very big apology. I rang you from New York to apologise, but…'

'Is that why you rang?' Erin asked, astonished. 'Oh, grief. I didn't give you very much chance, did I?'

'You sounded as mad as hell. Quite rightly too,' he approved. 'I'd behaved despicably. Insulted you with words, let alone brutishly manhandling you. I didn't deserve better. But I knew in any event that a telephoned apology was no way to go about asking your forgiveness.'

'You came in person!' she exclaimed. 'You came yesterday.' Though, since it was now the early hours of Tuesday, 'You came on Sunday,' she corrected.

'I came on Saturday too—when I got in from New York.'

'Saturday?'

'Several times,' he confirmed. 'Even though I knew you'd gone to spend the weekend with your father.'

'Mother, this time,' she murmured, but recalled he knew that from overhearing her speaking with Greg Williams on the phone. Though by then Erin was far more interested, avidly so, in hearing more of what he was so astonishingly saying than in dotting the 'i's and crossing the 't's of which parent she'd stayed overnight with. 'You must have wanted to apologise very much?'

'Apologise—and see you.'

'Ah, see me regarding the apology?' she slotted in. For goodness' sake don't start getting ideas that he was so desperate to see you that he dashed straight to your door from the airport. 'You—came back on Sunday.'

'I was here waiting, when you returned. With Richard,' he added succinctly.

'We'd both stayed Saturday night at my mother's.'

'You take a lot of your boyfriends to weekend with you at your mother's home?'

'I...' She hesitated.

'Be truthful with me, Erin,' Josh requested firmly.

It seemed oddly important to him that she be truthful. So, after a second or two of thought, Erin took a deep breath and said, 'I didn't want to tell you. Not for me, but for my mother.'

'Okay,' he answered slowly as he digested that part. 'Why for your mother?'

'Your opinion of her is already low. I—um—didn't want to give you fuel for despising her more than you do.'

Josh looked solemnly at her. 'I think we both have to agree that whatever has or has not gone on between our parents it must have nothing to do with us,' he said quietly. And her heart, that had been misbehaving for most of the time since she had opened the door to him, started leaping about all over the place again at that 'us'!

'I—er...' she said huskily, and realised she was think-ing nonsense. There was no 'us', and any minute now

one or other of them was bound to get angry and they'd
end up enemies again.

But she did not want that, and what Josh wanted was
that she be truthful with him. Though that would mean
breaking her mother's confidence. For a few seconds
Erin struggled between love and loyalty to her mother,
and love and trust for Josh.

She was feeling terribly torn, but in the end, she took
one very deep breath and risked, 'My mother has this
real and dreadful fear of marriage.' Erin dared a glance
at Josh. He wasn't uptight—yet. 'She's been married
twice and… Anyhow, she is popular with the opposite
sex—she's a fun sort of person.' Erin dared another
glance at him. He wasn't looking ecstatic to hear this
character reference for the woman who had dropped his
father like a hot coal the moment he had proposed, but
neither was he looking ready to go for her jugular.
'Nina—she prefers me to call her that—she—um—
doesn't much care for her friends to know she has a
grown-up daughter.'

'A beautiful grown-up daughter,' Josh inserted, to
make Erin's heart go crazy all over again.

'B-but I believe she always makes it clear to any new
f-friend that marriage is a no-no.' Erin paused. She
looked at Josh. He looked blandly back—she would
have loved to know what he was thinking. 'Why am I
telling you all this?' she asked.

'Because I need to know.'

'Oh,' she murmured, though was more confused, if
anything, by his answer. 'Anyhow,' she resumed, 'occasionally some man will think they know better, and
that she doesn't really mean it, and will propose.'
Another glance at Josh showed that, whatever his
thoughts on the subject of her mother, he was keeping

them well hidden. 'Two have attempted to break down her ''never again'' barrier recently.'

'My father,' Josh took up.

'And Richard,' Erin completed.

'*Richard!*' Josh looked astounded. '*Your* Richard?'

'He was never my Richard.'

'Never?'

Did she see a trace of a smile coming through? 'Never, ever,' Erin answered. 'I hadn't even met him until last Saturday. My mother had by then broken her golden rule and told him she had a daughter. Anyhow, Nina was committed to a charity thing at the weekend that included Richard. By then he had proposed and asked her to think about it. But because she no longer wanted to be alone with him...'

'She invited you to stay too,' Josh took up.

'Richard doesn't live far from here—my mother asked him to call for me on his way.'

'Because she wanted you in her home too, while he was there,' Josh documented. 'So when you said you wouldn't be seeing him again, it wasn't you who ended it but your mother?'

Erin wanted to make more excuses for her mother, maybe tell Josh that perhaps it wasn't the end for her mother and Richard. But Josh being here wasn't to do with her parent or his—her heart did a crazy flutter again—and, although it was too fantastic to be believable, he had used the word 'us'. And, while knowing she was heading for cloud cuckoo land, Erin felt she had explained enough about both her mother and Richard. 'That was one fine way to start off the apology you came to make on Sunday,' Erin mentioned as evenly as she could, recollecting that no sooner had

Richard gone than Josh had been there, demanding to know who Richard was.

'I was a bit—hmm—bad-tempered, wasn't I?' Josh admitted, looking only marginally shame-faced.

Erin wanted to smile, but settled for a simple, 'Why?'

And very nearly collapsed at his answer when, looking her straight in the eyes, he did his own version of drawing a steadying breath and quietly let fall, 'Jealousy.'

'*Jealousy!*' she exclaimed, her violet eyes huge in her face.

'Jealousy, pure and simple. I was green to the core with it.'

'B-but...' Words failed her.

And she had small chance of regaining her powers of speech either when, sincerely, he went on, 'You, Erin Tunnicliffe, have disturbed me and my peace of mind from the very beginning.'

She stared at him. 'No!' she denied faintly.

'True,' he replied, his grey eyes fixed nowhere but on her. 'I first met you that day you were having a break from shopping with Charlotte. You were seated at a window table when I came by. And I confess I couldn't take my eyes off you.' Erin's eyes were fixed nowhere but on him. 'Then I noticed Charlotte, and before I knew it I, who had only just had a cup of coffee, was joining you.'

'You said you could do with a coffee!'

'How else was I going to get an introduction to the most beautiful woman I have ever seen?'

Erin's mouth fell open. She closed it. Josh thought her the most beautiful woman...

'Oh!' she gasped.

'Exactly. I was bowled over by you. Wanted there and then to ask you out.'

She almost said Oh again, but with a drumming in her ears succeeded in holding it back. 'But—you didn't,' she managed, with what breath his statement had left her.

Josh sent her a wry grin. 'I had a big adjustment to make. I wasn't used to being bowled over. Things like that just didn't happen to me.'

'Mmm,' she murmured, playing for time, terrified of falling into some trap and of maybe revealing more than he should know. 'So you left it a week, and then rang me.'

'And arranged to call for you the following Friday. Only that dinner date didn't happen because you cancelled.'

Erin stared at him, recalling how back then he hadn't sounded in the smallest disappointed when she'd rung him to cancel. But only then did she realise that a man of his sophistication was hardly likely to fall about in a heap to have missed a dinner with someone who, at that time, was virtually a stranger.

'Would I be right in guessing that the complication you spoke of was your mother?' he asked, when she had nothing to say.

Erin nodded. 'I had no idea my mother even knew your father until she dropped in unexpectedly that Thursday. I'd bought an evening paper with the intention of looking for a job,' Erin explained. 'There was a picture of you with your father, tying in with a report that your father had suffered a heart attack. Unusually, my mother stopped by for a few minutes and spotted it. She told me how your father had proposed but that she had—er—felt she had to say no.' Erin tempered what her mother had actually said.

'And you were sensitive enough to see that her turning him down might have contributed in some major way to his heart attack,' Josh concluded gently.

Dumbly, Erin nodded. 'I knew then that I couldn't keep our date—not unless I told you. And had I done so you wouldn't have wanted to keep it anyway. Not without first having a potshot at my mother...'

'And loyalty to her meant you couldn't have that.'

Again Erin nodded. 'I wanted to tell you so many times. Though, to be honest, I had thought several times about ringing you to cancel before my mother turned up that night.'

'You didn't want to come out with me after all?' Josh asked, a frown creasing his brow.

'Not that,' Erin replied quickly. 'I was nervous, I suppose. You—someone like you was quite outside my experience.'

That took his frown away. He even smiled as he commented, 'You don't have a whole heap of experience, do you, sweetheart?' And as her heart pounded anew at his gentle, almost tender use of the word 'sweetheart', he added, 'As I discovered when, you having ditched me for the likes of the drunken Gavin, I found there was something about you—something I must have picked up from the way you were trying to cope in that hotel bar—that suggested you might be in need of assistance.'

'You followed us back here,' she commented. But quickly asked, 'Did you...were you upset that I'd ditched you? Even though I hadn't really,' she added, just as quickly. 'We were never that—um...' Her voice petered out, and Josh took pity on her.

'Close,' he finished for her, but went on to answer her question. 'I don't think I was so upset at being ditched, more fidgeting in my head about you—and quite intrigued,' he admitted. 'You were a new experience to me, so it was no wonder I should have had you on my mind so much.'

She'd been in his head? He had positively lived in hers! 'I was on your mind a little?' she queried—and immediately wished she hadn't fished. But she was discovering that in her love for him she sought every crumb of comfort.

'Oh, Erin, Erin,' he said softly. 'You were on my mind more and more. I should have accepted then what was happening to me—but didn't.'

'Er—what was happening to you?' she asked, that crumb-seeking creature pushing her on to want to know more.

Only for her to stare at him blankly when, quite calmly, quite quietly, Josh replied, 'Oh—I was falling in love.'

'With me?' she squeaked, swallowing hard, not believing her ears, wanting to believe her ears, ashamed of her question and getting abruptly to her feet and turning her back on him. She knew he did not like her to do that, turn her back on him, but she did not want him to see into her eyes. Of course he hadn't been falling in love *with her!* What an utter idiot she was.

Erin stood there, horrendously embarrassed and wishing she was ten thousand miles away—or, failing that, that Josh would just disappear and she might never have to face him again. But he had left his seat, firm hands were on her shoulders, and gently but determinedly those hands were turning her so that she had to face him.

She wouldn't look up. Even when Josh bent his head to hers to quietly say, 'That's why I'm here, Erin, to tell you that I love you,' and a spasm took her, shook her, still she wouldn't look at him.

She could not believe it. And dared not let herself believe it. This was some sort of game he was playing, because... 'It is revenge—vengeance... You said it wasn't, but—'

She broke off when Josh let go of her shoulders and gently gathered her in his arms in a loose hold. 'Forget revenge, forget vengeance,' he urged, giving her a small shake. 'You feel the same love and loyalty to your mother that I feel for my father. But much as we love them, and together, I hope, will deal with future situations, this is about you and me.'

Erin dared to look up then. He held her look steadily, his eyes saying that he was sincere. Oh, heavens—she started to shake. 'You and m-me?' she questioned chokily.

'Us,' Josh confirmed. 'This has nothing to do with anyone but us. You and me.' He took a deep drawn breath, and then confessed, 'I'm here because I've been in a living hell, and after your phone call tonight I just knew I couldn't wait any longer. I knew I just could not spend another wakeful soul-destroying night. I had to find out, now, if I have a chance with you.' A chance with her? 'Oh, sweetheart, you're shaking,' he murmured, and held her that bit closer to him. 'I've come to tell you that I care deeply for you, and...' his voice dipped slightly '...and to find out if there's a chance you might care for me.'

He sounded nervous! Erin couldn't believe what her senses were telling her. She dropped her eyes, but it was no good. She looked up again, straight into his dear grey eyes. He *was* nervous! She was sure of it. Her hands went up to his waist, but whether for his support or her own she knew not.

'You—care for me?' she asked hesitatingly, trying,

daring to try to believe that she was not such an idiot after all.

'I love you with everything that's in me,' Josh declared steadily, going on openly, 'I have, I confess, been in absolute torment over you. How could you possibly love me? I've agonised over how I didn't deserve that you should like me, let alone love me. Had I forgotten how, when pushed on and on, goaded by jealousy, I had shown you a side of me I didn't even know I possessed? How could you love me…?'

'Yet you—th-think I might?' she questioned huskily.

'Not think, hope,' he corrected, the tender light in his eyes threatening to melt her bones. 'I found hope when I recalled your response to our lovemaking in that hotel—but despair when I thought of how vilely I had treated you that day I discovered that Nina Woodward is your mother.'

'Y-you said you were a bit—er—brutish,' she conceded gently.

'Brutish! I wanted locking up!' He tenderly kissed her cheek, and went on to explain, 'I'd thought of you so much that morning that I almost invented an excuse to take a stroll down to Experimental. But, no, I had some of my father's work pressing, and my own diary was overflowing. Besides which, you'd got me in such a state I should probably ignore you, as I did the previous time I'd called in on your division.'

'When we were in the other building?'

Josh nodded. 'Charlotte mentioned in passing that you were now employed by the firm, and…' He smiled slightly. 'I'm not used to women telephoning to break dates with me, so was I going to ring you again? I was not. True, I did pick up the phone a couple of times to do just that…'

'But didn't?' Her heart was in overdrive. She held on to him. He seemed to like it.

'But didn't,' he agreed, firming his hold on her. 'I was a man who liked his freedom. Clearly you did not know the rules. Far better, I told myself, for you to cut your teeth on someone else. Little did I know then that the green-eyed monster was waiting to put me in purgatory should you dare to date anyone else!'

Erin knew a little of that purgatory, and as her faith started to grow that Josh wouldn't be with her here like this, telling her his innermost feelings, unless he meant it, so she felt herself blossoming in his love. Her shaking eased as her confidence took root.

'You came that time to the experimental division to check on matters concerning the move to—' His wry smile caused her to break off.

'Nothing of the sort. I told myself I was coming over to have a few words with the Professor, but, my dear Erin, I later acknowledged that all that had been driving me was a compulsion to see you.' Gently then he touched his lips to hers, and seemed encouraged when she showed no signs of backing away. 'So there am I, when you'd moved into the new building, doing nothing to jeopardise my freedom, but arranging to be able to see you daily by the simple expedient of having you work in my office.'

'Did you particularly ask for me?'

'Of course,' he owned. 'I was attracted to you, just a touch bewitched by you. But naturally I wasn't going to show it. You'd turned me down, remember?'

'I hadn't!' she protested. But, on thinking about it, realised that breaking their date could be seen that way. 'I couldn't ring you—' she tried.

'I know,' he cut in gently, understanding perfectly that

her 'mother complications' were still there. 'So there we are, working in my office, when the green-eyed monster began to appear when your ex-boyfriend Mark reared his ugly head.'

She laughed. Oh, how wonderful—Josh loved her. Oh, he must. She couldn't bear it if it were all a dream. 'Mark's quite good-looking, actually.'

'I didn't really need to know that,' Josh told her nicely, and she laughed again, and he looked as though he delighted to hear her laugh. He went on, 'But no sooner do I hear that Mark has had his marching orders than Stephen is there to plague me.'

'Stephen! Is that why you were so—um—crotchety?'

'I was jealous,' Josh admitted. 'And later annoyed that you refused my second invitation to dinner.'

'That "I'd better take you for something to eat" was a dinner invitation?'

'You've remembered?'

'Every word.'

He stilled. 'Like I've remembered, dwelt on, taken out and dissected every word of every sentence you've ever uttered?' he asked quietly.

She swallowed on emotion. It had been like that for him too? She was too full to answer.

'Love me a little?' he asked urgently.

'Yes,' she whispered.

'Darling!' His head came down and he kissed her. Gently she responded, and if she was dreaming then she wanted this wonderful dream to go on and on and on.

Their kiss ended and Josh continued to hold her gently to him. Then, keeping an arm about her, he led her to the sofa. They sat down and he turned to her, to look at her for long, long moments, seeming not to want to say anything more but to just sit looking into her beautiful face.

'Oh, my darling,' he breathed, looking as though he couldn't believe she was not rejecting him. But, perhaps remembering how he had rehearsed and rehearsed everything he did want to say to her if everything did go well, he began, 'So there am I—' but had to break off to give an unrehearsed kiss to the corner of her mouth. 'A man who never asks twice, and most certainly never three times,' he said with a self-deprecating smile, 'wanting to see you again but somehow managing to hold out until Robin and Charlotte's wedding.'

'You knew I'd be there?'

'I made it my business to find out,' he admitted. 'But only to get eaten up with jealousy for my sins when every blasted man at that wedding was after you.'

'Slight exaggeration?' she suggested demurely.

'There weren't many you didn't dance with.'

'I didn't dance with you,' she reminded him.

'I was too busy assuring myself I didn't care who you danced with.'

'You were too busy with the laughing bridesmaid.'

'I—' He broke off, a look of incredulous delight passing over his features. '*You*—were jealous!'

She had to grin. 'Pea-green, if you must know.'

'Darling!' he cried, and kissed her, feasted his eyes on her—and just had to kiss her again. 'I was just doing my best man's duty. Nothing more than that, I promise. Though at the same time I have to admit I was keeping a rather keen eye on what you were getting up to with Greg Williams. Then you went and knocked yourself out—and I knew that night what was wrong with me. That it wasn't just jealousy.'

'It—wasn't?'

He shook his head. 'It was there, battering down the

door of my stubborn refusal to acknowledge it, when I wouldn't allow anyone but the doctor and myself to look after you.' He smiled a tender smile as he told her, 'But I just didn't stand a chance of keeping it at bay any longer as you fell into a natural sleep and I continued to watch you. It was just there. I knew without the smallest doubt that I was in love with this sleeping beauty. I knew I loved you then, and ever would. It was there, and was not going to go away.'

'Oh, Josh!' Erin cried, awe in her voice. But suddenly then she felt able to tell him *her* innermost thoughts, and confessed, 'I knew that night, for all my talk about— um—having more fun, that you were the only man I ever wanted to make love with.'

'You loved me a little then?'

Erin nodded happily. 'I fell a little in love with you that night you sent Gavin home in a taxi.'

Josh stared at her incredulously. 'No!' he denied. 'That was months ago!'

'Months in which that little love has grown to be quite a lot, actually,' she admitted shyly. And absolutely adored him when, murmuring her name, he just had to hold her close and kiss her again and again.

When Josh finally drew back, while still keeping an arm about her, he seemed to have a need to explain why his subsequent behaviour had been as alien to him as it was to her.

'I confess, my love, this new emotion that had crept up on me when I wasn't looking—this deep and all-encompassing love I found I had for you—totally threw me. All I wanted to do was to be with you.'

'But—I didn't see you for over a week after the wedding!'

'Which should tell you what you've done to my confidence.'

Erin stared at him. He was the most supremely confident man she had ever met. 'H-how?' she gasped. 'I...'

'There was I, wanting to see you. In fact at times feeling quite desperate to see you. But I was in love with you, and flattened by that discovery,' he explained. 'My confidence took a pasting, a kind of nervousness setting in as again and again I asked myself—how did you feel about me? You responded to me physically—but that didn't mean you cared for me. You had never phoned me. In all those months since I'd suggested you should, not once had you called my number! I stewed like that for over a week. Then last Monday, after the most emotion-churning weekend I can ever remember, I decided it was no good but that I was going to have to contact you, to see you, to see if I could spot any small glimpse of anything at all remotely like love in your regard for me. But I was booked to fly to New York the next day— would it be better to leave it until I got back. Could I, in fact, wait that long?'

'That was before you saw me with my mother?'

Josh gave Erin a rueful look. 'Oh, it was,' he agreed. 'You weren't supposed to be there. You were supposed to be at your desk in the experimental division. So at first, in that first instant, I thought I'd had you so much on my mind that my imagination was playing tricks on me.' Josh tenderly kissed her before confessing, 'Such an explosion of warmth for you rushed over me when I saw you, I just knew I could not wait until I got back from New York.'

'Then you recognised my companion?'

'Recognised her and, if that wasn't enough to make me see red, there you are bidding each other a fond farewell.'

'You looked murderous!'

'I'm sorry, my darling. Forgive me. But I'd seen my

father with such high hopes, only to see him disbelieving, desolate and near destroyed when Nina Woodward not only turned him down but told him she didn't want to see him again. Not long afterwards he suffered a heart attack.'

'I'm sorry,' she apologised in turn.

'You have nothing to apologise for,' Josh told her lovingly. And, giving her a smile, as though to take the sting out of anything he had said or would say, 'I was blisteringly furious. Nothing would do but that I sorted out a few matters with you before my plane took off the next day.'

'You were still furious when you came here that night,' Erin remembered, without having to search very far in her memory.

'Don't remind me!' he mourned. 'I was downright insulting. When I think of how I treated you... The things I said...'

'Please,' Erin interrupted. He looked so mortified in recalling that time that she couldn't bear it. 'It doesn't matter. Not now. Not now you're here and—'

'It does matter,' Josh cut in. 'You were tearing my heart out. I loved you—yet hated you at the same time because you were doing to me what your mother had done to my father—and I couldn't take it.' Erin kissed him. She just had to. 'Oh, my love,' Josh said throatily. 'I was awake all that night, knowing that not only had I been wrong in what I'd done, in what I'd said, but that I had just blown any slight chance I might have had with you.'

'You did ring from New York to apologise.'

'A fat lot of good that did,' he said, but managed a smile for her. 'Nor was it any better when I came home. There you were, kissing Richard what looked a loving goodbye.'

'He'd just told me that Nina had said no. I felt for him.'

'You would,' Josh said tenderly.

They were lost for a few moments in that time. 'I hit you,' Erin said, still feeling dreadful about that. 'As your behaviour was alien to you, so mine was to me. I'm so, so sorry,' she apologised.

'Don't be—no one deserved it more,' he said with a grin. 'You kissed me better. But just as I'm beginning to find the comfort of holding you, responsive, in my arms, you leave my arms—and only seconds later you're on the phone, making a date with Greg Williams!' Josh sent her another self-deprecating smile. 'A man has his pride, you know.'

'That was why you went all narky!' Erin exclaimed. 'I thought it was because I'd mentioned my mother.'

Josh kissed her. 'You'll—hmm—cancel Thursday's date, I trust?'

Erin laughed. 'With pleasure.'

'And Wednesday's? And who the blazes is Stephen?'

'He works in Experimental. We're friends.'

'And nothing more?'

'Nothing.'

'And if I said I should like to see you Wednesday, and in fact every night this week?'

Her heart started beating erratically again. 'Then naturally I'd be delighted to fit you into my diary.' They kissed, and she just had to say, 'While we're on the subject of jealousy, there was a picture in the paper of you with a lady in New York...'

'You were jealous of...? Fantastic!' Josh exclaimed, truly appreciating that jealousy was not his torment alone. 'Her husband was close by somewhere—they're devoted to each other. I was more interested in getting back to you. In fact couldn't wait to get back to you.

But when everything went pear-shaped between us last night, and my trip to find you in Experimental this morning showed—'

'You went looking for me?'

'It was easy enough to find an excuse. But—did I expect anything else but that you'd had enough and decided to throw your job in? So, unable to see you then, I stewed some more for the rest of the day. But it was only when I started to think about how, only last night, you had said "I used to be a perfectly sane, rational person before I met you" that I began to wonder. Was that the same slightly demented, irrational person I too had become since knowing you? I started to hope.'

'You decided to come over.'

'I wanted to, straight away. But then I stopped to consider how, when I only ever wanted to be pleasant to you, my unannounced visits more often than not ended up being the exact opposite. I thought I'd ring first.'

'You reminded me I owed you a phone call,' she murmured dreamily.

'Waiting for your phone call tonight was one of the most traumatic times I've had to endure,' Josh confessed.

'You knew I'd ring?'

'I'd almost given up hope. Then there you were,' he said, 'and my heart turned over.' He was silent for long moments. And then, looking deeply into her lovely violet eyes, 'Marry me?' he murmured softly.

Erin experienced that drumming in her ears again. 'Yes,' she said, 'I'd like to,' and then quickly got up from the sofa. Oh, heavens, she'd misheard. He hadn't said what she thought he had said. 'I'll—er—make some coffee now, sh-shall I?' she asked, her voice all high and staccato-sounding.

But Josh was there by her side before she had finished.

'I think we'd better make that champagne, don't you, my darling?' he suggested.

'You did s-say what I thought you said?'

'Oh, yes, my love, I did. You once told me, when you shared my bed, that I'd have to marry you. I should have realised then that I was on the way to saying goodbye to my bachelorhood when, to my surprise, the thought of marrying you didn't have me bolting for the door. So, yes, dearest Erin, I did ask you to marry me.'

'You—did?' she questioned shakily, still doubting her hearing.

'Love me?'

'So much.'

Josh took a second or two out to kiss her, and then, looking deeply into her eyes, 'Then, my darling, since I very definitely heard you say yes, you'd like to marry me, I'm afraid I'm going to have to make you honour your promise.' He gave her the tiniest shake. 'All right?' he asked.

Erin, her heart full, nodded. 'Oh, yes. Yes, please,' she answered dreamily, and was held close to his heart for long wonderful seconds before, tenderly, Josh kissed her.

'Now, where, at this time in the morning, can we buy champagne?' Josh asked, looking deep into her eyes.

And Erin stared up at him. She guessed he already knew where; he was that sort of a man. This man, this wonderful man, this man she was going to marry.

He held her close. 'Oh, I do so love you, Erin Tunnicliffe,' he breathed, and just had to kiss her again.

HIS AFTER-HOURS MISTRESS

by

Amanda Browning

Amanda Browning still lives in the Essex house where she was born. The third of four children – her sister being her twin – she enjoyed the rough and tumble of life with two brothers as much as she did reading books. Writing came naturally as an outlet for a fertile imagination. The love of books led her to a career in libraries, and being single allowed her to take the leap into writing for a living. Success is still something of a wonder, but allows her to indulge in hobbies as varied as embroidery and bird-watching.

CHAPTER ONE

GINNY HARTE jumped at the sudden sound of a crash from the office next door, and glanced round to frown at the closed door which linked the two offices. As far as she was aware, her fellow director of the family-owned chain of hotels, Roarke Adams, was still at lunch. Her fingers paused over the keypad of her PC as she waited for another noise. There followed the distinct sound of something large, probably the wastepaper basket, hitting a wall. An unholy grin slowly spread across her face. All had not gone well, it seemed. What a shame. Couldn't have happened to a nicer guy, she thought, with a wry grimace.

Pushing back her chair, she rose gracefully to her feet, walked round the desk and headed for the closed door and the momentarily silent room. She was tall, even without her three-inch heels. Slim yet curvaceous, she had flashing green eyes, and the tempestuous nature her thick swathe of red hair indicated. Experience, however, had taught her to keep it in check and now, at the age of twenty-six, she presented a cool, calm demeanour to the outside world.

She had worked alongside Roarke Adams for a little over a year now, ever since his grandfather, the owner of the hotels, had hired her to co-ordinate the modernisation and decorating of the various properties. All other aspects of the business fell into Roarke's court, but when he bought a new property it was up to her to decide what was needed to bring it into line with the other hotels. When he did his regular tours of the hotels she went with

5

him to oversee any planned redecoration, and they had a surprisingly good working relationship. Which was nothing short of amazing considering the fact that they didn't actually like each other.

It had taken under a month for them to sum each other up and decide the other was wanting. Battle lines had therefore been drawn and their verbal exchanges had become a source of much interest and amusement to the staff. Skirmishes occurred on a daily basis unless one or other of them was out of the office. Roarke never missed an opportunity to get in a dig at her and, as she had never been one to refuse a fight, she gave as good as she got.

She knew he thought she had ice-water in her veins instead of blood. He didn't believe she had an ounce of passion in her whole body, and wouldn't know what to do with a real man. He viewed Daniel, her boyfriend, with open mockery because he was everything Roarke was not. Loyal, steadfast, undemanding. OK, so it wasn't a passionate relationship, but Ginny had trodden that path once, allowing her passions to rule her head, and it had led to disaster. It wasn't a road she intended to travel again. Daniel was what she wanted now, and she was pretty sure he was going to propose soon. When he did, she had every intention of accepting him.

If her lifestyle was a joke to her co-director, his was only worthy of her scorn. Roarke, in her opinion, was little more than an unprincipled womaniser. Women went in and out of his life in a more or less constant stream. Like a modern-day Casanova. Any woman who came within range was fair game to him, and even the strongest of them turned to jelly when he looked at them with his glittering eyes and disarming smile. It wouldn't surprise her in the least if he didn't carve a notch on his bedpost for every woman he seduced.

Though she didn't care for his love-them-and-leave-them lifestyle, she knew he was generous and knew how to treat a woman well, whilst his interest remained. And, to be fair, he never approached married women, or those who were otherwise spoken for. Roarke had a code of sorts. He only played the game with those women who knew the rules, and he never became involved with the women who worked for him. His life had two distinct areas, and the one only spilled into the other when she had to console the latest cast-off. A job she did not enjoy.

She had made her disapproval clear but, rather than taking offence, Roarke had been amused by it. He had mockingly informed her he wasn't going to be reprimanded by a strait-laced harridan. So it had begun, and that was the state of affairs between them now as she reached the connecting door. A wise woman might have drawn back, but Ginny recognised an opportunity when it presented itself. There was no way she could work on without knowing what had happened, so she reached for the door handle.

Pushing the door open, she had to duck hastily as an object hurtled in her direction. Straightening up, she stared down at the pencils which littered the floor around her like so much strange confetti, then back at the man who now stood immobile by the desk.

Honesty compelled Ginny to admit Roarke was, without doubt, the best-looking man she had ever seen. At thirty-two he was in his prime. Tall and leanly muscular, he had thick black hair, roguishly laughing grey eyes, and a mouth that could quirk into a smile to take the breath away. Right this minute, though, he wasn't smiling. On the contrary, his expression most closely approximated thunderous. It caused her lips to twitch.

'Nice lunch?' she enquired jauntily, and caught his fingers flexing as if he wished they were around something—like her neck.

His fine nostrils flared as he took a steadying breath. 'No, I have not had a nice lunch. In fact, I've just had the worst few hours of my life!'

'Don't tell me some little air-head actually had the sense to say no to you,' she drawled with heavy irony, and in a lightning mood swing he grinned at her.

'I don't date air-heads, sweetheart. I much prefer intelligent women; you know that,' Roarke drawled back, watching through glittering eyes as she squatted down and began to collect up the pencils. The process caused her skirt to ride up her thighs. 'Nice legs,' he murmured approvingly, then as she shot a narrow-eyed glare his way he changed tack. 'Did I hit you?' he asked with less than genuine concern, and Ginny snorted as she retrieved the holder and stood up again.

'No, but I might just hit you if you don't keep your eyes to yourself,' she warned as she set the holder on the nearest bookcase and folded her arms.

'It's your own fault for being so easy on the eye. A man just can't help himself,' he told her ironically.

He was flirting with her, a tactic he had used from time to time when he wanted to irritate her more than usual. She ignored it—as usual. 'Well, a man had better try,' she added firmly.

Roarke slipped his hands into the trouser pockets of his fashionable Italian designer suit, and rocked back on his heels. 'You're a hard woman. Does anything get through to you? Do you feel passion? Do you even know what it is? What about Daniel? How does that relationship work? Is he even allowed to kiss you, or does he go home each evening aching with frustration, whilst you sleep soundly in your virginal bed?'

Ginny kept her cool and raised her eyebrows at him mockingly. 'You don't really expect me to answer that, just because you're in a foul mood?'

'No, I expected you to up and slap my face. Why didn't you?'

She gave him an old-fashioned look. 'Probably because it was what you wanted,' she responded dryly and he laughed.

'You're learning, sweetheart. There's hope for you yet,' he taunted as he sauntered over to the window and looked out at the city below them.

'I'm not your sweetheart, Roarke. It isn't a situation I would ever aspire to occupy,' Ginny countered, though she didn't expect it to have any more effect than her previous attempts to have him stop calling her by the affectionate term.

He glanced over his shoulder at her. 'A man could get frostbite trying to warm you up. Daniel has all my sympathy.'

Ginny silently ground her teeth at his insolence. 'Fortunately, Daniel doesn't need it,' she said, which caused him to smile.

'No, he's pretty much a cold fish himself.'

She looked at him steadily. 'I don't find him in the least bit cold. There's a lot to the old adage that you shouldn't judge a book by its cover.'

'Which could equally apply to me, sweetheart,' Roarke pointed out, but Ginny immediately shook her head.

'Oh, no, you're an open book, Roarke. Everyone knows the plot where you're concerned. The wise ones put you back on the shelf,' she retorted mockingly, whereupon his eyes gleamed with mischief.

'Maybe, but the ones who don't have a much better time.'

Ginny shook her head sadly. 'You're incorrigible, and I have more important things to do with my time than waste it bandying words with you,' she told him bluntly, and made to leave, but Roarke held up a hand to forestall her.

'That can wait. Shut the door and sit down. I need to talk to you,' he commanded. His words were without a trace of his earlier mockery, and yet carried an edge of unease. Sensing something intriguing in the air, Ginny dutifully closed the door.

'I thought you didn't consider me qualified to be an agony aunt,' she remarked as she stepped over various objects which had borne the brunt of his temper.

'One of these days you're going to cut yourself on that tongue of yours!' Roarke warned her. 'Doesn't anything blunt it?'

'If you're after sympathy, you've come to the wrong woman,' she told him matter-of-factly. 'Just because you didn't get your own way for once, there's no need to destroy the place. So you met a woman with a brain cell or two. It was bound to happen some time.'

Roarke tutted reprovingly. 'You know something, Ginny? You're fixated with my love life. Who said this has anything to do with a woman?'

Now that did surprise her. Roarke was like a magnet for women. He didn't look dressed without one on his arm. That didn't mean to say he didn't work hard at the business. It wouldn't be among the top in its line if he didn't. But he played hard, too. She had listened to his tales of woe before, and a woman generally entered the picture at some point. But apparently not this time, if he was to be believed.

'It doesn't?' she queried, brows rising. If she had done him an injustice, then she was prepared to apologise, however much it went against the grain. She was about to open her mouth to do just that when his eyes fell away from hers and he rubbed an irritated hand around his neck.

'Actually, it is about a woman, but not the way you imagine,' he admitted reluctantly.

Intrigued by the palpable signs of his discomfort, Ginny slipped into the nearest chair and crossed her legs, decorously smoothing down the skirt of her violet-coloured suit. She had discarded the jacket earlier, and wore a simple cream silk sleeveless blouse for comfort in the oppressive summer heat.

'What do you imagine I'm imagining?' she challenged, her eyes following him as he walked to his leather chair and sank into it with a heavy sigh.

'The worst. You usually do,' Roarke shot back dryly, and Ginny laughed softly.

She spread her hands deprecatingly. 'Well, you've only yourself to blame for that. You've never had to console one of your exes. The tales I've heard make me shudder to think of them.' She gave a delicate shudder by way of example.

'Don't believe everything you hear. It isn't my fault if they got their hopes up. I never promised them for ever,' Roarke pointed out in his own defence.

'That's what I told them. He isn't a one-woman kind of man. You'd be better off cutting your losses and looking around for someone with more staying power,' Ginny agreed.

His brows rose at that, and then he laughed. 'You're referring, I take it, to that part of my life which I, clearly mistakenly, consider private. Hasn't anyone ever told you you aren't supposed to interfere in your employer's love life?'

'Your love life ceases to be private when you live it so

publicly. Why, scarcely a day goes by when you aren't photographed with one woman or another hanging on your arm! Your little black book must be bursting at the seams by now,' she protested scornfully.

Roarke steepled his fingers and looked at her over them. 'If I had one, which I don't.'

'No little black book? I don't believe it. Your sort of man always has one!'

'And just what sort of man is that?'

Ginny waved a hand airily. 'The sort who changes his woman as often as he changes his clothes.'

He tapped his thumbs together broodingly. 'I suppose a denial is out of the question?'

She shook her head. 'Hard to accept when I've seen the results of your handiwork.'

Roarke rubbed a finger down the bridge of his nose, then glanced at her sardonically. 'You disapprove of everything about me, don't you?'

'Not everything, just your treatment of women.'

'You make me sound like some sort of playboy.'

'Your affairs are well catalogued in print,' she reminded him.

He clucked his tongue at her. 'The women you see me photographed with are, for the most part, old friends. I'm often invited to events where I require a partner, and I'd rather take a woman I know than find myself seated next to a stranger. We spend an enjoyable evening together, and then I take her home. End of story.'

Ginny looked sceptical. 'You can't mean to tell me all your dates end so tamely,' she scoffed, and he grinned wolfishly.

'Not at all, but that's my business, not yours.'

She couldn't argue with him there. She was walking a fine line as it was. However, there was one thing she was curious about. 'Haven't you ever considered finding one woman and sticking to her? Haven't you ever been in love?'

That brought a mocking laugh from him. 'No, and I don't ever expect to be. In my experience, happy ever after is just a fairy tale, sweetheart,' he pronounced and she blinked, genuinely surprised.

'You don't believe in love?'

'What most people fall into is lust, though they prefer to give it the name love because it sounds better.' Seeing her frown, Roarke leant forward across the desk. 'I respect women for who and what they are. I enjoy them, but I don't make promises I can't keep, and I refuse to dress up the relationship as anything more than what it is.'

Ginny supposed she had to think well of him for that, but it was strange to her to hear him speak that way about love. Despite her own experiences, she still believed in love. She had just made the wrong choice, that was all. This time she wasn't about to let herself be blinded by passion into thinking love existed. Daniel was everything she wanted in a man, and she was sure that her liking for him would grow into love in the fullness of time.

'Don't you intend to get married and have children?' she couldn't help but ask curiously.

Sitting back again, Roarke shrugged. 'Sure, one day, but love will have nothing to do with it.'

'Your wife might disagree.'

'The woman I marry will know that she has my respect and loyalty. If and when I make a vow, I'll never break it. I only intend to get married once.'

'Sounds to me like you've had a nasty experience. What caused you to get so disenchanted with marriage?'

'Over-familiarity. My father has been married four times and my mother is currently on her third husband.

Both swore it was love each time, but as soon as the passion faded, they headed for the divorce courts. I have brothers and sisters dotted around the globe from their various forays into the wedded state.'

Not exactly good role models, she agreed. 'It doesn't have to be that way for you.'

He shrugged. 'It isn't going to be. I intend to honour my vows—when I make them.'

'I'm pleased to hear it, but have you heard the one about leopards not changing their spots?' she gibed.

Roarke smiled. 'There's always an exception to the rule, sweetheart.'

'True, but I haven't seen any flying pigs recently,' Ginny mocked.

He gave her a long look for that, to which she smiled sweetly and he grunted, 'I should have fired you months ago. Lord knows why I didn't.'

'Because it isn't in your power to do so. Your grandfather hired me, and only he can fire me,' she told him confidently, only to see him give a crocodile smile.

Tugging at the knot of his tie, he pulled it free and loosened the buttons of his shirt. 'On the contrary. I could fire you at a moment's notice. However, you're damn good at your job. You've a good eye for colour and style, and we've heard nothing but acclaim for what you've done so far.'

His praise gave her a warm glow inside, though she didn't let him know it. 'Would this be a good time to ask for a rise?' she asked, tongue-in-cheek, and he grinned appreciatively.

'You'd probably get it, too. A good worker is worthy of her hire.'

Ginny wasn't greedy. She had had a rise only a short while ago. The company rewarded its workers for their efforts without prompting, and she had received her share. That was enough for her. 'Don't worry, I have no intention of taking you up on that. So, what did the poor wastebasket do to incur your wrath?'

Reminded of what had happened earlier, Roarke let his expression become rueful. 'It grinned at me.'

Vastly amused, Ginny smiled. 'Grinned at you?'

'Knowingly,' Roarke confirmed.

'Ah,' she nodded wisely, knowing the feeling. 'Lunch was not a success.'

His laugh was scornful. 'To put it mildly. Which is why I need your help.'

Her mind was rioting with questions. Ginny reined them in. 'Things must be bad if you need my help.'

'You have no idea!'

Ginny waited for more, but when none came she frowned. 'Are you going to tell me, or is it a game of twenty questions?'

Roarke took a deep breath and swung his chair round so that he was facing her. 'My sister's getting married at the weekend.'

Whilst interesting, it was not quite what she was expecting. 'I'm sure I'm pleased for her, but what's that got to do with me?'

His eyes flashed sparks at her interruption. 'I was coming to that. I've been invited.'

It occurred to Ginny that he was uneasy about asking her for whatever it was, and that was quite unlike the usual confident Roarke Adams. Bemused, she nodded. 'OK, that was to be expected, but I still don't see what that has to do with me.'

There followed a momentary hesitation, then he took the bull by the horns. 'I need you to go with me...as my lover.'

That took the wind out of her sails like nothing else. 'What?' she gasped out, sure she must have misheard somehow.

Having broached the subject, Roarke quickly regained his composure. 'I want you to attend the wedding with me,' he repeated.

She had that part; it was the other she took exception to. 'As your lover?'

Roarke hastily held up a hand to forestall the protests he knew were hovering on her lips. 'I didn't mean that the way it sounded. I need you to *pretend* to be my lover.'

Ginny felt as if she were gaping at him like a fish, her mouth opening and closing repeatedly but nothing coming out. She shut her mouth with a snap of teeth and took a steadying breath. 'You have to be joking!'

'I only wish I were. Believe me, I wouldn't be doing it if it wasn't important.'

Instinctively she knew that was true. Neither would seek help from the other unless business was involved. But what he was asking was out of the question. 'What about what's-her-name, the brunette you're dating? Why don't you ask her to help?' That would be the ideal solution.

The question had him grinding his teeth again. 'She was going to go with me, but as we are no longer an item, I'm left without a partner.'

Ginny stared at him, aware that there was a story he wasn't telling her, and he wasn't going to get away with keeping it to himself if he wanted her help. Not that she was promising anything. 'What happened?'

Roarke's fingers tapped out an irritated tattoo on the desktop. 'She informed me at lunch that her stars told her the weekend was a bad time to travel, so she wouldn't be going. I told her only an idiot would believe such rubbish.'

Ginny winced. 'Bad move,' she pronounced sympathetically and he grimaced.

'Tell me about it! The upshot was she took offence. Apparently, her stars also said it was a good time to end relationships that were going nowhere.'

'Oh, dear!' Ginny commiserated, biting back a laugh.

Sensing it, he sighed ruefully. 'I know, I know. Things went from bad to worse. Which brings me to you. Will you help me out?'

'Why me?' Ginny asked, spreading her hands questioningly. 'Why not ask one of those women who aren't in the little black book you haven't got?'

She got some idea how serious the situation was when she didn't get a smart comeback to her remark. 'Because most of them are known to the family, and I need someone who is a complete stranger. Grandfather won't be there and he's the only person that knows you.'

'Now, that you've simply got to explain,' she insisted.

His reluctance was palpable. 'It's complicated. There are…family complications.'

Family complications covered a multitude of sins, as she knew only too well. As an explanation, it fell way short of the mark. 'You're going to have to come up with a better reason than that if I'm to help you,' she declared bluntly, and his eyes snapped to hers.

'Does this mean you're going to do it?' he wanted to know.

Ginny shrugged, kicking herself for the slip. 'It means I'm thinking about it,' she conceded. Families were a touchy subject. Her inclination, due to her own experience, was to help if an injustice was being done, but otherwise she preferred to keep out of it. Roarke was going to have to do some fancy talking. 'Just tell me, Roarke. Whatever you say, and whatever my decision, nothing is going to go outside this room.'

He looked at her for so long a time she thought he would refuse, but then he nodded. 'OK, listen up. My latest stepmother's name is Jenna. When she was still my father's fiancée, she thought it would be fun to make it with father and son. To put it bluntly, she did her best to seduce me. Contrary to your beliefs, I don't sleep with every woman I meet. I especially do not get involved with those attached to my own family. Jenna did not take kindly to my refusal to play the game with her. She went running to my father with the tale that I had tried to force myself on her. Naturally, I denied it, but my father has always been jealous of his women, and he chose to believe her rather than me. The consequence was that he refused to talk to me for the better part of three years.

'We are back on speaking terms now, but the relationship is still fragile. Which brings me to the problem. When I visited him recently on his birthday, Jenna started getting up to her old tricks again. I managed to fend her off without upsetting my father, but I know how she works. If I turn up alone, she'll try again, and heaven alone knows what my refusal will lead to this time.'

Ginny studied his grim face and sympathised with his dilemma. 'Perhaps if you were to go to your father first, this time he would react differently,' she proposed, without any real expectation of that happening. Her own experience with her father had taught her that they didn't change that easily.

Roarke grimaced. 'I thought about it, but I can't take the risk. I decided my best option was to arrive with a woman on my arm. That way Jenna will have to keep her distance.'

'And if she doesn't, I'll be there to ward her off?' she murmured, following his line of thought easily. Roarke looked at her sharply.

'*Will* you be there?'

Ginny glanced down at her hands. Though he didn't know it, he had her. When it came to families she had her own vulnerabilities, which made it virtually impossible for her to walk away from helping someone else. She didn't want what had happened to her to happen to Roarke, whether she liked him or not.

'I must be crazy to even consider it,' she sighed as she raised her head.

'But you'll do it?' he urged hopefully, and she rolled her eyes.

'Yes, I'll do it,' Ginny confirmed, and was instantly consumed by doubts. But it was too late to back out. She had given her word, and it was a matter of honour with her that she kept it. Ever since the man she had trusted had abandoned her after making all sorts of promises, she had vowed that any she made she would keep, no matter what.

Roarke's famous smile appeared, but there was no glitter of satisfaction in his eyes at having won her over, only gratitude. 'Thank you, Ginny. You've probably no idea what you've done, but you've just saved my relationship with my father from total meltdown.'

She understood better than he thought, but that was another story. 'Just remember you owe me one.' She dismissed his thanks uncomfortably. 'So, what time is the wedding, and how are we getting there?'

'Saturday afternoon, so if we fly out Friday evening, we'll have some time to settle in before the ceremony,' Roarke obliged, sending a shock wave through her.

'Fly out? What do you mean, fly out?' she demanded

to know, sitting up straighter. 'Just where is this wedding taking place?'

'Switzerland. Lake Constance, to be exact. At my mother's summer residence. You'll like it there,' he declared confidently.

Ginny ignored that last point and concentrated on the first. 'Switzerland! Damn you, Roarke Adams, you said nothing about the wedding taking place abroad. You know darn well I thought it was in this country!' she remonstrated with him.

Now there was a gleam in his eye as he grinned at her. 'I thought you'd refuse to go if you knew.'

Ginny ground her teeth helplessly. She might well have refused, but the die was cast. She had given her word and that was that. Getting to her feet, she glowered down at him. 'You are an impossible man. You don't just owe me, you owe me big time,' she pronounced, then promptly spun on her heel and headed for the door.

'Ask for anything you like, and it's yours,' Roarke called after her.

She halted but didn't turn round. 'Anything?'

'Just name it.'

A catlike smile curved her lips. 'Very well, I'll get back to you when I've made up my mind,' she agreed, closing the door behind her. Roarke Adams was about to find out her help didn't come cheap.

CHAPTER TWO

GINNY went out to dinner with Daniel that evening. She liked him a lot, but it wasn't always easy to enjoy his conversations, because he could be rather stuffy. He could also, though it pained her to admit it, be something of the cold fish Roarke thought him. Tonight, though, she had to work extra hard to concentrate whilst he told her about his terrible day. Unfortunately, Ginny's thoughts were miles away, and that irritated her, because she didn't like the fact that Roarke kept floating into her mind. Thankfully, Daniel didn't appear to notice her distraction, and she made a concerted effort to be more attentive whilst they waited for their desserts.

When Daniel reached across the table and took her hand, she smiled at him just a little curiously, because he wasn't a 'touching' sort of person.

'I have a surprise for you,' he declared with boyish enthusiasm, and Ginny's heart suddenly leapt into her throat as she wondered if this was to be the moment he proposed.

'You have?' she asked a tad breathlessly, whilst mentally she prepared herself for what she would say in response. The surroundings could have been more romantic—the restaurant was chosen for its convenience, not its ambience. 'What sort of surprise?'

Daniel's smile broadened at her apparent eagerness. 'My parents have invited us both to their place for the weekend. When I told them how wonderful you are, my mother insisted that she had to meet you. I know she'll adore you as much as I do.'

Ginny tried her best to hold on to her smile, but she could feel it fading and her facial muscles stiffening. It wasn't that it hadn't been the question she had hoped for, but rather the fact she was going to have to refuse what was close to being a royal summons.

'Oh, Daniel, I'm so sorry, but I can't go. I was going to tell you later. I have to go to Switzerland this weekend,' she told him apologetically, hoping to soften the blow, but she could tell from the way he dropped her hand that he was not best pleased.

'With Adams, I presume!' Daniel responded frostily, causing her to blink at his tone.

Ever since she had agreed to this trip, Ginny had been wondering what she was going to tell Daniel. She abhorred deception, but his reaction told her clearly that the truth was out of the question. She had known for a long time that Roarke didn't think highly of Daniel, but she hadn't realised until now just how deeply Daniel disliked Roarke.

'Of course. It's business,' she lied, watching him sit back and fold his arms.

'I don't trust him,' Daniel pronounced bluntly, and Ginny frowned just a little. She could see where this was going, but she had never given him cause to worry. It surprised her to think he had given the possibility credence. He had no need to be jealous.

'You trust *me*, don't you?' she asked soothingly, and he instantly reached for her hand again.

'I do. Of course I do. It's just that that man...' Daniel let the sentence hang, and she knew what he meant. Roarke's reputation went before him.

She squeezed his hand. 'Is someone I have no interest

in at all. However, the trips are part of my job.' OK, not this one, but he didn't need to know that.

Daniel nodded reluctantly. 'I know, but Mother won't be best pleased. She hates having her arrangements altered. She won't like it, and I need her to like you.'

Ginny did a swift mental double-take. Daniel made the visit sound as if she was being presented for inspection, and whether or not he married her depended on his mother's report. She didn't much care for the sound of that, for good reason. Her father had insisted on vetting her boyfriends, and for the most part had found them wanting. They had not been welcome in his house and she had been compelled to follow his dictates until she was old enough not to need his approval.

To find herself on the receiving end of a similar situation now, when she had put all that behind her, made the hairs on the back of her neck stand up. There was no way she was prepared to go through that.

'Does it really matter if she likes me, Daniel? After all, I'm going out with you, not her.' She tried to make light of it, seeking reassurance.

She got it—of a sort. 'I suppose not,' he agreed uncomfortably, then laughed. 'No, no, of course it doesn't. Though I would prefer her to like you. There's no reason why she shouldn't, of course. It's simply that I've always sought her opinion on the important things,' Daniel explained, as if that would make it acceptable.

Ginny swallowed her unease. The situations weren't the same. All she would be doing was meeting his parents. It had to happen eventually. 'I shall do my best to make her like me, if that will make you happy. All we have to do is postpone the visit for a few weeks.' If it was important to him, then she would bite the bullet. As he said, there was no reason why his mother shouldn't like her. She shouldn't allow the past to cloud the present.

Daniel looked relieved. 'That would be wonderful. I just know she's going to like you. My mother has a very discerning eye.'

Ginny let the matter rest there, but later, when she was lying in her bed trying to sleep, the conversation went over and over in her mind. An uncomfortable feeling of *déjà vu* came over her. Daniel was the man she'd settled for, but she didn't want to have to battle his mother for him, and that was what she feared was going to happen. She had been through that, and wasn't about to let it happen again. But maybe she was seeing bogeymen where there were none. After all, she was predisposed to balk at the idea of being inspected. It would be best to reserve judgement until she had met his parents.

They couldn't be as bad as her own. Nobody's could. With which comforting thought she was finally able to drift off to sleep.

The rest of the week was hectic, and Friday came round all too quickly. As she packed for the trip that evening, Ginny decided she was out of her mind. Not only had she bought a new outfit for the occasion, which would have been acceptable, but she had bought several other things as well. For a trip she hadn't wanted to go on, and certainly wasn't looking forward to. The truth of the matter was that she couldn't just turn out in any old rag. Never mind she was going to be playing a part, these people were Roarke's family, and a wedding was a very special occasion. She couldn't bring any sort of disharmony to the day by treating it as a non-event. Besides, she had the feeling Jenna Adams would be dressed in only the best, and there was no way she would let the woman upstage her.

A glance at her watch told Ginny that Roarke would be here soon. Closing the case, she took it out to the hall, then double-checked that she had her passport in her handbag. Which left her with nothing to do but wait, and nerves started to churn in her stomach. They had nothing to do with flying, because she was well used to it. Nor was it due to the fact that she was travelling with Roarke, for she had done that countless times too. No, the nerves were due to the fact she hated waiting. Waiting gave her time to think, and her thoughts were rarely pleasant.

She had learned to keep herself busy, to always have something on hand in which to engross herself, but she couldn't do that now because Roarke was due any minute. She paced to the window of her flat and stared down at the road, but no car was pulling up. Where was he?

The silent question triggered a memory, and she could see herself looking out of the window of that grotty bedsit, waiting for Mark to come home so she could tell him her news. He had never come. Instead he had abandoned her to a terrifying future which had ultimately led to tragedy. She had waited that night, too. Alone in the dark, in pain.

'No!' With a low moan Ginny spun round, closing out the thoughts. She wouldn't go there. Not again.

The sound of the intercom buzzing made her jump, but it was closely followed by a sense of relief. He was here. She crossed to the intercom.

'Hello?'

'It's Roarke,' his disembodied voice informed her.

'Top floor, on the right,' she directed him, pressing the door release. She just had time to catch him muttering, 'It would be, wouldn't it!'

Ginny went to the door to meet him. To her eyes he didn't look the least bit out of breath when he reached her.

'Hasn't anyone ever thought of installing a lift?' he complained, and she shook her head at him.

'It's only three floors.'

'But six flights,' he was quick to point out.

'Quit complaining. You're the fittest man I know,' Ginny responded dryly. She knew for a fact that he worked out regularly, and though she had never seen it, she suspected there wasn't a spare ounce of flesh on the whole of his body.

'Remind me never to come to you for sympathy,' Roarke muttered as he glanced around. 'Is this it?' he asked, pointing to her single case.

Ginny nodded. 'It's all I shall need for a few days,' she confirmed, though she was well aware she had packed too much.

Roarke hefted her case and laughed. 'My mother never travels with less than thirty pieces of luggage.'

Ginny couldn't imagine having the clothes to fill them. 'Think about the excess she must have to pay!' she exclaimed in amazement.

'Think of the pandemonium that arises every time she thinks a piece is missing!' Roarke countered sardonically, and Ginny winced.

'Ouch. Does that happen often?'

'Nearly every time. You see, life has to be a drama for her. She's the prima donna to end all prima donnas. It wouldn't surprise me if my sister is marrying this man just to get away from our mother,' he declared outrageously.

'Oh, but surely she loves him,' Ginny protested, uneasy at the idea that any woman would do such a thing.

Roarke shrugged indifferently. 'She probably thinks she does.'

'Thinks she does?' Ginny challenged as she pulled the door closed behind her and checked it was securely shut.

Roarke started down the stairs. 'Caroline is very much like our mother. She can convince herself of anything. If she wants to get away from Mother's influence, she could well have convinced herself she loves this guy.' He took time out to shoot her a mocking glance over his shoulder. 'You might have gathered that relationships aren't our thing. Caro's a brilliant flautist, but emotionally she's caught in the fallout of our parents' broken relationships like the rest of us. I give this marriage a fifty-fifty chance at best.'

Having reached the ground, Roarke held the door open for her. 'You don't expect it to last?' Ginny asked as she walked outside.

Taking her arm, Roarke guided her to where he had parked his car. 'None of the others have, so the odds are against it.'

'Which is why you aren't even going to attempt a proper marriage,' she pronounced, and Roarke grinned at her over the boot before closing it with a solid thunk.

'Got it in one.'

He helped her into the car, but there was very little time for talking as the traffic that evening was heavier than usual. In fact, they only just made it to the airport in time, and their flight had already been called. Ginny didn't have time to catch a breath until they were in the air and the seat belt sign went out.

'There's nothing like a frantic last-minute dash to set you up for the weekend,' Roarke drawled sardonically as he made himself comfortable in the spacious first class seats.

'I look at it this way, things can only get better,' Ginny responded lightly.

He laughed. 'Don't you believe it. You haven't spent any time with my family before.'

Ginny frowned at him. 'Nobody can be as bad as the picture you're painting,' she argued, though she knew full well that they could be as cold and unforgiving as an arctic winter. 'Your grandfather is always a gentleman.'

'True,' Roarke agreed easily. 'He's one member of the family I'd do anything for. Unfortunately, he won't be there. Pressure of work, he told me, but I think he just doesn't want to run into my mother. They don't see eye to eye on anything.'

The affection in his voice when he spoke of his grandfather caused Ginny to look at him curiously. 'So there's one human being you do care about. You aren't quite the lost cause you like to make out. Why do you hide it?'

Roarke glanced round at her, a mocking smile back on his lips. 'Wait till you meet the family. Then, if you're half as smart as I think you are, you'll understand.'

Ginny looked away, fixing her attention on the view from the window. She wasn't sure she wanted to meet any of his family. Then a small smile tweaked at her lips. Well, they were the *Adams* family, so what else could she expect?

'What's so funny?' Roarke enquired, and Ginny, who hadn't realised she was smiling, hastily composed her features.

'Private joke,' she murmured with a shrug, hoping to put him off asking further, which it did, but only set him off in another unexpected direction.

After giving her a doubtful look, as if he had guessed what she was thinking, he said, 'So what about your family? They can't be as gruesome as mine.'

It was an automatic response for Ginny to tense, though she had battled hard to feel nothing over the years. She tensed because the memories were as painful as they had ever been. Try as she might not to care, she knew in her heart of hearts that she always would.

'I have no family,' she told him shortly, knowing she sounded far too abrupt, which would only pique his irritating interest.

There was a second of surprise while he assimilated this, then he frowned as he made the logical assumption. 'I'm sorry. I had no idea your parents were dead. You must miss them.'

Ginny had no intention of explaining anything to him, but, on the other hand, he was offering sympathy, and she couldn't take that under false pretences either. Caught between a rock and a hard place, she felt compelled to put him straight. 'They're not dead,' she corrected bluntly.

Beside her, Roarke's eyebrows rose, then drew together in another frown. 'You're saying you don't know who they are? That would explain the lack of photographs in your flat.'

Gritting her teeth, Ginny swivelled her head to give him a darkling look. 'I'm not saying that at all. Now, if you don't mind, I'd rather we changed the subject.' She couldn't be more pointed than that, but, as she had expected, Roarke ignored the heavy hint.

'Hey, you can't leave it there. You've got my mind buzzing with off-the-wall scenarios here. Besides, I told you about the skeletons in my family closet, so it's only fair you should do the same,' he cajoled her.

'You volunteered the information,' she was quick to point out. 'I could have done with knowing less.'

Roarke grinned. 'Come on now, sweetheart. You know you found it fascinating in a sort of perverse way.'

'I did not!' she denied, though she knew that wasn't totally true.

'Did too!' he quipped back, making them sound like two children sniping at each other. It made her want to laugh, and she hated that he could do that to her.

She narrowed her eyes at him. 'OK, so I didn't find it completely uninteresting,' she admitted, and held up her hand as he started to speak. 'But that doesn't mean I have to tell you anything about my family.'

'So you do have one. I was beginning to think you sprang into this world fully formed,' he mocked her, and Ginny sighed. He wasn't going to give up unless she said something.

There was no way she could keep the reluctance from her expression, and she wasn't laughing when she spoke. 'I'll tell you one thing, but only if you promise not to ask any more questions.'

The laughter faded from his grey eyes. 'You make it sound like the end of the world.'

She held his gaze. 'Your promise, Roarke.'

'OK, I promise. No more questions, no matter what you say.'

Ginny glanced down at her hands, composing herself so that she would reveal nothing, not by a look or an expression. Her gaze was bland when she looked at him again. 'Very well, I'll tell you this much. I no longer exist,' she told him quietly, and saw the myriad questions forming in his head. Yet she knew he wouldn't let one of them pass his lips, for he had given his word and she knew that, once given, he would not go back on it.

Roarke sat back in his seat, puffing out a frustrated breath. 'You realise this is going to drive me mad?'

That wasn't her intention, for she wasn't deliberately cruel. It had been her only defence to his probing questions. She couldn't tell him that her family wasn't dead to her, but that she was dead to her family. He would want to know why. She had had to shut him up and that had been the only way.

'Best not to think about it, then,' she advised, picking up one of the magazines she had bought to while away the flight with.

'God, you're an aggravating woman! Why didn't you just say nothing?' he demanded testily, and that made her lips quirk.

'I tried that, but you insisted. You only have yourself to blame. Something for you to remember in future. Curiosity can be a dangerous thing,' she told him with a husky laugh.

The sound of her laugh brought a rueful expression to his face. 'You're enjoying this, aren't you?'

Ginny couldn't help but laugh again. 'There's a certain amusement in the situation.'

'I had no idea you could be so nasty.'

She shook her head sadly. 'I told you. You…'

'…only have myself to blame. Thank you for rubbing salt into the wound. It's made me feel a lot better,' Roarke muttered grumpily, but she could tell there was no real animosity in it. He had been well and truly hoist by his own petard.

Secure in the knowledge that she had headed him off at the pass, Ginny concentrated on her magazine until her eyes began to close. Knowing sleep would make the journey pass more quickly, she settled her seat into a more comfortable position and was asleep in seconds.

It was a hand gently shaking her that brought her awake some time later, and in that moment of slight disorientation she glanced round to get her bearings and found herself looking into Roarke's concerned eyes no more than inches away from her own.

'What—?' she croaked, inexplicably fascinated by the depth in those grey orbs. She experienced the fanciful notion that they were bottomless. Perfect for drowning in.

'You were having a bad dream.' Roarke's soft words cut into her errant thoughts, causing her to blink and really see him. The words sent a chill through her and she shivered. 'I thought you'd rather I woke you up.'

Ginny licked her lips and swallowed, suddenly aware of a warmth on her shoulder. Glancing down, she discovered Roarke's hand still rested there from when he had shaken her to rouse her. It was this that was creating the only hot spot on her body, but it was radiating warmth. Disconcerted by the effect, she touched the button which brought her seat upright and removed his hand at the same time.

'Thanks,' she muttered awkwardly. 'Was I making much noise?' she added, glancing round surreptitiously to see if anyone was looking at her. Much to her relief, nobody was.

Only Roarke was studying her with any interest. 'Just whimpering sounds that warned me whatever was happening in that head of yours, it wasn't pleasant. Do you often have bad dreams?'

Glad to hear that she had stopped short of one of her more explosive nightmares, Ginny shook her head. 'Only now and then,' she revealed. Once she had been plagued by them. Driven to the point of exhaustion by nights of broken sleep. Time had seen them fade until now she only dreamed when she was worried or upset. It must have been Roarke's questions about her family which had set her off this time.

She'd been dreaming of the last time she had seen her

family. Her father had been as cold and remorseless as ever. Denying her entry to the house. Saying things in that harsh voice he used to show his disapproval. Things that had cut her pride to ribbons, though she had held her head high. He had seen her off as if she had been a creature from the gutter. But that was what she was to him then. No longer his daughter, just a thing he would step over in the street.

Roarke's hand on her arm gave her a start. 'Don't,' he ordered gently when she looked a query at him. 'Come back. Wherever you just were, you clearly don't want to be there.'

His perceptiveness brought an unexpected lump to her throat, and she had to clear it. 'Some dreams are hard to shake off,' she confessed, and he smiled faintly, as if he knew from experience.

'For some of us the past isn't a pleasant place to be, is it?'

That wasn't a path she wanted to travel, and in order to fend him off Ginny eyed him ironically. 'You have bad dreams? I would have thought you'd need a conscience for that.'

He wagged an admonitory finger at her. 'Now, that wasn't nice, sweetheart. As it happens, I do have a conscience, but I doubt very much if I could convince you of the fact. You have this habit of expecting the worst of me.'

'A side you delight in showing me,' she was quick to point out, and he laughed.

'Ah, well, if you expect to catch fish you have to use the right bait, otherwise they won't rise,' he explained, and Ginny's eyes narrowed.

'Implying that I rise to the bait, I presume?' she charged wrathfully.

'Which you do beautifully.'

She wanted to respond to that with a furious denial, but to do so would be to rise to the lure he had just put out, and therefore confirm what he was saying. She had to satisfy herself with a baleful look and one word.

'Snake.'

Roarke chuckled. 'Damn, but I have to admire your self-control. You are one cool customer.'

She might look cool, but inside Ginny was seething to the point of incandescence with frustration. 'You're too clever by half, Roarke Adams. People like you have been known to come to a sticky end.'

'There, you see, there's something for you to look forward to. My comeuppance. Will you look on, gloating with satisfaction?' he teased her, and she rolled her eyes.

'Oh, please, gloating is so passé. I'll probably be leading the cheering section. It will be made up of all the women you've toyed with over the years.'

'I'm afraid it won't be as large a group as you imagine. I'm on pretty good terms with most of my exes,' he reminded her, and she knew that basically it was true. She might rag him over the ones who had taken it badly, but they were in the minority.

Ginny had never been able to understand it. How could women allow themselves to be used as they were, and still like the man when he decided it was over? 'You must be related to Svengali,' she said now, and Roarke smiled rakishly.

'Sweetheart, I don't have to hypnotise a woman to, as you'd put it, have my wicked way with her.'

'No,' Ginny agreed with a grimace. 'You merely smile at them, and they turn all weak at the knees.'

'What turns you weak at the knees, Ginny? What's Daniel's secret weapon?'

There was no way Ginny would tell him that if Daniel had a secret weapon he kept it well hidden. He didn't turn her weak at the knees, and she wouldn't want him to. She'd done that, and it wasn't all it was cracked up to be. 'That's none of your business.'

Roarke's smile suggested he wasn't taken in by her response, but at least he didn't follow it up. No, he took a different tack. 'So, what did dear Daniel say when you told him where you were going this weekend?'

The nerves in Ginny's body jolted uncomfortably. Picking up her magazine, she flipped it open. 'He said nothing. Why should he have anything to say?' she responded in an offhand manner designed to tell him how unimportant the situation was.

Roarke studied her downbent head curiously. 'You mean he saw nothing odd in you going away with me? How open-minded of him. I didn't think he had it in him, to be frank.'

Ginny shrugged. 'We travel together too often for him to be upset this time,' she offered, recalling with a tiny frown just how upset he had been.

'True, but this is different...or doesn't he know that?' Roarke added thoughtfully, and Ginny groaned silently at his persistence. 'You didn't tell him, did you? Where does he think you are?' The amusement in his voice made her wince.

Slapping the magazine closed, she turned to stare him out. 'This is a business trip as far as he's concerned. When I realised how much he dislikes you, I chose not to tell him. Are you satisfied now? Can I read my magazine in peace?'

'Daniel dislikes me?' he asked, sounding even more amused. 'The man has a hidden depth. Well, well, well.'

Exasperated, Ginny was tempted to hit him with her

magazine. 'It's not uncommon for people to dislike you, Roarke, hard as that is to believe. I dislike you too.'

'Ah, but does he dislike me for the same reason? You see me as a womaniser. Is that what Daniel thinks too?' Roarke mused, then snapped his fingers as an idea struck him. 'Of course, that's it. He's afraid I might turn my attention to you.'

It was irritating that Roarke should hit the nail on the head so quickly. 'I told him he had nothing to worry about. I'm not the least bit interested in you. I think I may even have mentioned a ten-foot bargepole. That desperate I'm not,' she added sardonically for good measure.

'Besides, you have Daniel,' Roarke put in sagaciously.

'Exactly,' Ginny agreed, returning once more to her magazine. 'I have Daniel, and I'm not in the market for anyone else.' Saying which, she turned her shoulder on him and concentrated on the words on the page.

Roarke wasn't to know that they were little more than a jumble of letters because her thoughts were concentrated on those brief moments when a pair of roguish grey eyes had set her nerves skittering and her heart skipping. Why they had become fascinating, she couldn't say, but she was seeing them in a way she never had before. Added to that, she could still feel where his hand had touched her. She was aware of him, too. Physically. Suddenly she could sense him, when she had sat beside him before and never felt a thing. It was as if something had been switched on inside her, and she was far from comfortable with it. She had to be losing it to find Roarke Adams even remotely attractive. That damned chemistry had picked a fine time to rear its ugly head. However, what could be switched on could also be switched off, and that was what she was going to do. All she had to do was will it. She was a sensible person, so it shouldn't be that difficult... should it?

CHAPTER THREE

IT WAS evening when they landed, but as it was summer the sun hadn't quite set and it was still warm. Someone had sent a car to collect them, and Ginny was more than a little surprised to find herself being ushered into a luxury limousine.

'Somebody's pushing the boat out,' she murmured as she ran an appreciative hand over the soft leather seat.

'Mother never travels in less than the best,' Roarke explained dryly as he joined her in the back, having passed a few friendly words with the driver, whom he obviously knew well.

'Hasn't she heard of energy saving?' she charged, judging that the limousine would guzzle petrol as if it was going out of fashion.

Roarke uttered a bark of laughter. 'She never hears anything that would be to her disadvantage. Which is why she insists her children call her Marganita and not mother. The surgeon's skill has maintained her youthful looks, which would be undermined by having a son my age.'

'What do you call her?' Ginny wasn't sure whether the woman sounded likeable or not, he was painting such a dreadful picture of her. Her eyes narrowed. Just a minute, why was he doing that? It wasn't like him at all to be so openly critical. She began to smell a rat.

That roguish smile reappeared. 'Mother, of course. I think it's important somebody keeps her in touch with reality.'

'Why bother if she's such an ogre?' Ginny countered,

definitely getting the idea that something was more than a little fishy here.

'She's my mother. I can't just abandon her,' Roarke replied carelessly, and Ginny knew she was right. She sent him a narrow-eyed look.

'You, Roarke Adams are a twenty-four-carat fraud,' she accused, which had him looking at her with what she could clearly see was feigned surprise.

'I have no idea what you're talking about.'

'Your family is gruesome and your grandfather is the only one you'd give the time of day? Ha! The fact that I'm here gives the lie to that. You care so much for your father you don't want to hurt him, and as for your mother... You love every larger than life inch of her,' Ginny declared roundly, the glow in her eyes daring him to deny it.

One eyebrow quirked. 'Is that so?' he said softly, and she nodded, quirking an eyebrow right back at him.

Roarke glanced away, scratching his ear. When he looked back, his expression was ruefully impressed. 'You aren't just a pretty face and a fabulous pair of legs, are you?'

'I was hired for my brain,' she confirmed, but Roarke smiled.

'And a humdinger of a brain it is, but a mere brain didn't see what you did. How does a woman who's locked up in layers of permafrost get such an accurate insight into man's deeper emotions? Sort of begs the question: were you always as frosty as you are now?'

Ginny gave him a sad look. 'Just because I don't choose to live my life as a high drama like your mother doesn't make me frosty,' she said, and received a look of high scepticism.

'I beg to differ. A glance from those eyes of yours can

deliver a serious case of frostbite,' he drawled humorously.

'The answer to that is to not say anything to provoke me,' she advised, glancing out of the window and enjoying the view as the car began to circle the lake. They must be getting closer to their destination, she decided, and a tiny flutter of nerves started up inside her.

It wasn't that she was really worried, for she was used to meeting new people, and all she had to do was be there to show Roarke's stepmother that he was spoken for. Money for old rope, really. By Sunday evening she would be back in her own home again, and he would owe her one *big* favour.

All the same, the situation was just that little bit different. This was a family function and, Lord knew, she had never been a whizz at those. Doing what was expected of her, for a father who was notoriously hard to please, had been difficult. He had hated her spirit, and had done his best to crush it. That he had failed was due to her inner strength. She had refused to give in, and it had taken her along paths leading to betrayal and rejection. Her determination to be free had cost her dearly, and the memories were painful to this day.

She was distracted from her uncomfortable thoughts by the driver turning the car in through iron gates set in a wall that appeared to stretch for ever. It was a winding drive through natural forest, and Ginny wasn't in the least surprised when they finally came out of the trees and found themselves drawing up before a large turn-of-the-century mansion. The views over the lake were spectacular.

Climbing out of the limousine, Ginny stared up at the impressive frontage. Goodness only knew how many bedrooms there were.

'It's not much to look at, but it's still home to us,' she sighed dramatically.

Roarke slipped his hands into his trouser pockets and rocked back on his heels. 'Impressed?' he queried, tongue-in-cheek.

'I'm impressed by the size of the fuel bills. It must cost a packet to heat this place,' she exclaimed in awe.

He grinned. 'Which is why it's the summer place. Summers are hot, so there's no need to heat it. There's a cool head under all that passion and flamboyance.'

She looked at him speculatively. 'Aha, I'm beginning to see where you get your cunning from. What characteristics did you inherit from your father, other than an eye for the ladies?'

His laughter sent a trickle of pleasure down her spine. 'Why, good looks, charm and wit, of course.'

'Very useful,' she drawled ironically.

'All depends what you want to use them for,' he countered smoothly, and she had no trouble guessing what he meant.

'So, why isn't your father in the hotel business?' Ginny asked as they walked to the front door. Lawns stretched out on either side and were immaculately kept.

Roarke shrugged. 'He's better at spending money than making it. Fortunately, he can never spend what he has. He inherited a tidy fortune from his maternal grandmother, and has been living on the interest ever since. Oh, he isn't a fool where money is concerned. It's all stashed away, making more money than he could spend in three lifetimes, but it means he doesn't have to work.'

'So what does he do all day?' Ginny wanted to know, frowning up at him in disapproval.

Seeing the look on her face, Roarke quirked an eyebrow

mischievously. 'I told you, he spends money,' he said mildly, just as the door opened as if by magic.

Ginny had been going to pursue the subject, but the vision before her took the words out of her mouth. Standing deferentially in the doorway was a butler. Not just any butler, but a genuine English one from the way he wished them good evening. He could have stepped right out of that well-known series of humorous novels.

Roarke stooped down to whisper in her ear. 'If the wind changes, you'll stay like that,' he said and, realising she was staring with her mouth open, Ginny closed it with a snap of teeth.

'Is he real?' she asked, stepping inside in response to Roarke's hand in the small of her back.

'The lady wants to know if you're real, Watson,' Roarke promptly addressed the question to the butler, much to Ginny's discomfort.

'Indeed I am, sir,' Watson replied with gravity, but Ginny thought she caught the faintest of twinkles in his eyes.

'He's real,' Roarke reported back, and Ginny sent him a look sharp enough to slay him where he stood.

'Very funny,' she growled, then gave the butler a friendly smile. 'Take no notice of him, Watson. He has a warped sense of humour.'

'Mr Roarke's foibles are well known to me, miss.'

Laughing, Roarke turned back to the butler. 'Are we the last to arrive?'

'Of those expected today, yes, sir. Madam had dinner put back to coincide with your arrival. Cocktails will be served in the drawing room in half an hour.'

Roarke glanced at his watch. 'We can make that. There's no need to show us up, I know the way.'

Watson inclined his head in assent. 'Very good, sir. I'll have Carl bring your luggage up directly.'

The staircase was beautifully carved in wood and, climbing up it, Ginny could imagine elegant *fin de siècle* ladies swaying down it in their waspwaisted dresses, bent on making a spectacular entrance.

'Has Watson been with your family long?' The man was clearly somewhere around retirement age, but he still had a straight back and a full head of silvery-grey hair.

'Since I was a boy. He's had to rescue me from more scrapes than I care to remember,' Roarke enlightened her as he ushered her down one corridor, then left into another. It was very confusing.

'Could you draw me a map. I think I could get lost in here,' Ginny declared wryly. 'Has anyone disappeared never to be seen again?'

'Not recently,' he responded with a teasing grin. 'Here we are.' Stopping by a door, he opened it and pushed it wide.

It was a beautiful room, with a double bed at one end and a sitting area complete with couch and armchairs encircling a fireplace at the other. There were two large windows opposite, one giving access to a balcony, and Ginny went to look out, delighted to realise it offered a grand view of the lake. She decided she would be very comfortable here.

Turning, she found Roarke had followed her in. 'Like it?' He sought her approval, and she nodded, walking past him to take hold of the door.

'It's absolutely perfect. Now, if you wouldn't mind leaving, I would like to clean up before dinner.' She stared at him, urging him to go, and noticed that Roarke looked oddly discomfited.

'I would, but there's a problem,' he said uneasily.

Her eyes narrowed. 'Problem?'

He winced. 'Something I forgot to tell you.'

Feeling uneasy herself now, Ginny was about to ask what it was when a figure appeared in the doorway. He was carrying their bags, so she identified him as Carl. What she didn't expect was that he would deposit all the luggage on the chest at the foot of the bed and leave again, as quietly as he had arrived. Understanding was swift, and Ginny looked up at Roarke with eyes that registered first surprise, then anger. She let the door go in order to point an accusing finger at him.

'If you think for one minute that I am going to—' The words were abruptly cut off as Roarke closed the gap between them in no time and clamped one hand over her mouth and used the other to swing her away from the door, which he shut with a flick of his foot.

'For the love of Mike, keep your voice down,' he ordered in an urgent undertone, whilst Ginny glared at him over his hand.

'Take your hands off me!' she ordered, sounding both angry and garbled.

'What?' Roarke asked absently, intent on listening for sounds outside the now closed door.

Ginny chose a more direct method of communication, and the business end of her heel connected with his shin.

'Ow!' he exclaimed, releasing her to rub at the damaged area.

Stepping out of reach, Ginny folded her arms wrathfully. 'I said, take your hands off me,' she repeated for his benefit, and Roarke straightened up. 'Why didn't you tell me we would be sharing a room?' she demanded to know.

'Because I forgot,' he growled back.

She laughed incredulously. 'You forgot? You can't seriously expect me to believe that?'

Grey eyes glowered at her. 'Right now, I don't care what the hell you believe. The truth is I forgot. I use this room when I'm alone or when I'm not, and you aren't the one I was supposed to be with. The arrangements were made ages ago, remember?'

Some of the initial anger drained out of her at his explanation, but that didn't mean she was happy with the situation. 'OK, you forgot, but that doesn't mean I intend to share this room with you, Roarke.'

Satisfied that there was no serious damage, Roarke abandoned his examination of his shin and gave her a blunt look. 'You're going to have to.'

That set her nostrils flaring. 'I don't have to do anything!' she declared, bringing a mocking smile to his lips.

'The woman in my life shares my room, and so far as this family is concerned you are the woman in my life. Get used to it. You're staying here.'

Ginny would have given anything to be able to counter his argument, but she could not. She had agreed to play a part, and apparently that meant sharing this room with him. That being the case, she was going to lay down some ground rules right now.

'OK, so we share the room. We don't share the bed. You can sleep on the couch,' she ordered coldly, and that brought a glint of amusement back to his eyes.

'Sure you don't want me to sleep in the bath?' he mocked, and she returned the smile with saccharine.

'Don't tempt me!' she threatened, and went across to the bed to pick up her case. 'Before I get changed, is there anything else you've forgotten and would care to tell me about?'

He shrugged, hands busying themselves with the buttons of his jacket, which he removed and tossed on to the bed along with his tie. 'Nothing springs to mind,' he declared, starting on the buttons of his shirt.

Ginny found herself staring as if hypnotised. For reasons she couldn't afterwards explain, she couldn't seem to take her eyes off the movement of his fingers. It was only when they paused near his waist that she blinked and looked up—to find him watching her with a wicked glint in his eye.

'Want to help?' he invited in an ever so slightly husky voice.

Realising what she had been doing, and how it would be perceived, Ginny felt a wave of heat storm into her cheeks. 'You've been undressing yourself long enough to know what you're doing,' she responded tautly, swinging on her heel and heading for the nearest door.

Opening it, she came to a halt. It wasn't the bathroom. She closed her eyes, waiting for the remark that was bound to follow. He didn't keep her waiting long.

'You can use my dressing-room if you like, but yours is the other side of the bed, and the bathroom is to the right of the fire,' Roarke said in that friendly, helpful way that made her want to commit serious bodily harm.

Bracing herself, Ginny turned and met eyes dancing with amusement. 'Thank you,' she gritted out through her teeth, and followed his directions to the other side of the room. Once safely inside the bathroom, she shot the bolt and leant back weakly against the door.

Oh, God, she had just made a complete and utter fool of herself. And why? Because she had been unnerved by finding she had been staring at him whilst he began to undress! What on earth had made her do that? She groaned aloud. He would never let her live it down. She just knew in her bones that he would be throwing it in her face from now till kingdom come.

To cap it all, she was having to share the room with him. Sometimes life was darned unfair. Thank goodness she had thought to bring a robe with her, for, although it was made of some silky material, it covered her from neck to toe. She wouldn't have to swan around in next to nothing in front of him.

With that grateful thought, Ginny set her case down on top of the laundry basket and drew out the two-piece she would wear that night. It didn't take her long to wash off the dust of travel and refresh her make-up, then slip on her stockings and shoes. Finally, she reached for the two-piece. The skirt was simple, black and clingy, whilst the top had a beadwork pattern all over it that glittered in the light and was held up by two thin straps. Ginny had a feeling that Roarke's mother always dressed for dinner, so the evening wear would not be out of place. She ran a brush through her hair, gathered up her belongings and let herself back into the bedroom.

Roarke was already dressed in a dinner suit, and Ginny was compelled to acknowledge once again that she'd rarely seen a man who looked better formally dressed. Probably because he was at home in formal clothes. Mind you, she also had the idea that he would look equally good in informal clothes. Because if Roarke Adams was nothing else, he was a man who was comfortable with who and what he was. It was probably one of the main reasons he was so attractive to women. Women always appeared to go for men who were sure of themselves. Roarke had...the only phrase that really said it all was that old one—*savoir-faire*.

He turned at the sound of her return, and a slow smile spread across his face. 'Very nice. I've always said it, you know how to wear clothes, sweetheart,' he complimented her, which, as it was virtually what she had been thinking about him, made her feel a little strange inside.

Setting her case on the nearest chair, Ginny smoothed away invisible creases from her skirt. 'You didn't say, but it seemed to me, if your mother has a butler she must dine formally.'

'Right down to the napkins and finger bowls,' he confirmed ironically. Then, seeing her sceptical expression, he amended the statement. 'OK, so the finger bowls are a slight exaggeration, but you get the picture.'

Ginny shook her head at him in mild exasperation. 'You enjoy painting your family as a bunch of wildly eccentric loonies, don't you?'

'Makes it less of a shock when you finally get to meet them,' he replied with a chuckle.

She rolled her eyes. 'I'm beginning to believe half of what you say isn't true, and the rest is just plain lies.'

His lips twitched and he quirked an eyebrow at her. 'So, you think you're getting to know me, do you?'

Ginny folded her arms, and tipped her chin challengingly. 'A little. About your family. I said you were a fraud, and nothing has changed my mind since.'

'Hmm,' Roarke mused just as a soft knock came on the door. They looked at each other questioningly, both wondering if this was where the real deception would begin. Bracing himself, Roarke went to the door and opened it.

Immediately the room was pervaded by the scent of Opium. For a moment all Ginny could see was Roarke's back, and then two arms slinked their way around his neck, causing her eyes to widen in surprise.

'Roarke, darling, Watson told me you were here, and I

just had to come and say hello,' a sultry voice declared, and the hairs on the back of Ginny's neck rose.

Ginny watched silently as Roarke attempted to back away, but, tentacle-like, the arms closed around him, drawing him in. She saw Roarke's hands fasten on those arms, trying to dislodge them, but the woman they belonged to wasn't about to let go. Ginny didn't like that one little bit, but didn't have time to analyse why.

Crossing to the door, she pulled it open wider to reveal Roarke and the sexy blue-eyed blonde who had him in her feline grasp. There was no doubt in Ginny's mind that this could only be Jenna Adams. In which case, she had a job to do.

'Hello,' she said mildly, though someone who knew her better would have been uneasy at the glitter in the back of her eyes. Reaching up, Ginny took hold of one of the woman's wrists. 'Let me help you. You seem to have got caught up on something that doesn't belong to you,' she said with a smile that belied the strength with which she pulled the woman's arm down. There was no harm in letting the other woman believe she was fiercely territorial. It was, after all, what Roarke wanted.

Taken by surprise, Jenna Adams gasped and took a hasty step backwards, releasing Roarke, who took the opportunity to put some distance between them.

Warming to her theme, Ginny slipped her arm through Roarke's proprietorially, and kept smiling at the other woman. 'You really should be careful who you get snagged on, Mrs Adams.'

Jenna might have been temporarily knocked off her stride, but she was not the sort of woman to remain so for long. She rallied instantly, looked Ginny up and down, then tossed her head dismissively. 'And you are?' she asked disdainfully, which made Ginny's lips twitch.

'Ginny Harte,' Ginny introduced herself, holding out her hand.

Jenna deigned to touch it briefly. 'You must be Roarke's latest,' she said snidely, but that only got Ginny's dander up. It wasn't often that she took an instant dislike to anyone, but she was willing to make an exception for Jenna Adams. The woman was trouble with a capital T. She had been poured into a glittery red dress that clung to every curve lovingly, leaving little to the imagination.

'That's right,' she said brightly. 'And you're Jenna... his father's wife.'

The reminder caused Jenna to flash her eyes at Ginny, sizing her up as she realised Ginny was possibly a force to be reckoned with. 'Roarke, darling, she sounds positively possessive. I'd be careful, or she'll be putting a ring through your nose before you know it,' she teased with a gurgling laugh, but she was far from amused.

Roarke smiled faintly and covered Ginny's hand with his own. 'I'll take my chances.'

Jenna's lips parted in surprise, and the flash in her eyes became almost feral as she looked from one to the other. 'My, my, she must have something all your other women didn't.'

Roarke glanced down at Ginny, and secretly winked at her. 'She certainly does,' he agreed with feeling, and Ginny almost laughed because she knew what he meant and Jenna didn't.

Jenna took a deep breath, which put her dress under great strain. 'Do let us into the secret. What has she got that the others don't?'

Ginny looked her squarely in the eye. 'Well, for one thing, I don't have a husband,' she said with the precision of a master swordsman, not caring if she offended the other woman or not. It was plain as the nose on her face that Jenna wouldn't like any woman Roarke had. She wanted him for herself.

In response, Jenna laughed grimly. 'Darling, don't think you've almost got one yourself. Roarke isn't going to marry you. He isn't the marrying kind,' she warned, no holds barred.

The statement hung on the air, destined never to be countered, for, as if on cue, a male voice called out from further along the corridor.

'Ah, there you are, Jenna,' Lewis Adams exclaimed. 'I thought you were going to wait for me,' he added just a little testily as he came level with the doorway.

Quick as a flash, Jenna smiled lovingly at the older man and slipped her arm through his. 'Sorry, darling, but I just had to come and say hello to Roarke and his latest lady friend.'

There was a moment when Lewis Adams did not look best pleased, but then he smiled at his son, and Ginny believed she could see genuine warmth there. 'Good to see you, Roarke. And you, too...' He smiled at Ginny and she could see where Roarke had got his charm.

'Ginny,' Roarke introduced her, and Ginny found her hand swallowed in a firm male one.

'Hope you enjoy your stay here, young lady. Now, we'd better get downstairs before your mother pitches a fit,' he added with a significant glance at his son. 'She's been in diva mode since this morning.'

Roarke urged Ginny out of their room ahead of him. 'Never let it be said she missed an opportunity, Dad,' he responded to his father, who was leading the way with his wife sashaying on his arm.

Ginny attempted to remove her hand from Roarke's arm, now that the need for it was past, but he quickly closed a hand over hers again, and when she glanced up he shook his head. Which was just as well, for Jenna looked round then, and would have thought it odd for Ginny not to be clinging to Roarke. She subsided, but holding Roarke's arm was a completely new experience, and she found herself becoming aware of his strength. He was a powerful man in both senses of the word, yet there was nothing threatening about the strength of his body. In fact, for some weird reason, being this close, far from making her uneasy, was strangely comforting. Not a word she would usually use in connection with Roarke, but it certainly made it easier to resign herself to having to remain in close contact with him, at least for the moment.

'Marganita always has to be the centre of attention!' Jenna said irritably, and Ginny guessed she preferred to hold that position.

'She can act how she wants in her own home,' Roarke put in ironically.

'That's what I keep telling you, Jenna,' Lewis told his wife.

'Well, I don't like it,' Jenna complained with a toss of her head.

'You knew how it would be. You didn't have to come, but you insisted, so quit complaining,' her husband advised with a touch of asperity, and Ginny's brows rose thoughtfully.

It seemed to her that Lewis Adams was not as uncritical of his wife as Roarke assumed. Which might suggest that he was beginning to see how wrong he had been. She hoped so, for Roarke's sake.

Back downstairs, they made their way to the drawing room, which opened on to a terrace overlooking the lake. The daylight was fading fast now, and through the opening Ginny could see lights beginning to flicker on in the houses over the water. The room itself was ablaze with light from two elaborate crystal chandeliers, which were reflected back from strategically placed mirrors, and was full of people making quite an incredible amount of noise.

'Mother appears to have invited the whole family to dinner,' Roarke murmured in her ear, and Ginny thought he was probably right.

She was aware that they were drawing some attention. No doubt Roarke's family were speculating as to who she was—and how long she would last. Ginny relaxed, secure in the knowledge that she knew there was nothing between them, and that the 'relationship' would be over in something like forty-eight hours.

'Your family are wondering who I am,' she remarked to Roarke as they ventured further into the room.

'Do you mind being the centre of attention?' he asked, attracting the eye of a passing waiter and handing her a glass of champagne before taking one for himself.

Ginny sipped at the drink and found it a little too dry for her taste. 'Actually, it's quite amusing. If they only knew! In different circumstances, you and I wouldn't come any closer than a ten-foot bargepole would allow. The sad thing is, when you turn up next time with someone else, they won't be the least bit surprised.'

Roarke shrugged that off easily. 'I try not to disappoint them. Ah, I think Mother is holding court over there.' He nodded in the direction of the far end of the room. 'We'd better go and say hello. Brace yourself.'

Ginny felt her stomach lurch. Brace herself for what? She soon found out.

When Marganita Toscari—she always preferred to be known by her maiden name—saw her eldest son making his way towards her through the crowd of guests, she let out a cry and jumped up from her seat to envelop him in a bruising hug. She broke into a veritable spout of Italian, which Ginny found hard to follow, but which Roarke responded to in the same language.

Only when she finally held him at arms' length, did she return to English. 'Roarke, you are a rogue. I may never forgive you for not coming to visit me for months and months. What have you got to say for yourself, you devil?' She didn't wait for his answer, for she caught sight of Ginny hovering behind him and let out another cry, albeit softer. 'Is this your young lady? But she's beautiful, Roarke. Why didn't you tell me how beautiful she was? Introduce us. I insist,' she urged her son, all the time beaming at Ginny, who was beginning to feel uncomfortable at all the attention.

'Ginny, this is my mother. Mother, meet Ginny Harte,' Roarke dutifully obliged, and Ginny just caught the faint gleam in his eye as he took her glass from her before she was overwhelmed by an embrace almost as effusive as the one Marganita had given her son just minutes before.

'Ginny, *cara*, I'm so happy to meet you. Come, give me a hug, for any friend of my son's is welcome here.'

Marganita was a large lady, along the lines of the older sopranos, and hugging her was no easy matter. Ginny did her best, and surfaced pink-cheeked and flustered.

'I'm pleased to meet you, Miss Toscari,' she returned the greeting politely.

The older woman waved her hands and shook her head. 'Marganita. You must call me Marganita, and I shall call you Ginny.'

It was more of a royal pronouncement than a suggestion and Ginny, getting over the shock, smiled. 'Marganita, then.'

'And we shall be friends, and you shall tell me all about yourself. Only not yet. Don't go away, Roarke, there's someone I want you to meet.' Without further ado, Marganita scanned the room with the eye of an expert and set off in search of her quarry.

Grinning, Roarke handed Ginny her glass, and she took a much needed drink. 'My goodness, is she always so... so...?' Words failed her.

Roarke laughed affectionately. 'I thought she was remarkably restrained. As a rule, she can be quite voluble. I expect it's because her soon to be in-laws are present. She's making an extra effort so as not to scare them off.'

Ginny pulled a face. 'I think she's probably easier to get along with in small doses.'

'That's the consensus of opinion of all her children. Otherwise, she'll try to take over our lives—with the best of intentions, of course. My father finds it easier to get along with her now that they aren't actually married,' Roarke explained.

'Roarke, *caro*.' Marganita's mellifluous tones drew their attention, and they both turned towards her. She was smiling broadly and trailing a rather disgruntled man in her wake.

Ginny took one look at that stern face, and her blood turned to ice. No! It couldn't be, she told herself, and yet she knew that it was. Walking towards her was the man she had thought she would never see again, and had been comforted by that thought. That man was none other than her own father. Shock held her to the spot, and she was sure the colour must have drained from her face.

All she could think was: what was he doing here?

Of all the people it was possible for her to run into, her father had never been on the list. They didn't inhabit the same world any more. Yet he was here, and any second now he was going to see her. She didn't know what he would do, but instinct told her it would not be good. He had made his position very clear. So far as he was concerned, she did not exist. Tensing, her heart starting to beat faster, she waited for the moment when he would notice her and recognition would come. Unknowingly, she tightened her hand about the stem of her glass.

'Mother,' Roarke was saying beside her, but Ginny couldn't take her eyes off the man who had come to a halt beside Marganita and who looked first at Roarke and then at her.

Recognition was as instantaneous for him as it had been for her. His reaction was also typical. Drawing himself up, his expression tightened and his face grew red with anger and distaste. If Ginny had held any hope that he might have softened his stance with the passing years, she would have been left in no doubt. That look said it all. He despised her now as much as he had ever done. Only the dictates of good manners stopped him from turning his back and walking away. After that initial moment he kept his gaze firmly averted from her.

It shouldn't have hurt. After all this time, his displeasure should have left her cold, and yet it didn't. Hate him though she might, for what he had done, he still had the power to wound her with his disdain. Yet she was stronger now. Tougher. She wasn't about to turn and run. He might not want to see her, but he had no option. He would be forced to recognise her, and that brought her chin up.

Marganita was still making the introductions. 'Roarke, this is Brigadier Sir Martin Beavis. Caroline is marrying his son, James. Sir Martin, this is my son, Roarke Adams.'

Ginny's breath caught in a tiny gasp when she heard that. Roarke's sister was marrying James? Her heart leapt into her throat. That meant her family were here. Eagerly, she began to look around her, searching for those familiar figures of her mother, brother and sister.

'Pleased to meet you, Sir Martin.' From a long way away she heard Roarke's response, but she was diligently scanning the crowd.

Try as she might, she couldn't see them, and was so intent on what she was doing that Roarke's hand on her arm made her jump. 'Sorry, did you say something?' she asked, glancing round unwillingly. She wanted to find her family before her father knew what she was doing, for he would prevent it by any means.

A tiny frown appeared between his brows at her abstraction. 'I wanted to introduce you to Caroline's future father-in-law,' he said. 'Sir Martin, this is a good friend of mine, Ginny Harte.'

Ginny had no trouble reading the look in her father's eyes. He interpreted 'friend' as 'lover', and made his judgement. In his eyes, she hadn't changed, and that made her so angry. She knew he didn't want to have anything to do with her, but right here he had no option, and she was determined to make him speak.

Raising her chin, she held out her hand. 'Brigadier,' she said challengingly, and knew he was caught by his own notion of what was good manners. He was forced to shake her hand. 'It's been a long time. You haven't changed.' She had always called him Brigadier, for he treated his family as if they were part of his army, laying down rules that had to be followed to the letter. Something she hadn't done.

Sir Martin's lip curled disgustedly. 'Neither have you, it seems,' he responded in his clipped military fashion, with a brief glance towards Roarke, which Ginny understood perfectly. He dropped her hand after the merest touch as if it were a live coal. Which it probably was to him.

Ginny was aware that Roarke was looking at her

thoughtfully, but his mother clapped her hands in delight. 'What's this? You have met before?' she beamed, believing she had brought old friends together.

'Miss Harte was once known to my family,' Sir Martin explained tersely.

Ginny smiled mockingly. 'I shall look forward to meeting your son again,' she told him, and knew he wanted to warn her off there and then, but dare not.

'My son is very busy. I don't think he'll have time to meet everyone,' her father declared, being as blunt as he dared.

'And what of your other children?' Ginny went on turning the screw. 'Are they here with you?' As soon as the question left her lips, she knew it was a mistake. She had given him an opening, and she knew he wouldn't fail to take it. All she could do was brace herself.

Contempt flared in Sir Martin's eyes as he went in for the kill. 'I only have one son and one daughter. Surely you remember that?'

Ginny stared him out, but they both knew she had lost ground in their personal battle. 'I had the impression there were more. Never mind. I must reacquaint myself with your wife and daughter, too.'

'I'll be sure to tell them you are here, Miss Harte,' he responded politely, which she knew meant that he would warn them off from seeking her out. 'Now, if you'll excuse me, I think I'd best see what my wife is doing.' With a nod to Marganita and her son, he turned and walked away.

Ginny felt a hard cold knot settle in her stomach as she watched his retreating back. He wouldn't let her see them if he could prevent it, yet he couldn't be watching them all the time. There would be moments when his back was turned, and she would take her chance. Only…what if they didn't want to see her? James had always followed their father's instructions, whilst Lucy had been so young the last time she had seen her. And Mother... Her mother had been worn down years ago. She would take the chance, though, even if it turned out badly.

She sighed and looked away from him to find herself facing Roarke wearing a very serious expression.

'So you've met Sir Martin before?' he said softly, and that gave her nerves a severe jolt. She had been so intent on squaring up to her father, she hadn't considered what Roarke was overhearing. He would have been tantalised, and she knew he was puzzling over the facts, trying to put two and two together.

She shrugged, determined to keep him off the path she knew he wanted to follow. 'It was a long time ago. We didn't get on,' she added and he laughed.

'That was patently obvious, to anyone except my mother. She still believes she's brought two old friends together.'

They had never been friends. 'I preferred his family to him. He isn't an easy man to get along with.'

Roarke glanced off to where Sir Martin had vanished into the crowd. 'He didn't appear to want you to meet his family.'

Ginny let out a hollow laugh. 'There's nothing new in that.'

Roarke's expression went from thoughtful to amused. 'But you're going to do it anyway, aren't you?'

Ginny met his look and started to smile with genuine amusement. 'I never have liked being ordered off,' she confirmed.

'Which makes you a woman after my own heart,' Roarke declared. 'This is turning out to be a far more interesting weekend than I had imagined.'

Interesting wasn't the word she would have chosen, she thought, as she sipped her drink. Dangerous seemed to fit better. Running into her father had been unpleasant, but there was a brighter side. Her family was so close, she could almost touch them. All she had to do was reach out. Life had a way of throwing you a crumb of hope just when you least expected it.

CHAPTER FOUR

DINNER was a sumptuous affair, and Ginny could only wonder what the wedding breakfast would be like. It seemed to her it would be hard to top this. Not that she had a large appetite. Half of the guests had melted away before dinner was announced. They had been invited for cocktails to meet the bride and groom, so it was a smaller number of people sitting around the long table in the formal dining room.

Ginny had caught sight of her mother and sister as they sat down, but they must have received orders not to acknowledge her. Whenever she glanced in their direction they looked away hastily. James had been more subtle. He had simply looked right through her. Not surprising then that her appetite had disappeared.

'Looks like Sir Martin has had a word with his family,' Roarke observed dryly from beside her, and it didn't really surprise Ginny to realise he had seen what was happening. He sensed a mystery, and mysteries had only one reason for existence—to be solved.

'All done with military precision,' she joked.

Roarke reached for his glass of wine and took a sip. 'What did you do to get on the wrong side of him?'

She poked at a piece of chicken with her fork. 'Marching in step was never my forte.'

'If you aren't going to eat that, leave it alone,' Roarke ordered mockingly. 'Didn't your parents tell you not to play with your food?'

Spearing the chicken, she raised it to her mouth with a

challenging look. 'Constantly, but I didn't listen to them,' she declared, and popped the morsel into her mouth. It was dry by now, and she was forced to wash it down with some wine.

'So,' Roarke went on. 'How did you get to meet James Beavis?' he asked curiously.

Ginny toyed with her glass, watching the golden liquid swill from side to side. 'You could say we grew up together,' she admitted wryly.

'I thought he might have been an old flame,' Roarke put in, surprising her into looking at him.

'James?' she exclaimed with a laugh. 'No, there was never anything like that between us.' No doubt he would be angry with her if he ever discovered the true nature of her relationship with James but, as she had no intention of telling him, there was no way he would find out. Her private life was going to remain private.

'Good. I didn't really think he was your type.'

Ginny followed his gaze to where her brother sat talking to Caroline, Roarke's sister. There was nothing animated in his features. Nothing to show he was looking forward to marrying the woman he was talking to. She frowned. She hoped Caroline was doing the right thing. If James had become more like their father... But it was not her decision.

'How on earth did they meet?' she asked, and Roarke shrugged.

'At some charity dinner, so Mother tells me. Perhaps they exchanged horror stories and decided they would be better off together,' he said with a laugh, and Ginny winced.

'Talking of horror stories, your stepmother is unbelievable!' she pronounced in an undertone.

'Oh, yes,' he agreed dryly. 'I liked the way you sat on her. She was no match for you.'

Ginny was pleased he was pleased, but shrugged in an offhand way. 'I was only doing my job.'

'You seemed to be enjoying it,' Roarke pointed out sardonically, and she chuckled.

'OK, so I admit it gave me a certain satisfaction to peel her off you. I didn't like her.'

'The feeling was mutual,' he responded with a laugh.

Ginny laughed too, and as she turned towards him their eyes met in shared enjoyment. Then it seemed to her that something changed, and for a wild moment there was a connection between them. Something other than shared laughter. Her heart lurched, and she saw the tiny frown that appeared between his brows. He started to reach out a hand to her, and she held her breath, waiting...

'Hey, you two, break it up,' one of Roarke's half-brothers called from across the table, and suddenly they were the centre of attention.

Ginny came to with a jolt and felt colour storm into her cheeks. Roarke handled the matter with more *élan*.

'Mind your own business, Tom. Ginny and I are having a private conversation,' he declared, grinning at her. 'Ignore him, darling. He's just jealous because I happen to have the most beautiful woman in the room sitting next to me.'

The endearment took her by surprise, but a second later she realised he was acting a part. His statement was hotly refuted up and down the table and she was able to use the time to gather her composure. Whatever had happened in those odd few seconds, it had been quite unsettling. She didn't know why it had happened, but she would have to take care that nothing like it happened again. Which, she acknowledged wryly, might prove difficult as she hadn't anticipated anything like it happening once.

It was quite late when they left the table and returned to the drawing room. Roarke took her round and introduced her to the other members of his family. They all appeared to be nice, friendly people, who accepted her presence without question, which made her feel something of a fraud, until she reminded herself the deception was in a good cause.

She kept an eye out for her family, but it was an hour or so before she saw James standing on his own for a moment. Knowing there would be few opportunities like this one, she excused herself from the group she was with and made her way towards him. Her brother didn't notice her approach until the very last second, by which time it was impossible for him to escape. He tensed visibly, clearly unhappy with the situation.

A lump of emotion lodged itself in her throat as she smiled at him. 'Hello, James,' she greeted huskily, willing him to respond.

For his part, her brother's eyes darted about the room, and she had no doubt who he was looking for. Not wanting to be interrupted too soon, she placed herself in a position to shield as much of him as she could from the room at large.

'You can speak to me, you know. I won't bite,' she urged softly, trying to tease him as she had been wont to do when they were at home.

Finally he looked at her. 'Go away, Ginny.'

It was hardly encouraging, but she persevered. 'Can't we talk, James? We used to be able to talk, at least.'

James looked angry. 'That was before. Things have changed. I can't talk to you. I won't,' he declared, and made to move away, but her hand on his arm forestalled him.

'Can you still be so afraid of him, James? Even now?' she asked unhappily, and he paled, jerking his arm free.

'I'm tired of hearing that from you. It was so easy for you, Ginny. You had nothing to lose!' he snapped angrily, keeping his voice down with an effort.

Ginny almost laughed as she shook her head. 'You're wrong. I had everything to lose. I lost you and Lucy and Mum. I've missed you. All I want to do is talk to you.'

For the space of a heartbeat James appeared to hesitate, but then something over her shoulder made him shut down tight. She glanced round and saw their father watching them, his expression grim. No wonder James was in retreat.

'Get lost, Ginny!' he snarled at her, and this time he did walk away.

Ginny didn't try to stop him, for she knew there would be no point. James had never been strong enough to fight their father's strictures, even when she had been there to back him up. He hated unpleasantness and rows and angry voices. He had been a gentle boy, which had irritated their father and made him send his son to a military school to toughen him up. James had returned more buttoned-up than ever, and Ginny would never forgive her father for that.

Feeling as she did, she couldn't stay in the same room with him right now, for she didn't know what she might do. She had to get away to calm down. Which was why she didn't return to where Roarke stood talking to another of his sisters, but headed for the terrace and the fresh air. Nor was she aware that he watched her go, a frown of concern creasing his forehead.

Outside, she headed away from the light cast by the doorway, into the peace of the shadows further along where few people had wandered to. Resting her hands on the parapet, she tipped her head back, allowing the breeze that blew in off the lake to cool her face. It lifted the hair from her neck and she rolled her head slowly from side to side to get maximum benefit. It felt wonderful, and she could feel herself relaxing.

She might not have felt so relaxed had she been aware of the man who had followed her out and who now approached her from behind. She had only the briefest of warnings given by the sound of a footfall, then Sir Martin's hand took her by the shoulder and spun her round roughly.

His face was livid with anger. 'My God, why must you constantly defy me? I told you to stay away from my son. We want nothing to do with you.'

Ginny had never been afraid of confrontation, no matter how threatening her father could be. Now she rested back against the stonework of the low wall and tipped her chin up at him.

'You disowned me, remember? Which means you no longer have the right to tell me what I may or may not do,' she shot right back, unaware of a dark figure who slipped out of a window further along the veranda and settled into the shadows. 'I'm no longer your daughter, Brigadier.'

Sir Martin's lip curled scornfully. 'You were never that. A daughter doesn't disobey her father. She doesn't mix with riff-raff, nor sleep with gutter trash! A daughter thinks more of herself than to bed down with any man who asks her!'

Ginny could feel the same old anger balling up inside her, threatening to choke her. 'My friends were not riff-raff,' she insisted, enunciating each word carefully. 'Nor did I ever sleep around.'

He laughed harshly. 'No? You went off with the first man who came sniffing round you. You couldn't wait to get into his bed!'

The accusation was true, but only to a point. 'I loved him. I thought he loved me.' She had been desperate for affection, starving for it. So much so that she was blinded to Mark's true nature.

That made Sir Martin laugh again. 'And all he really wanted was *my* money. When he knew he would never get his hands on it, he couldn't drop you quickly enough.'

Ginny crossed her arms over her chest to hide the fact that her hands were shaking with suppressed emotion. 'I wasn't the first, and I certainly won't be the last woman who's been made a fool of by a man.'

'Nor been left pregnant by him,' Sir Martin added sneeringly.

There was nothing Ginny could do to ward off the shaft of pain his words drove through her. She gasped as the old wound was torn open. Straightening up, her eyes flashed a warning he was treading on dangerous ground.

'That has nothing to do with you.'

Her father bent over her, using his height and size to dominate. 'It has everything to do with me, young woman. I have to live with the knowledge that there's a fatherless child out there bringing disgrace to an old and honoured name!'

Oh, if ever there were a few words that summed up what really mattered to her father, those were the ones. His name and position meant more to him than his family. Well, he didn't have to worry about it any longer.

Strong emotions threatened to choke her, but she forced herself to speak clearly. 'You can put your mind at rest, Brigadier. There is no child to put a blot on the family escutcheon.'

He was brought up short temporarily. 'You had it adopted after all?'

That was what he had demanded in exchange for his help. It had never been an option for her. Ginny shook her head. 'She died.' Her voice broke on the word, and her eyes glittered like diamonds with unshed tears. 'That should give you cause to celebrate,' she went on, rallying. Determined not to break down before this unforgiving man.

Sir Martin straightened up, folding his hands behind his back, military fashion. 'Probably the best thing to happen,' he declared shortly, and Ginny drew in a shocked breath.

'You are incredible. There isn't an ounce of compassion in you. Well, this will come as a surprise to you, Brigadier, but it wasn't the best thing for me that my baby died. I wanted her. I would have loved her in a way you could never comprehend.'

Sir Martin set his jaw. 'Children are for continuing the family line.'

How many times had she heard that? It had been no more true then than it was now. 'That's archaic! You would have had me marry a man of your choice, just to enhance the family connection!'

'Precisely. James and Lucy are doing their duty by the family, as you should have done.'

Ginny paled at his revelation. 'You're forcing Lucy into marriage, too?'

'Nobody is forcing her to do anything. I've simply placed the names of suitable husbands before her so that she can make her own choice,' her father denied.

'And if she doesn't want to marry one of those?' Ginny enquired, feeling her stomach tighten as Sir Martin smiled smugly.

'Lucy is not like you. She will do what she knows is right, or end up like you.'

Ginny stared at him, aghast. 'You're using me as a threat to get her to do what you demand?' Her brain was whirling. Oh, God, Lucy, not you too!

Sir Martin smirked down at her. 'Did you think you would be sowing the seeds of rebellion when you left? That was a serious tactical error. All you did was remove a thorn in my side. Your name is never mentioned. You don't exist so far as this family is concerned, Virginia. My game, I think.'

Ginny closed her eyes as she made a sickening discovery. By staying away she had given her father the opportunity to force her brother and sister into line. Too late she realised she should have stayed in touch with them somehow. She could have helped them to see that they didn't have to obey his unreasonable demands. As he said, it had been a tactical error on her part, but he had just made one of his own. He had told her about it, and now she knew she had to do something. James might be beyond her reach, but Lucy was not. What she must not do now was show her hand.

'You may think you've won, Brigadier, but it's an illusion. You're going to end up a lonely, bitter old man. Now, if you don't mind, I came out here for some fresh air, and you're sullying it with your presence.'

'I have no intention of staying out here any longer than it takes me to get your promise not to talk to my family,' Sir Martin responded coldly, but Ginny laughed and shook her head.

'Hell will freeze over before that happens.'

Angry colour mottled his cheeks. 'You refuse?'

'You can bet your life I do. You can't browbeat me

like you do James. I'm made of stronger stuff.' Hopefully, Lucy would be made of stronger stuff too. Lord, she hoped so.

He looked as if he wanted to throttle her, but that was one thing he had never done—harmed any of them physically. He preferred to dominate mentally. 'You'll regret defying me. I'll make sure you do,' he threatened, and spun on his heel and marched off.

Shaking more than a little, Ginny turned and rested her hands on the parapet again, closing her eyes.

'Damn him! Oh, damn him to hell!' she gritted out through her teeth, slamming her fist on to the concrete.

Her father had dominated her life, turned it into an unending war for independence. She had thought she was free, but it had been a temporary reprieve. She would not be able to breathe freely again until she had saved Lucy from a marriage of convenience. Lucy had been scarcely ten years old when she had left—a child—now she was a young woman. Perhaps it was too late. Her father might have done his work too well. It was something Ginny was going to have to find out...

Suddenly she froze. There had been a noise off to her left followed by a stifled sound. Turning round, she tried to probe the darkness.

'Hello? Is anybody there?' she called out, and was almost on the point of deciding it must have been a cat or some other animal, when the darkness shifted and she could make out the shape of a man walking towards her.

Seconds later, Roarke stepped into the soft moonlight, a wry expression on his face. 'I should tell my mother to move some of her potted plants. I gave my knee a nasty rap,' he said with a laugh, but Ginny didn't smile.

'What were you doing, hovering in the shadows like

that?' she demanded to know, whilst a cold lump settled in her stomach. How long had he been there? What did he know?

'Enjoying the moonlight?' Roarke ventured, but when she continued to stare at him coldly, he shrugged and confessed. 'Waiting for Sir Martin to leave.'

Her eyes narrowed. 'How long have you been standing there?'

Roarke came closer, hands tucked into his trouser pockets. 'I saw him follow you out, and, as I didn't like the look on his face, I decided to keep tabs on him. I slipped out through the library window.' He jerked his head in the direction of the window she could barely make out.

Her nerves jolted anxiously at that, and though she was sure she knew the answer to her next question, she braced herself to ask it anyway. 'How much did you hear?'

Stopping before her, Roarke looked her squarely in the eye. 'Pretty much everything,' he confessed, and Ginny drew in an angry breath. By her sides her hands balled into fists.

'Damn you, Roarke, you had no right to listen! What you eavesdropped on was private.'

He raised his hands placatingly. 'I know. I'm sorry. In my defence, I can only say I was more interested in making sure you were safe. I told you, I didn't like the look on your father's face.'

The casual use of the word 'father' underlined just how much he now knew, and how pointless it would be to attempt to deny it. The cat was out of the bag and, much as she might wish otherwise, it could never be put back. Roarke now knew the most sordid details of her past, and she was sure he could make a good attempt at filling in the blanks of what he didn't know. The protective wall she had built had been breached, leaving her feeling more exposed and vulnerable than she had in years. Impotent rage bubbled inside her, and she hated him for knowing what he did. It was none of his business.

'What you did was despicable, and a sheer waste of time.' She hit back at him the only way she could. 'I was never in any physical danger from him. That isn't how he works.'

Roarke's expression grew grim. 'No, I realised that after a while. He prefers to use mind games, doesn't he? Where the scars won't show. It's still abuse in my book. Your father is little more than a bully, and I have an intense dislike for bullies.'

Ginny folded her arms and paced up and down. 'Maybe you do, but that didn't give you the right to follow us. Besides, I can take care of myself,' she insisted, ending up before him and glaring at him frostily.

Roarke smiled, but it was far from pleasant. 'I'm glad to hear it, but if I hear him threatening you again I'll knock him into the middle of next week, and I won't ask your permission first.'

The statement so surprised her that Ginny blinked at him. 'You'll what?'

Roarke continued to look grimly purposeful. 'You heard me.'

Nobody had ever come to her defence before. Ginny had always fought a lonely battle, for herself and her brother and sister, and to have someone say what he just had drained her anger and left her more than a little bemused. She sat down a tad hurriedly on the parapet.

'But I'm not your responsibility, Roarke,' she felt compelled to remind him, to which he shot her a level look.

'You're my responsibility if I choose to make you so...and I do choose to make you so.'

That caused her to laugh mockingly. 'Oh, yeah? You don't even like me!'

Roarke shrugged. 'You're growing on me,' he admitted, and moved round to rest against the wall beside her. 'So that's your family, huh?'

She pulled a face. 'Not any more. You heard the Brigadier say so himself.' It felt strange to be talking openly about them after all these years. Because it had hurt so much to be cut off from them, it had been easier not to talk about them at all. By overhearing what he had, Roarke had just broken down that barrier too. Though she hated that he knew, he was one person she had no need to lie to now. Surprisingly, that gave her a new-found sense of freedom.

Roarke glanced at her sideways. 'Why do you call him Brigadier?'

'Because he was never a father. He issued orders, or gave us rules and regulations which had to be followed to the letter and, if we didn't, privileges were withdrawn. Our friends had to be vetted before they were allowed in the house. We were his family, but he treated us as if we were part of the army.'

'Charming man,' Roarke remarked scathingly. 'I'm not surprised you rebelled. I'm just surprised you stayed so long.'

'It wasn't through lack of nerve,' she hastily justified herself. 'If I had run away they would only have brought me back home, and that would have been worse. So I decided to wait it out until I was old enough to leave. It was while I was waiting that I met Mark the Snake,' she added, keeping her tone level with an effort.

'There are a lot of those around,' Roarke pronounced wryly. 'It isn't always easy to pick the good guys from the bad guys, sweetheart. For one thing, the bad guys have good camouflage.'

Ginny shot him a whimsical look. 'Where were you when I needed some good advice?' she asked sardonically, and he chuckled.

'Creating my own kind of hell, probably. Do I take it your romance with Mark the Snake followed the usual pattern?'

Ginny had never thought she would find anything amusing about the past, but Roarke's comments made her smile and eased the remembered sense of despair. 'You do. I thought he loved me, but the Brigadier was quite right. All he wanted was the money that would come with me. When I was cut off he vanished quicker than you can say it.' Leaving her pregnant and without the means to support herself, but she wasn't ready to talk about that to Roarke yet.

'Snakes have a habit of doing that. You were better off without him in the long run,' Roarke observed evenly, and Ginny nodded.

'True, but I was still living short term. There were… complications.' She had struggled on, but it had been a downward path which had eventually sent her back to her family, only to be rejected because she wouldn't give up her baby. She shivered at the memory and took a slightly ragged breath. 'It was the worst time of my life and I prefer not to think about it.'

Roarke nodded. 'I can understand that. You have to move on.'

His understanding was unexpected but welcome. 'I made another life for myself and I thought I'd left the past behind.'

'Until you discovered your brother is marrying my sister,' he mused thoughtfully.

'Seeing the Brigadier again after all these years was a nasty shock. I couldn't think why he would be here,' Ginny confirmed.

'I can't say I like the sound of the family Caroline's marrying into.'

Ginny could well understand his concern. He cared about his family, and wouldn't want his sister to walk into the lion's den. She glanced down at her fingers, knowing it was within her means to put his mind at rest. It would mean revealing more of herself to a stranger, but the thought of doing nothing didn't sit easily with her.

'Listen, I can talk to her if you like. Tell her what my father can be like. She's in no danger, though. After all, she's the good connection the Brigadier wants for his son. If she produces an heir in nine months' time, she'll be his pride and joy.'

Roarke glanced at her downbent head. 'A legitimate heir,' he said gently, and Ginny stiffened at the reminder. Her eyes darted to his, saw the ready sympathy there, and rejected it. He was going too far. She jumped to her feet, crossing her arms and taking a hasty step away.

'Don't even think of going there, Roarke. You overheard things that were none of your business. The subject isn't open for discussion,' she told him forthrightly, her eyes sending sparks his way as she looked at him.

'I merely wanted to say I'm sorry about your baby.'

Ginny fashioned a shrug of sorts, although her heart twisted painfully. 'It was a long time ago.'

Roarke shook his head. 'Sweetheart, it was only yesterday for you, and always will be,' he countered gently, bringing a lump to her throat and tears to her eyes.

She held up a hand to silence him. 'So help me, Roarke, if you say another word...' Her throat closed over at that point, and she turned her face away, closing her eyes, pressing her lips together tightly to still their trembling.

She didn't hear him rise and come up behind her, just the gentle touch of his hands on her shoulders.

'Forgive me. I'm not usually so crass,' he apologised and his thumbs took up a sensuous circling motion.

'You weren't crass. You were trying to be kind, and I thank you for that, but I'd rather just forget this whole episode.'

Ginny knew she ought to shrug him away, but his touch was giving off an incredible amount of warmth that was sending tingles through her bloodstream. It had the strange effect of making her want to lean back against him. It was very tempting, hypnotically so, and she might even have done it if a couple hadn't walked out of the open door, laughing at something someone had said. She was brought back to the present with a jolt.

'Hey! Cut that out!' she ordered immediately.

Stepping away from him, so that his hands fell to his sides, she asked herself just what she thought she was doing letting him touch her at all, let alone leaning in to him! He was the man she loved to hate, though she had to admit there were aspects of him which weren't as bad as she had thought. Her heightened emotions were no doubt playing tricks on her after the encounter with her father.

Roarke held up his hands and backed off. 'Sorry. I thought you liked it.'

She had, but that was hardly the point. 'Look, I know you were trying to help, but keep your hands to yourself in future.'

He winced and glanced towards the couple who were strolling towards them. 'OK, OK, just keep your voice down. We're supposed to be an item, remember?'

How could she forget? 'We'd better go in,' she suggested.

'Are you still willing to talk to my sister?'

'Of course.' Ginny wasn't about to withdraw her offer. Caroline needed to know what she was taking on.

'Let's go find her, then.' He led the way to the door, but halted short of entering the crowded room. 'Wait a second.'

Ginny halted obediently. 'What's wrong?'

He grinned wolfishly. 'Nothing—just checking you look as if we've been up to something.'

Ginny shot him a withering look. 'Well, do I?'

'Don't worry—only you, me and Sir Martin know what really went on. To the rest you look interestingly mussed.'

'Oh, good!'

Taking her arm, he slipped it through his and laughed huskily. 'Behave yourself, we're about to walk out on stage again.'

Ginny rolled her eyes, then plastered a smile to her lips. 'If I wish you to break a leg, you won't misunderstand my meaning, will you?' she hissed out of the side of her mouth.

'Ouch!' Roarke laughed again and they stepped inside.

CHAPTER FIVE

UNFORTUNATELY Ginny and Roarke didn't get the chance to talk to Caroline before the party wound down. They mingled and waited and watched, but James stayed firmly by his fiancée's side, making it impossible for them to speak to her freely.

'We'll catch up with her later, after the others have gone to bed,' Roarke decided as the clock slowly ticked towards midnight.

'What if James is with her?' Ginny pointed out, but Roarke shook his head.

'In this house? Not a chance.'

Her brows rose. 'We're together.'

He grinned roguishly. 'That's because I'm a hopeless case, and we aren't getting married tomorrow, or is it today? Now, if we should find my mother with her, offering her some last-minute unwanted advice, that wouldn't surprise me at all.'

Ginny had been carrying an untouched glass of wine around with her for ages, and now set it down on the nearest table. 'This is getting ridiculous. I'm tired. Let's go to bed,' she grumbled, stifling a yawn.

'Now, that's the best offer I've had all day,' Roarke flirted wickedly.

'It wasn't an offer,' she refuted immediately, knowing that, had she been less tired, she would have chosen her words more carefully. 'It was a statement. I'm tired,' she repeated grumpily. It had been a long day, and unexpectedly emotional. She was drained.

'You're no fun, sweetheart,' Roarke teased. 'You were supposed to get affronted and flash those fascinating eyes at me,' he added, causing her to frown.

'I'm too tired to get affronted. And what do you mean, fascinating eyes?' she asked in surprise.

He laughed softly. 'When I've made you really mad at me, you spear me with a look.'

'I do not,' she protested, still unexpectedly unsettled by his description of her eyes.

'Sure you do. Lesser men would tremble, but I'm made of sterner stuff. I can take it.'

'Which is just as well, because you probably deserve it,' she riposted smartly, then a movement across the room caught her eye. 'Oh, look, I think your sister may be calling it a night.'

Roarke glanced round in time to see Caroline kiss her mother and say a general goodnight to whoever was left in the room before leaving with James.

'We'll give them ten minutes to say goodnight to each other, then we'll follow her. Can you last out till then?'

Ginny nodded. Another half an hour wasn't going to make a lot of difference. 'If we go outside, the air should wake me up a bit,' she suggested.

'Come on, then. We'll stroll round the house and go up by the back stairs.'

The cooling midnight air did clear her head as they slowly strolled along the terrace. At the corner they halted by mutual consent to study the view over the lake. It was such a clear night, with the lights of the town glittering almost as much as the stars overhead.

'It really is beautiful here,' Ginny observed with an envious sigh.

'I try to come over several times during the summer,' Roarke agreed.

She quirked an eyebrow at him, lips twitching impishly. 'To visit the ogre? Isn't that taking filial duty a little too far?'

His laugh was rueful. 'You're never going to let me forget that, are you?' he said, reaching out to brush a strand of red hair from her cheek.

'Hey!' Ginny protested without any great force. 'We're not on stage now,' she reminded him. Much to her surprise, he didn't remove his hand but brushed an imaginary strand from her other cheek.

'As a matter of fact, we are,' he countered softly, and her eyes widened. 'We're being watched.'

She went still. 'Who is it?'

'My over-sexed stepmother. She must have seen us come out here and decided to follow to see what we get up to,' Roarke enlarged and met her eyes. 'She knows I wouldn't miss an opportunity like this for a little romancing. We're going to have to give her a show, I'm afraid, or she'll start to smell a rat.'

Ginny desperately wanted to look round, but that would have been too obvious. All she could do was hold his gaze. 'What do you mean? Exactly what kind of show?'

With a casual movement Roarke stepped in front of her and set his hands on her shoulders. 'Brace yourself, sweetheart. I'm going to have to kiss you. Nothing else will do.'

He began to lower his head towards hers, and Ginny raised her hands to his chest. 'I didn't agree to any of this hands-on stuff.'

Roarke's lips twitched. 'What did they used to say: close your eyes and think of England? Don't worry, it will all be over in a minute,' he joked, and brought his mouth down on hers.

And that was how it began.

The kiss started out as a simple pressing of lips on lips, and probably would have stayed that way, only something happened that changed everything. Ginny was thinking she would give him 'think of England'...when her brain stopped functioning. She was unexpectedly swamped by a powerful wave of electricity which lit her up from inside and set her nerve-ends tingling. Heat surged through her system, bringing with it a sensual response that had her lips softening and parting. Before she knew it one kiss became two, then many as they sought more of the same, tasting and exploring with ever-deepening need. They couldn't seem to get enough.

Without conscious thought she let her hands slip up around his neck, her fingers fastening in his hair, whilst at the same time Roarke let out a purely male groan and slid his arms around her, pulling her tight up against himself. When Roarke's tongue sought her mouth Ginny welcomed him with a sigh of pleasure, matching him stroke for stroke. They drowned in the kiss, and at the same time it began to spiral out of control. Neither seemed able, or willing, to stop it.

The angry banging of a door echoed across the night and startled them back to the present. The kiss ended, leaving them staring at each other in slowly dawning realisation that they were in each other's arms and couldn't remember how they had got there. Of course, that situation didn't last. They simultaneously recalled that the kiss was supposed to be no more than a gesture, and their shock was mirrored on both faces.

'Oh, my God!' Ginny declared thickly, very much aware that her heart was racing, her knees were trembling and her breathing was ragged.

'What the hell—?' Roarke muttered unevenly, and released her just as she stepped back from him.

They stared at each other in disbelief. Roarke raised a faintly trembling hand and dragged it through his hair.

'Well, that was unexpected!' he attempted to joke, but the words came out heartfelt. He meant what he said and it was no laughing matter—for either of them.

Ginny touched a finger to lips that felt slightly swollen. 'Tell me that didn't happen,' she commanded in horror.

Roarke laughed hollowly. 'What did just happen?' he wanted to know, but Ginny couldn't help him.

Of course, they both knew what had happened, but neither wanted to believe it. The kiss was supposed to have been a token gesture. It had turned into a passionate conflagration that still had their bodies tingling.

Ginny turned away from him, striving to get her breathing back to normal. 'This isn't happening. I don't want this.'

'You think I do?' Roarke growled behind her.

Ginny licked her lips, but that was a mistake, for she could still taste him. 'Just…don't start getting any wild ideas, OK.'

'Sweetheart, I don't want to have any ideas about you!'

She spun round again, eyes flashing accusingly. 'Then why did you kiss me like that?'

'Why did you?' Roarke countered, and they were left staring at each other in angry silence.

It was Ginny who finally broke the hiatus. 'This is a silly thing to be arguing over. Neither of us planned it, it just happened. It must have been moon madness. Things like this often happen at weddings, but it doesn't mean anything. It isn't going to happen again.'

'You can say that again,' Roarke agreed dryly. 'Hopefully, Jenna will have got the message.'

Their eyes met, and both knew the other was thinking that the message she had got was more than either had bargained for. Then it hit them that they hadn't given Jenna a thought, and they turned as one to find the terrace empty.

'She's gone,' Roarke confirmed. 'It must have been the door closing that...' He left the sentence hanging for Ginny to fill in the blanks.

'Yes, well, I think we should draw a veil over the last ten minutes and call it a night,' Ginny suggested uncomfortably.

'We still have to see my sister,' he reminded her.

'It's getting late, Roarke. She could be asleep already. We can see her first thing in the morning. Your mother isn't going to let James anywhere near her before the wedding, so the coast will be clear,' Ginny pointed out, wishing she had thought of that earlier, then that kiss—or kisses—need never have happened.

'You're right,' Roarke agreed, clearly in no mood to prolong the evening either. 'Tomorrow will be better.'

By which time she should have got her head round what had happened tonight, and put it in perspective. It was laughable to think that she and Roarke could be attracted to each other. It had been a momentary aberration, and the clear light of day would put their relationship back on its customary footing. She had no doubt of that...no doubt at all.

Back in their bedroom, they barely spoke. Ginny collected her night things and disappeared into the bathroom. When she came out again, Roarke had taken a pillow and cover from the bed and made up the couch. Without a word, he went into the bathroom whilst Ginny hung up her things in the dressing room and hurried into bed. She had turned out the light and closed her eyes when Roarke reappeared. She heard him move about carefully in the darkness, then all noises ceased.

It wasn't easy to sleep, and she tossed and turned for some time before her exhausted body gave up the struggle and she slept. Roarke tucked his hand under the pillow and studied the moonlight on the ceiling. On the bedside table her travel clock slowly ticked on.

Ginny was dreaming. It was a dream she hadn't had for a long time, but it was no less powerful for all that. It was not a pleasant dream, but good dreams rarely returned to haunt a person. She was caught in the past, trapped by memories that came thick and fast. Unable to break free, she tossed and turned restlessly.

The nightmare was always the same. It was night, but she dared not put the light on, for the landlord of the grotty bedsit she called home was due to call to collect the rent and she didn't have the money. She had a job washing dishes—it paid little, but it was all she could get. She had been sick all through her pregnancy, and it had lost her the few better paid jobs she had managed to get. Now her boss had threatened to fire her if she was late again—and she was late already...

The scene changed. Now she was standing outside the cheap restaurant, with the manager telling her to clear off. She tried to plead with him, but he didn't want to know. She had to turn, had to take the next step. Anxiety began to rise in her, and her head thrashed about on the pillow. She didn't want to go on, but the dream was remorseless. It took her back down that dingy street as she made her way home. As always, she didn't hear the approach of the person who jumped her, just felt a shove in the back and hands grabbing for her bag. Beneath the covers her legs and arms thrashed about as, in her dream, she fought him, hanging on to the bag, for it contained all the money she had. But her pregnancy had made her clumsy and weak, and with one last shove he had got the bag and run.

She cried out, but it didn't wake her, and for the hundredth time she careered into the heavy-duty bins and fell to the floor of the alleyway. And, as night followed day, there came the pains, making her groan in her sleep. In her dream she called for help, but nobody came, and she lay there in the dark, in pain, knowing her baby was coming and that she had to try to help herself. Tears streamed down her face as somehow she managed to get to her knees and crawl out to the road. Then more pain and she collapsed, and she knew she was going to lose her baby...

Dragged from an uneasy sleep, Roarke lay on the couch and tried to get his bearings. Then he heard sounds from across the room and sat up, glancing to the bed Ginny occupied. He could just make out the thrashing movements beneath the covers, and it was closely followed by a sound that turned his blood cold. Ginny was crying. Painful sobs that tore into the very heart of him and brought him to his feet in a hurry.

Padding to the bed, he stared down at her, knowing she wouldn't want him anywhere near her, but knowing too that he couldn't leave her trapped in the midst of the despairing dream she was having. Easing himself on to the edge of the bed, he reached out to gently shake her awake.

'Wake up, Ginny. Ginny, can you hear me? It's a dream. Come on, sweetheart, snap out of it!'

Ginny heard a voice calling her from a long way away. An insistent voice that dragged her out of the depths of her nightmare, leaving the pain behind but not the sense of loss. She felt hands lifting her, shaking her, and with a ragged gasp she woke.

She blinked at the figure who sat on the bed, holding her by the shoulders. 'Roarke?'

'You were crying in your sleep. Must have been a very bad dream.' He explained his presence, eyes quartering her face in concern.

Ginny touched her hand to her cheeks and they came away moist. 'Oh, God!' she whispered achingly. She knew what dream it had been; the tendrils of it came drifting back, coiling around her heart, making her shiver in remembrance. 'Did I wake you? I'm sorry. I should have known...'

Releasing her now that she was awake, Roarke sat back. 'Known what? That seeing your father again would bring the memories back?'

She nodded, not really surprised by his astuteness. 'I haven't had that one in a while.' She had been hoping she would never have it again, but she should have known better.

'Was it about your father?'

Ginny rubbed her hands over her arms, warding off a chill that came more from inside than out. 'Not really.'

Indirectly, her father's refusal to help her had set her along a path which had ultimately led to the loss of her baby, but she wouldn't put the blood on his hands.

'Do you want to talk about it?' Roarke offered. 'I've been told I'm a very good listener.'

Ginny shook her head in swift refusal. 'No. I don't even want to think about it.'

He accepted that without argument. 'Can I get you anything? Hot milk? Chocolate?'

'I'll be fine,' Ginny declared confidently, though she knew from experience that she wouldn't be. Whenever she had had the dream before, sleeping afterwards had been impossible. But she wasn't his problem. She would deal with it. She had always dealt with it.

'OK, but you know where I am if you need me,' he told her as he got off the bed.

Ginny lay back against her pillows and listened to the sound of Roarke returning to his bed on the couch. She tried to keep her breathing light and did her best not to move about too much, wanting him to go back to sleep. Time passed slowly, but eventually she was sure he must no longer be awake, so she sat up, plumping the pillows behind her and stared out of the window, watching for a sign that would tell her dawn was approaching.

'What's the matter, Ginny?'

The disembodied voice drifting to her from the couch made her jump. 'I thought you were asleep.'

'I was waiting for you to drop off. At this rate, it looks as if neither of us will get any more sleep tonight,' he remarked without rancour.

The last thing she wanted to do was disturb anyone other than herself. 'Don't let me keep you awake,' she urged him, but should have known better by now.

'Ginny, you can't expect me to turn over and start knocking out zeds when I know darn well you're afraid to sleep.'

Her heart leapt into her throat at his intuition. 'I'm not…' she began, but the rest of the sentence trailed off, because it was a lie and they both knew it. 'You're right, I am scared. I know from experience that if I sleep now I'll only have the dream again. Once is enough for any night,' she added with a shudder.

'What's it about, this dream?'

Ginny pulled her legs up and wrapped her arms around them protectively. 'The worst day of my life,' she admitted scratchily.

'I guess that would have to be the time you lost your baby,' Roarke stated softly, not wanting her to draw back into her shell.

She was getting used to him pulling rabbits out of the hat this way. 'You guessed correctly.'

'Have you ever spoken to anyone about that time?' Roarke probed carefully.

Ginny shook her head, then, realising he couldn't see the gesture, cleared her throat. 'No.' Who had there been to talk to? Her family had been denied her, and her old friends had drifted away into their own lives.

'Talking helps, Ginny. Keeping it locked up inside yourself is asking for bad dreams to come.'

She knew he was right. The past was festering inside her, never healing. She had to get it out in the open for her own sake. He wasn't the person she would have chosen to talk to, but he knew so much already there seemed little point in hiding the rest.

'How good a listener are you?' she asked wryly.

'The best. I don't judge, and I don't tell tales. Try me.'

Ginny sighed heavily. 'Where do I begin? My life had become such a mess by then. The start of it all was when I left with Mark. Nothing went right from then on.'

'Except the baby,' Roarke corrected evenly, and she smiled faintly.

'You're right. Except the baby. I wanted her. I was prepared to move mountains to give her what I had missed.' Her smile faded away. 'The day I discovered I was pregnant was the day Mark left me. He never knew about the baby. My father had cut me off, and Mark saw his meal ticket slipping out of his grasp. I didn't know at the time, but he had gone to see the Brigadier, to try and get him to change his mind. I could have told him it wouldn't work. He said no, and a week later Mark disappeared. Whilst I was waiting for hours for him to come home so I could tell him about the baby, he was miles away cutting his losses.'

Roarke made himself comfortable with his hands behind his head, listening to the flat voice tell its tale. 'You never saw him again?'

'I had no idea where to look. He told me very little about himself. Besides, when the bills that he had run up started to come in, I fell out of love very quickly. It wasn't hard to decide to bring up my baby on my own, but from the start things were against me. I had an awful pregnancy. The sickness they told me would eventually stop, never did. I lost I don't know how many jobs because the sickness prevented me from working. Money became tight.'

'So you went to your father?'

Ginny closed her eyes against painful memories. 'He wouldn't let me in the house, even when I told him about the baby. He said things...'

Roarke's face grew tight. 'I've heard him. I can guess what he said.'

Ginny dropped her head to her knees. 'He said I could come back, so long as it was without the baby. I refused, and he shut the door in my face.'

'The man wants taking out and shooting!'

'Amen to that.'

Roarke let a little time pass before pressing on. 'What happened then?'

On the bed, Ginny shrugged, keeping her voice level, trying not to feel anything as she told the sorry story. 'I went back to my grotty bedsit and did the best I could. Things got worse, though, and by the time I was seven months' pregnant I owed back rent and was down to washing dishes. That last day I was sick again, and I had this ache low down in my back all day. When the landlord came for the rent, I hid in the dark. I had to wait ages for him to go and that made me late for work. I lost my job.

'I thought that was the darkest moment, but I was wrong. As I walked home, wondering what I was going to do now, someone snatched my bag. I fought them, because I couldn't afford to lose the money in it, but they were stronger than I was and shoved me into an alley.' She felt again those hard hands pushing her. 'There were several large metal bins in there and I must have hit one of them, because I ended up on the floor.' Ginny felt her pulse pick up, and she licked her lips to moisten them. 'That was when the pain started.'

'Go on,' Roarke urged her, even as his own stomach twisted into a knot at what he knew was coming.

'I managed to crawl out of the alley, but that was all. Someone must have found me, because the next thing I can remember I was in an ambulance. Then everything begins to blur. I remember patches. People bending over me. Lights. The smell of disinfectant. Voices telling me to do this or that.' She swallowed hard as memories came rushing back, but the lump remained in her throat. 'Do you know what sound echoes the loudest in my mind? Her cry when she was born. It was so weak, barely there, and I knew then that something was wrong.' Tears welled up in her eyes, and her lips trembled. 'In my heart I knew I wasn't going to have her for long.'

A teardrop overflowed, and then another. She felt the bed depress, and only then realised that Roarke had left the couch. She stared at him, her eyes filled with an unutterable sadness. 'She lived for six hours. I held her hand. It was so tiny, Roarke. She seemed to hold on to me for a while...and then she died. My beautiful baby daughter died,' she whispered achingly, and the tears that she had held back all these years finally found release.

She didn't feel Roarke take her in his arms and rock her whilst the tears fell and she gave vent to her despair in long raking sobs. She cried until her throat ached and there were no more tears to shed. She wept for a life that had been cut tragically short, and for the love she had been unable to give. Finally she was still, and she sighed raggedly.

'I loved her,' she said huskily.

'Only a fool would doubt it,' Roarke returned gently, stroking a soothing hand down her back.

It was that which made Ginny aware of where she was, cradled against the warmth of his strong male chest. She could have felt awkward, but she didn't. For the first time in for ever she felt…comforted. It was a strange sensation, considering who it was who held her.

'I never meant to cry all over you,' she apologised a little awkwardly.

'Something tells me those tears have been a long time coming,' he observed, looking down at her, and Ginny sighed.

'I couldn't cry, because I knew that if I started I would never stop, the pain was so bad. Instead I put all my energy into making something of my life. I got a job, took evening classes. Found a better job, and so on.'

Driving her on had been the need to stay one step ahead of her grief. Allied to a determination to never allow her emotions to blind her. Passion was a drug that scrambled the mind, leaving her open to hurt and betrayal. But she had learned her lesson and passion was out. This time she was going to be in control of her life. This time…

A yawn took her by surprise.

'Think you can sleep now?' Roarke queried.

'Um-hum,' she mumbled. Her eyelids felt weighted, and she decided to shut them for just a few seconds, then she would send him back to the couch.

Roarke listened to the measured sound of her breathing and smiled wryly. She was already asleep but he didn't want to disturb her, so he would wait a few minutes before settling her back on the bed. Making himself comfortable against the pillows, he hooked her in more securely and closed his eyes.

CHAPTER SIX

GINNY drifted to consciousness feeling warm and cosy. Sighing, she rubbed her cheek against the pillow—and something tickled her nose. She moved her hand to brush it away, and her fingers encountered more of the tickly material. Puzzled, she opened her eyes and discovered her 'pillow' was a man's chest, and the 'tickly material' the silky hairs that grew there. Furthermore, her 'pillow' was rising and falling rhythmically as it breathed.

Lifting her head carefully, she could see a stubbly jaw and ruffled black hair and recognised both as belonging to Roarke. Her eyes widened in surprise, and then the memories slowly returned. Last night she had had that dream again. Roarke had heard her, and he had urged her to talk about it. She had, and she had cried too. Cried tears that had been battened down inside her too long. The crying had drained her, and she must have fallen asleep in his arms, but why was she still there? Why hadn't he gone back to the couch? Because he had fallen asleep too, came the obvious answer.

Ginny bit her lip and glanced down at the body she was literally draped around. She had certainly made herself comfortable, she thought dryly. He had some body, though, was the thought that swiftly followed. She had been right; there wasn't an ounce of spare flesh on him. Her eyes began a lazy perusal of long legs and strong thighs, skipped over loins hidden by his shorts, and roved on over a flat stomach, that powerful chest and broad shoulders. Tanned and healthy and pretty much perfect, she decided whimsically.

She wondered what all that bronzed skin felt like to the touch. Her pulse-rate increased slightly as she considered the prospect of running her hand over his chest. A tiny voice in the back of her mind asked her what she thought she was doing, but with the thought had come a need to touch him, to know, and the voice was quashed.

Ginny set her hand down gently and held her breath as she moved it through the forest of silky hair. His skin was smooth, and touching it sent a tingle up her arm that slowly spread through her whole system. Her senses sprang to life, and she could feel her heart racing. That tiny voice urged her to stop, to be sensible, but she was enthralled by the sensations she was experiencing.

So caught up was she that it took a while for her to register that his chest was no longer rising and falling gently but much more powerfully as he dragged in air. Shock at the knowledge that Roarke was awake brought her head up, startled green eyes locking with smouldering grey ones. Time seemed to stand still, but then those eyes dropped to her lips, and they tingled as if he had actually touched them. She couldn't help but moisten her lips with the tip of her tongue. With a growl Roarke's fingers tangled in her fiery hair and eased her up those few inches necessary to allow his mouth to take hers.

It was no gentle kiss, but a sensuous invasion that sought pleasure even as it gave it. The intensity was mind-blowing, for it seemed as if they were intent on devouring each other. Ginny could feel her body responding to the stimulation and, as she moved against him instinctively, she felt the powerful response of his body too. Her stomach clenched, and that familiar ache started deep within her. She wanted him…badly.

'Roarke...' His name was a low moan in her throat as he tore his mouth from hers only to plunder the sensitive cord of her neck. She felt dizzy. Caught up in an overwhelming maelstrom of sensations. Her heart was tapping out a crazy beat...

But it wasn't her heart she could hear. Penetrating through the passion-induced mists in her brain, she slowly realised that what she could hear was a frantic tapping on the bedroom door. Roarke must have heard it too, for they both froze at the same time. Staring at each other, both recognised the look of disbelief each wore at the realisation that they had responded to each other again. Yet there was no time to discuss it, for the tapping continued, managing to sound even more frantic.

'I'll get it.' Feeling self-conscious, Ginny clambered awkwardly off Roarke and scrambled to her feet. Smoothing her nightdress down, she composed herself as best she could before going to answer the door. A glance back at the bed showed that Roarke had vanished, then moments later she heard the shower running.

Taking a deep breath she opened the door, and gasped at the sight of her sister standing outside. 'Lucy!' she exclaimed in surprised delight.

Lucy, however, looked ill at ease, constantly glancing over her shoulder—and Ginny instantly knew what she was afraid of. Grasping her by the arm, she pulled her sister inside and hastily shut the door.

She was so pleased to see her younger sibling that she immediately enveloped her in a hug. 'It's so good to see you! I've missed you so much,' she declared in a voice thick with emotion, and only then became aware that her sister hadn't responded. Her heart sank as she realised she could have misinterpreted her sister's reason for being there. Lucy might well feel as James did, which wouldn't be so surprising. Bracing herself for rejection, she released her sister and stepped back.

'Sorry. You probably didn't come here for a family reunion at all,' she apologised uncomfortably. 'I got a little ahead of things,' she added with a laugh that teetered off-key.

Lucy's expression immediately became contrite. 'No, no, don't be silly. That was exactly what I came for, but I wasn't sure that you wanted to see me!'

'Not want to see you!' Ginny exclaimed in astonishment. 'Lucy, not a day has passed when I haven't wished I could see you.'

'I missed you, too,' Lucy confessed, and this time it was she who threw her arms around her sister. They shared laughter and brushed away a tear, and then Ginny held Lucy away from her.

'Let me look at you. You've grown so, I would hardly have recognised you.' Lucy had turned from a gangling youngster into a beautiful young woman of eighteen.

Just at that moment the bathroom door opened and Roarke stepped out. He wore nothing but a towel and a smile. The sight of him took Ginny's breath away and knotted her stomach. She could feel telltale warmth invading her cheeks.

'Ladies.' Roarke greeted them with charming panache, considering the situation.

Ginny decided to ignore his lack of clothes—as much as she could, anyway. 'Lucy, this is Roarke. James is marrying his sister. Roarke, my sister Lucy.'

Roarke's grin was dashing. 'Pleased to meet you, Lucy. Let me get some clothes on, and then we can talk and spare Ginny's blushes.' With which taunting statement he crossed the room and vanished into his dressing-room.

Lucy giggled, and Ginny rolled her eyes. 'Don't encourage him!'

'No, I'll leave that to you,' her sister returned, tongue-in-cheek. 'Thank goodness your taste in men has improved. I never did like Mark,' she added seriously, surprising Ginny.

'You didn't?' she asked falteringly.

Lucy pulled a face and shook her head. 'He was a phoney. I bet he didn't do half those things he said he did.'

Mark had bragged about where he had been and who he had met. Ginny had pretty soon discovered none of it was true. 'I wish you'd told me,' she drawled wryly. She could have saved herself a lot of grief.

'You wouldn't have believed me,' Lucy replied with a fatalistic shrug, and Ginny knew she was right.

'Probably not,' she conceded.

Lucy suddenly laughed brightly and gave Ginny a knowing look. 'But I like what I've seen of this one,' she said saucily, which made Ginny laugh. 'He's delicious.'

'And unavailable,' Ginny countered swiftly, surprised by the way her nerves had leapt at the notion that Lucy found Roarke attractive.

Roarke chose that moment to reappear, dressed in the trousers of his morning suit, white silk shirt and bow tie. Pausing by the couch, he retrieved the blanket and pillow he had used to make his bed.

'Come and sit down,' he invited.

'I can't stay long. Dad will be looking for me,' Lucy warned them, though she went to the couch, giving the bedding an odd look.

Roarke was equal to the unspoken question. 'We argued. I spent part of the night on the couch,' he admitted easily.

'Only part?' Lucy queried archly, and Roarke laughed, looking right at Ginny.

'We made up,' he said huskily, causing Ginny's cheeks to burn hotter.

'Making up's the best part,' Lucy agreed flirtatiously.

Roarke dumped the bedding on the bed and took one of the chairs whilst Ginny joined her sister on the couch.

'I'm glad you didn't respond to Ginny the way your brother did,' Roarke observed, and Lucy sighed.

'It isn't easy going against a man like our father. James collapses under pressure, and there's no one who can exert pressure as well as Dad.'

Ginny had firsthand knowledge of that. 'I'm sorry I wasn't there to help.'

'You had to get out. I understood that.' Lucy immediately waved away the attempted apology. 'When Dad told us we weren't to see you or speak to you, it made me angry. Later, he said your name wasn't even to be mentioned, and I really hated him. I used to mention you all the time, just to annoy him. It was worth being sent to my room to see his face go red. You were my sister, and nothing he said or did was going to change that. I'm really sorry I didn't speak to you last night, but he was watching, and if I'd attempted it he would have made Mum's life a misery. So I waited until this morning and snuck out before he did his rounds!' she finished with a spirited laugh.

Roarke grinned at her. 'Seems the women of your family are a strong-willed bunch. Could it have something to do with the hair?' Lucy's hair was red, too, if less vibrant than Ginny's. 'I'll have to watch what I say around you two.'

'Oh, I'm a kitten compared to Ginny,' Lucy contested. 'Just don't get in her way when she's really mad.'

'Lucy!'

'Well, it's true! You're by far the most passionate of us all!'

Ginny couldn't help her gaze drifting to Roarke, saw in his eyes the acknowledgement that he had already discovered the passionate side of her for himself. She hadn't wanted it to resurface, but it had. Twice now she had found herself a captive of her sensual response to this man, and she didn't like it. It wasn't part of her plan.

'I'm not the person I was, Lucy,' she denied, turning back to her sister. 'I learned the hard way not to be so foolish. The world didn't stand still these last eight years.'

'Why didn't you keep in touch?'

'Not because the Brigadier told me not to, but because I thought you would fare better if I stayed away.'

'You were right in a way, it was better—until recently,' Lucy confirmed, then her expression clouded.

Ginny's stomach knotted. 'What happened?'

Lucy opened her mouth to explain, but the clock on the mantelpiece began to chime, and she got to her feet quickly. 'Half past eight already! I can't talk any more now, Ginny. Dad asked for breakfast in his room for all of us, so I'd better go. We'll talk again, I promise,' she insisted as she made her way to the door.

'Let me make sure the coast is clear,' Roarke commanded, taking a swift look up and down the hall. 'It's OK.'

The two women hugged each other swiftly, and then Lucy left, walking briskly down the hall. At the corner she glanced back and waved, then she was gone.

'Nice girl,' Roarke remarked as he shut the door again. 'I find it amusing that a man like Sir Martin, who likes to throw his weight around, should have two daughters strong enough to fight him. He can't have expected that his son would be the weaker one.'

'He should have done. The red hair comes from his side of the family. James takes after our mother,' Ginny responded with heavy irony, and their eyes met as they shared the joke. However, when the laughter faded, they found themselves remembering what it was that Lucy's arrival had interrupted, and the air around them began to crackle with electricity.

Ginny licked her lips and took the bull by the horns. 'What happened earlier... That was a mistake,' she declared firmly.

Roarke had no trouble following her. 'I couldn't agree with you more.'

She folded her arms protectively. 'I'll play the part as I promised, but we'll have to keep our distance. I don't intend for anything to happen a third time.'

'I'm with you all the way, sweetheart. Finding myself physically attracted to you wasn't on the cards for me, either,' he acknowledged. 'Discovering this unexpected fire in you doesn't help. It would have been better if that ice in your blood hadn't melted!'

'I never had ice in my blood. That was your invention. If I appeared frosty, it was because I didn't like you.'

'Well, sweetheart, we would both have been better served if you'd continued to dislike me,' Roarke shot back.

'I never stopped. In fact, right now, I dislike you every bit as much as I ever did!' Ginny returned fire swiftly.

'Then why didn't you put up more of a fight when I kissed you?' he wanted to know, incurring her wrath.

Her lips parted in an angry gasp. 'Are you suggesting this is all my fault? You should learn to keep your hands to yourself!'

His lips twisted into a mocking smile. 'I would, if you didn't keep responding to me!'

Green eyes narrowed wrathfully. 'So it is my fault!'

'I didn't say that.'

'Not in so many words, but I got the message. Damn, none of this would be happening if you hadn't kissed me last night!' she exclaimed accusingly.

'Cut it out, Ginny. Neither of us expected the response we got. Besides, whilst we're on the subject, who was exploring whose body no more than an hour ago?'

Of course she had no answer to that. Roarke had been asleep. It had been all her own idea. All she could do was draw herself up to her full height. 'Thank you for throwing that back in my face!'

Roarke took an impatient step towards her, which she countered by taking a step back. 'I wasn't about to touch you,' he protested irritably.

'I wasn't taking the chance!'

'Now you're just being ridiculous. I have no intention of touching you…in that way…ever again,' Roarke snapped back testily.

'You can't know how happy I am to hear that!' Ginny snorted, fully aware that she was overreacting, but not seeming to be able to stop.

'Oh, for the love of God! Nobody has to take all the blame. We're both at fault. It turns out this response we have to each other isn't going to vanish as easily as we expected. We didn't ask for it, but we have to deal with it. We can't expect someone to always bang or knock on a door to stop us doing something rash.'

Ginny knew he was right. They had to get control of the situation. 'OK. No kissing, no touching—no anything. We keep our distance from now on.' How hard could it be? They would be leaving the next day, so there was something like twenty-four hours for them to get through. They could do this. All it would take was self-discipline.

'Fine,' Roarke agreed, dragging a hand through his hair.

'OK, then,' Ginny retorted, facing up to him.

An uneasy silence fell, during which time each observed the other warily. This was a new situation, and neither wanted to precipitate another incident. Roarke's eyes dropped, taking in her apparel.

'You can help by putting some clothes on, or are you going to stay like that all day?' he asked sarcastically, waving a hand at her nightdress.

Not for the first time, she was tempted to hit him. 'Of course not! I'm going to shower and change, and then we're going to see your sister,' she exclaimed, putting action to the words by heading for her dressing room. 'And if I don't murder you before the day is out, you can consider yourself lucky!' she added, before vanishing inside.

Of all the nerve, she thought, as she collected together underwear and the dress she intended to wear for the wedding. She had been respectably covered in her nightdress, whilst he had wandered around in a towel. Talk about a double standard. Obviously she had become Eve, the temptress, and he was the poor hapless male. Hah!

Gathering up her things, she re-entered the bedroom. Roarke was on the telephone. Ginny crossed to the bathroom without looking directly at him, but she felt his eyes on her all the way. Her spine tingled. Only with the bathroom door shut did the feeling go away. Setting her clothes down and hanging her dress on the door, she stripped off her nightdress and stepped into the shower. The warm water was refreshing and she stood under it, savouring the pleasure.

However, as she stood there, thoughts of Roarke and her response to him trickled back into her mind. There was no denying the response, but how had it happened? She would have bet anything that she would never feel anything for him. She disliked him and his attitude to women. Or did she…?

Hadn't it always been the case that she disliked his attitude to women more than she disliked him? When she had first met him, hadn't there been a moment when he had set her nerves jangling? Before she remembered his reputation, and that he was exactly the kind of man she was determined to avoid?

If she was honest with herself, then she knew that attraction didn't just flare up. It had to have been there, unacknowledged. They had been fighting for so long that neither realised it had masked what they were now discovering was a pretty powerful mutual attraction. It had been hidden because neither wanted to acknowledge a response to the other. They called it dislike and fought like cat and dog. Now the blinkers were gone and they were left to face the passion.

Which they still didn't want, because they were the same people. Only it was going to be harder to ignore, because they had had a taste of what it could be like. Temptation hovered, however inconveniently. At least things hadn't gone too far. They could retrieve the situation. That, at least, they were agreed upon.

With renewed determination Ginny washed, then dried herself on the softest towel she had ever held, and dressed in the pale lavender shift dress. She emerged from the bathroom feeling much more confident, only to have that confidence tilted dangerously by the view she had of Roarke standing at the dressing table combing his hair. The action was stretching the cloth of his silk shirt over powerful shoulder muscles, and that reminded her of what he had felt like to touch. Her mouth went dry.

'Something wrong?'

Roarke's eyes met hers in the mirror, and she hastily shook her head. 'I was just wondering what I did with my shoes,' she lied, giving herself a mental ticking-off for allowing the erotic thought to enter her head. The few seconds it took her to retrieve her far from lost shoes allowed her to regain her composure.

'Will your mother be with your sister?' Ginny asked in concern, fixing tiny diamond studs to her ears as she emerged from the dressing room.

Roarke laughed at the mere idea. 'Mother never puts in an appearance until lunchtime. She'll make a concession today, but I still don't expect her to emerge before eleven. We should be able to get a short time alone with Caroline before her bridesmaids turn up, if we're quick. Are you ready?'

'Yes. I won't put on the matching jacket until we leave for the church,' Ginny added as they headed out of the door.

'I'm resisting wearing the rest of this monkey suit until the last minute myself,' Roarke remarked wryly.

'Morning dress suits you,' she felt compelled to admit.

He quirked an eyebrow at her. 'Are compliments allowed under the rules?'

'I've complimented you before,' Ginny pointed out, which caused him to grin.

'But that was before we discovered we were attracted to each other,' he countered, setting her nerves leaping.

Ginny winced. 'Comments like that are definitely out,' she declared.

'Hiding our heads in the sand isn't going to help.'

She knew that. All the same... 'Can we not discuss it right now?' she begged, hurrying to keep up with him. 'Where on earth is your sister's room—on the moon?'

'The other side of the house. Caroline prefers mountains to water. She has a morbid fear of it.'

'That's a shame!'

'It's a shame somebody didn't drown her father. He was the individual whose idea of teaching her to swim was to chuck her in the deep end!' Roarke explained, and clearly he had no love for his ex-stepfather.

Ginny felt a sympathetic anger too. 'He was husband number two, I take it?'

'Correct. He was a flautist of international renown, but a dead loss as a human being. Fortunately, Caroline inherited his talent and not his ego. Here we are.'

Roarke halted at a door and tapped out a particular series of knocks. Catching Ginny watching him in amazement, he shrugged. 'We all have our own knocks—that way, the person whose room it is knows whether to answer or not.'

Ginny's lips twitched. 'Who were you trying to avoid?'

'Mother, mostly.' He grinned unrepentantly, and looked so boyishly handsome that her heart skipped a beat and her breathing went awry.

Something must have shown on her face, for he frowned. 'You OK?'

'A touch of indigestion,' she invented hastily.

That brought his brows arcing. 'You haven't eaten anything.'

There were times when his persistence could be downright irritating. 'Must be an empty stomach, then,' Ginny countered and was relieved to hear the door open.

'Honestly, Roarke, where have you been? I expected you earlier,' Caroline complained as she looked out, then caught sight of Ginny. 'Oh!'

Roarke stepped forward, hustling his sister away from

the door and back into her room. 'Caro, meet Ginny. Ginny, Caro.' He introduced them to each other as he did so.

'Pleased to meet you,' Ginny murmured politely, following them in and shutting the door at a jerk of the head from Roarke.

'Likewise,' Caroline returned, then pulled an angry face at her brother and slapped his hands away. 'Stop it!'

Roarke held up his hands repentantly, then bent and kissed her cheek. 'Sorry, darling, but we need to speak to you alone, and we don't want to be seen coming in here.'

'Why? What have you done?' she asked suspiciously.

Roarke straightened up. 'Why do you always assume I've done something?'

'Because you're a rogue,' Caroline observed simply.

Unsure how long this sibling badinage was likely to go on for, Ginny cleared her throat to attract their attention. Caroline was instantly contrite.

'Now look what we've done. We're upsetting your... friend.' The fractional hesitation was glossed over by a friendly smile.

'Ginny is more than a friend,' Roarke amended, and his sister glared at him.

'I was trying to be polite,' she hissed through her teeth.

'There's no need to worry,' Ginny interrupted. 'I'm used to your brother's shortcomings,' she added sweetly.

Caroline frowned. 'I don't understand.'

'No, but you will,' her brother declared, leading her by the arm to a nearby chair and urging her to sit. 'We want to talk to you about Sir Martin.'

The other woman couldn't have been more surprised. 'Sir Martin? What about him?'

'For one thing, Ginny is his daughter,' Roarke said without preamble, and his sister blinked.

'His daughter? But I thought…' The sentence tailed off as she looked steadily at Ginny.

'He only had one?' Ginny finished for her, taking the spare seat. 'That's because he disowned me many years ago. I was shown the door and told never to darken it again, because I chose to follow my own path. I took my mother's maiden name, Harte.'

Caroline had been studying her closely. 'Yes, now that you mention it, I can see the likeness between you and Lucy.'

'Please don't think I'm here to try and talk you out of a marriage, because I'm not. Your brother asked me to tell you something about the family you're marrying into, that's all. You see, the Brigadier, my…father, is a very…forceful man.'

Caroline looked from her brother to Ginny, and just the faintest of smiles curled at the outer edges of her lips. 'I've always thought of him as a bully,' she remarked, taking the wind right out of their sails.

'You do?' Ginny gasped in amazement.

'I never thought of calling him the Brigadier, but it's a good name for him,' Caroline added with a wry laugh, before looking at Ginny. 'It was good of you to come, but you didn't have to. I've known for a long time just the sort of man Sir Martin is. Your brother James is a decent man, but whenever he comes into contact with his father, he changes. He's intimidated and he knows it, so he becomes angry and aggressive. He isn't the man his father would have him be, and he has anxiety attacks because of it. Yet when he's with me he's a different person, softer, calmer. James is a talented man. He's a brilliant watercolourist, did you know?'

Ginny shook her head. 'No, I didn't. What my father deemed as ''sissy subjects'' were banned in our house.'

A determined look settled on Caroline's face. 'Maybe in his house, but not in mine. I love James, and I fully intend to get him away from your father's influence just as soon as we are married.'

The unexpected declaration, said with such determination, brought a lump to Ginny's throat. She stared at her soon to be sister-in-law with growing respect. 'So you do love him.'

Caroline frowned a little. 'I wouldn't be marrying him if I didn't. Does that surprise you?'

'No,' Ginny denied hastily. 'It was suggested to me that you might be marrying him to get away from your mother,' she added, with a pointed look at Roarke.

'You'll pay for that,' he promised, and Ginny raised her eyebrows.

'Oh? And just how do you propose to do that?'

'I'll think of something.'

Following the exchange with interest, Caroline laughed. 'Roarke has this thing about love and marriage. One doesn't exist and the other doesn't last.' She looked at her brother fondly. 'I wasn't too sure myself at one time, but I am now. Love exists, and marriages don't have to fail if you work at them. Our parents find it easier to flit from one to the other, because it's easier than making a proper commitment. They fail, but I don't intend to. You'll find you think the same yourself one day, Roarke.'

Her brother was quick to shake his head. 'I'm not looking for love,' he pronounced, which only made her smile broadly.

'Good, because that's just the time when you'll trip right over it. I wish I could be there to see the moment when you realise that old magic has got you too!'

Roarke laughed along with her. 'Never going to happen, darling,' he insisted, taking her hand and pulling her to her feet. 'We'd better be off. Time's getting on and you've got to get ready.' Taking her in his arms, he gave her a powerful hug. 'Be happy.'

'I intend to,' she responded in a watery voice when he released her.

On impulse, Ginny hugged her too. 'James is very lucky,' she said gruffly, knowing that her brother might just have found salvation.

'I'm the lucky one,' Caroline corrected. 'You must come and see us. I'll have Roarke give you our address.'

Ginny stepped back with a wince. 'You might want to check that out with James first, but thanks for the invitation. It was a kind thought.'

Looking troubled by Ginny's response, Caroline took her hands. 'I can't imagine what it must have been like to be cut off from your family. I know it would hurt me, so I'm sure it must have hurt you. But that's over now. Trust me, James will want to see you.'

Ginny didn't believe it, but she wouldn't spoil Caroline's day by saying so. 'Maybe you can work miracles.'

They were interrupted by a knock on the door.

'That will be my bridesmaids come to help me dress. Mother will be descending on me too, soon.'

'Which is our cue to leave,' Roarke said with heavy irony. 'See you in church, Caro.'

They left Caroline in the capable hands of her four bridesmaids and headed back the way they had come.

'I have to hand it to my little sister. She surprised me with that one,' Roarke commented.

'That's because she isn't a little sister any more. She grew up. Like Lucy. We think we know them, but we don't really. Do you think she could be right about James?'

'After this morning, it wouldn't surprise me. Have faith in Caro. If anyone can help your brother, she can.'

'Mmm, I liked her. In fact, the more I see of your family the more I like them. You're even likeable yourself when you're not being obnoxious,' Ginny admitted reluctantly.

'Ditto,' Roarke returned promptly, and their eyes met. Not for the first time sexual awareness ignited between them, and the air began to thicken. Ginny found it hard to look away, and when she did she still felt as if she had run a race.

They hadn't touched or anything like that. All they had done was look at each other, and that chemical reaction started all over again. It was getting ridiculous.

'Let's get some breakfast,' she suggested tersely, not because she was hungry but because right now she would rather not be alone with him. So far as she was concerned, the sooner this weekend was over the better.

CHAPTER SEVEN

THE wedding service was beautiful. The bride was radiant and the groom looked nervous, but that was how it should be. She and Roarke were seated on the bride's side of the church. If she glanced to her right she could see her parents and Lucy in the front pew but, so far as she could tell, nobody had looked her way. Doubtless her father had laid down the law again.

The church was packed with relatives and other well-wishers, which was why Ginny found herself pressed up close to Roarke's side. She had tried to make more room for herself, but that had only had the effect of brushing her thigh against his. A manoeuvre which had caused him to look at her mockingly and she had desisted. However, the warmth coming from him was impossible to ignore, as was the far too intoxicating scent of his cologne.

Just being close to him was turning her on, and she had known how it would be. That reckless side of her nature, which she had relentlessly suppressed for so long, was coming to the fore again. Her sensuality had come out of her self-imposed deep freeze and was being bombarded by signals it didn't want to ignore.

She was doing her best, though, but it didn't help that she still had a role to play. When the service was over, and they all rose to follow the bride and groom out of the church for the taking of photographs, she would have preferred to walk alone, but she became aware of Jenna watching them, and was forced to take Roarke's arm, holding on to it far more tightly than was comfortable.

Roarke glanced at her, brows raised questioningly, and she sighed, knowing he wanted to know why she was holding him when she had been the one to insist on no touching. 'We're being watched,' she explained in an undertone, and he nodded, placing his hand atop hers to add to the illusion, unwittingly sending her temperature rising.

They wandered outside with the rest, but there was scant relief for Ginny. To her dismay Roarke insisted she joined in all the family group photos.

'You're part of the family, even if only a few of us know it,' he informed her when she attempted to protest. 'You have more right than some to be here.'

To which she had no response. And seeing the annoyance on the Brigadier's face did make her feel better. Of course, she didn't move when the groom's family were called for, because that would raise some pretty difficult questions.

There was, however, no getting away from the traditional greeting of the guests by the bride and groom and their immediate families, when the guests moved on to the hotel where the wedding reception had been arranged. If anyone thought it odd that the bride should greet her as warmly as she did her brother, whilst the groom barely shook her hand, nobody remarked upon it.

Naturally, Jenna took advantage of the situation to kiss Roarke far too enthusiastically, which brought a dark look to Lewis Adams's face, despite the fact that Roarke pulled himself free almost immediately. At his side, Ginny could feel his anger and when it was her turn to shake hands with the woman, she gripped her hand tightly so that Jenna was forced to look at her.

'Do that again, Mrs Adams, and you'll be sorrier than you can possibly imagine,' Ginny promised softly, attaching a friendly smile to the words that didn't reach her eyes.

'I don't know what you mean!' Jenna protested her innocence, trying to free her hand without drawing attention to herself.

'I'm not Roarke, Jenna, and I have no qualms about calling a spade a spade,' Ginny had time to add before finally releasing the other woman and moving on.

This brought her to her sister, who gave her a swift smile and an even swifter shake of the hand. Sir Martin was next, and Ginny made no attempt to shake his hand. 'Brigadier,' she said coolly, before passing on to her mother.

Emily Beavis was patently nervous, and looked everywhere but directly at her eldest daughter, which saddened Ginny. 'James looked very handsome today, Mum. You must have been proud of him,' she said, willing her mother to say something, anything.

Her mother jumped, but at last she did meet her daughter's eyes. 'Oh, yes...I...er...'

'Emily!' Sir Martin's stern warning lashed out, making his wife blanch.

'Oh, dear!'

Ginny could have killed him for that, but she took pity on her mother and, defying the man standing by, she gave her a brief hug. 'I love you,' she whispered gruffly, then quickly turned away.

Her eyes were dazzled by unshed tears, and it was just as well that Roarke slipped an arm about her waist and guided her away from the group by the door, because she couldn't see where she was going.

'Here, take this.' He urged a glass into her hand, and Ginny took a bracing sip of what turned out to be a fine champagne.

'Sorry about that,' she apologised a little while later, once her composure had returned. 'I hate to see her so cowed, but I can't really remember her any other way.'

'Why doesn't she leave him?' Roarke asked the obvious question.

'Because he has her so much under his thumb, she can't do a thing without his approval. Besides, the family and her home is all she has. If she had any courage once, he's bullied it out of her by now,' Ginny answered dispiritedly.

'Just as well you got away from there when you did,' Roarke observed grimly.

'Amen to that,' she answered with a heartfelt sigh.

'So now all we have to do is make sure your sister Lucy breaks free too,' he went on, causing her to stare up at him.

'We?' she queried with a tiny frown.

'Did you think I was going to let you go into battle for her alone?' Roarke challenged, and Ginny's heart did a strange little flip-flop in her chest.

'It isn't your fight, Roarke,' she reminded him, at the same time feeling oddly unsettled inside.

'It is now,' he insisted calmly, and Ginny didn't know whether to be pleased or angry.

Her laugh sounded odd to her own ears. 'Because your sister married my brother?'

Roarke shook his head, and the look he held her eyes with was compelling. 'Because that man has done all I intend he should ever do to hurt you, sweetheart. What he does to your sister hurts you, and that's all I need to know. Got it?'

Oh, she got it all right, but she didn't believe it. He took her breath away. He made it sound as if how she felt was important to him, and she wasn't used to that. Not from anyone, least of all Roarke Adams. She had no idea what to say.

'Why are you doing this?' she had to ask, though her voice was a croak, her throat was so tight.

'Because somebody has to,' he responded forcefully.

Ginny drew in a very shaky breath. 'I'm having trouble seeing you as a white knight.'

Roarke's laugh was wry. 'That's because you've painted me as an unsavoury Lothario ever since you met me. If I did a good deed, you would have ignored it.'

He wasn't far off the mark, and that made Ginny feel uncomfortable. 'You're right, and I apologise. You aren't all bad.'

'Damned with faint praise,' he exclaimed in amusement.

She had to smile ruefully. 'It's hard to let go of the image I have of you.'

His brow quirked. 'That's the one of me bed-hopping and writing notes in a little black book?'

It did sound like a ridiculous stereotype put like that. 'It's more comfortable thinking of you that way,' she admitted reluctantly.

'I know what you mean,' Roarke put in feelingly. 'I'm trying to hold on to my image of you as a cold-blooded harridan, but this sexy redhead keeps getting in the way!'

The whole of her body seemed to jolt at his description of her, and her stomach knotted. She could feel heat flooding into her cheeks. 'Cut it out, Roarke!' she ordered thickly. 'I'm not…what you said!'

'Sweetheart, you should try looking at yourself from my point of view,' he drawled huskily, setting her nerves tingling like crazy.

She didn't dare when she was having her own problems. When he was just Roarke Adams, vile womaniser, she could pigeonhole him and carry on her way. Since he had become Roarke, the man who could make her blood sing, she didn't know what to make of him, and he was impossible to ignore. Now she also had to try and forget the fact that he thought her sexy. They had come a long way in a very short time, and the end result was far from ideal.

At least she had recovered from the emotional turmoil of the brief meeting with her mother. Which, now she came to think of it, might have been his intention all along. Proving yet again that he was not the man she had always thought him. There were layers to him that she had never suspected, and each time she uncovered one her idea of him changed, making it impossible to dislike him. It was very disconcerting, because her dislike of him had been a fire wall behind which she had hidden. With that removed, she was once more in danger of feeling the heat of her sensuality.

Like now, for instance. Roarke wasn't watching her, giving her the chance to observe him unobserved. There were lines beside his eyes and mouth, which suggested he laughed easily and often. She liked men who laughed. Her father was a sober man, too full of his own importance to damage his dignity by laughing. Roarke's eyes twinkled, too, at thoughts he generally kept to himself. Physically, he looked powerful, but she knew how gentle he could be, and that was a big turn-on. There didn't seem to be an inch of her that wasn't aware of every inch of him. She had never experienced so strong a pull, and it was downright scary.

'Have I grown another head?' The amused question reached her ears and brought her out of her reverie.

Naturally she looked up and green eyes met grey. She was getting a little more used to the thrill that went through her whenever that happened, but it didn't stop her nerves from tingling.

'No, thank goodness. One of you is enough!' she returned with heavy irony.

His lips twitched. 'Really? I thought you might be memorising my features so you can dream about me later,' he countered equally mockingly.

'I don't need to do that. Your face is unforgettable. More likely to bring on a nightmare than a pleasant dream.'

'Now, that wasn't nice. It was also untrue,' Roarke dismissed easily, not in the least offended. 'You're no more afraid of me than I am of you. I know what gives you nightmares, remember, and I'm not it.'

'In that case, it's awfully big-headed of you to assume I'd dream about you,' she told him in her coolest tone, to which he merely laughed.

'Sweetheart, I doubt you can get me out of your head any more than I can get you out of mine, right now,' he remarked dryly, and she knew what he meant. He was occupying far too much of her thoughts.

'Well!' she exclaimed with false brightness. 'This isn't turning out at all the way I expected!'

'Oh, yeah!' Roarke agreed. 'Life has a way of knocking the ground out from under you all right.'

She grimaced at him helplessly. 'Why did you have to turn into a nice guy?'

He spread his hands. 'Why did you have to thaw out?'

Stalemate.

Ginny groaned. 'This is getting us nowhere.'

'Fighting the inevitable is generally a waste of time,' Roarke pointed out, and Ginny rounded on him.

'Nothing is inevitable. We still have a choice. I choose

to do nothing about it!' she insisted, and once again their gazes locked. An electric silence fell.

'How come I never noticed that your eyes are such a startling green before?' Roarke wanted to know. 'It would be very easy to drown in them.'

She knew the feeling. She only had to look into his to feel the same. 'I'll throw you a life preserver,' she returned a tad breathlessly.

'Hey, you two!' A voice right beside them made them both start. They looked round to find one of Roarke's brothers grinning at them. 'This isn't the time or place for what you two were contemplating! Besides, lunch is being served. The amount of electricity coming off both of you, you'll need to stoke the boiler or you might run out of steam just at the wrong moment!' he added, and walked away laughing and grinning from ear to ear.

'Thanks for the advice, Jack!' Roarke called after him, whilst Ginny stood there with beetroot-coloured cheeks. She was very much aware that others had heard what Jack had said, and they were smiling as they went past.

'Sorry about that,' Roarke apologised, taking her arm and joining in the exodus to the dining room. 'One day I expect him to grow up.'

'Why is it the ground never opens up and swallows you just when you really wish it would?' Ginny groaned, glancing round under her lashes. It came as no surprise to meet the Brigadier's inimitable stony look, and realise that he had overheard what Jack had said too. 'Oh, great!' she muttered. It never rained but it poured. Still, his opinion of her was so low, this would hardly make a difference.

'What's up?'

'The Brigadier heard everything.'

'Forget it. Some people have the unhappy knack of being where you least want them to be,' he passed it off, then shot her a look. 'Does it bother you that he heard?'

Ginny sighed. 'No...maybe a little. It's the child in me that somehow still hopes to win his approval. Not very rational, but that's the way it is.'

'Sweetheart, he's a man who knows the price of everything and the value of nothing. He won't change. He doesn't want to. It's his loss, but he'll never see it that way.'

Once again he astounded her with his perceptiveness. 'You've known him five minutes. How can you understand him so well?'

'Because I meet people just like him all the time,' Roarke returned with a faint shrug. 'They tend to have no sense of humour. It comes from taking themselves too seriously.'

'Something you could never be accused of,' she quipped, to which he chuckled.

'Life's hard enough without being able to find the funny side of it. Look at us, for instance. Now, that is funny.'

'Highly amusing, but I don't see you laughing,' Ginny pointed out sardonically.

'Somebody up there is having a huge joke at our expense, wouldn't you say? We've been skirmishing since the moment we met, and yet since yesterday what I want to do is get you alone somewhere, rip our clothes off and indulge in some indoor pursuit that I guarantee will give us both a great deal of pleasure.'

Instantly, Ginny's mind was filled with the vision exactly as he had described it, and it sent her temperature soaring. 'You don't go in for false modesty about your prowess, I notice,' she managed to say reasonably calmly, when she felt anything but calm.

Grey eyes glittered rakishly. 'I've had no complaints.'

'Yes, well, there's always a first time.'

Roarke laughed huskily. 'You'll be too out of breath to complain!'

She very nearly choked at that. It had to be the most downright arrogant thing he had ever said. 'I'd watch my step if I were you, or you'll be tripping over your ego!'

'I'm just telling it like it is.'

'Well, cut it out. You aren't helping to cool things down.'

He shrugged. 'The curse of an agile imagination. My mind insists on seeing the possibilities in vivid Technicolor.'

Ginny held up a cautionary hand. 'Don't tell me. I don't want to know. But you're right about one thing—the joke's on us. What I wouldn't give for a bargepole right now!' she added with wry amusement.

Roarke laughed softly, and the sound tingled its way along her nerves. She liked the sound of that laugh, which only went to prove she was losing her grip. Somebody up there was most certainly having the time of his life.

Several hours later, having consumed good food and good wine, with an appetite she hadn't expected, Ginny was feeling much more relaxed and at ease with the world. Fortunately, the seating arrangement had been traditional, so Ginny's family were on the top table, along with Roarke's. They themselves were on a table sufficiently far away to allow Ginny to forget them temporarily. The other guests at their table turned out to be distant cousins of Roarke's, and were a friendly group who had plenty of tales to tell about him, which he listened to with wry good humour, and kept the laughter bubbling.

They had just finished the inevitable speeches and

toasts, and now the wedding guests began to mingle once more and let their hair down. A band arrived and began playing dance music, and slowly couples began to filter on to the floor. Ginny found herself in constant demand by Roarke's male relatives, and for most of the next hour she was barely off the dance floor for long. Finally she pleaded exhaustion and returned to the table. Roarke was already there, though she had seen him dancing occasionally as she circled the floor.

He watched her flop into her chair and take a much needed drink from her glass of now tepid white wine. 'I had no idea you were so popular,' he observed coolly, and Ginny looked at his set expression and burst out laughing.

'I do believe you're jealous!' she gurgled, emboldened by the wine, though she was not even close to being tipsy.

'Not jealous, but I didn't find the sight of you being fondled by so many of my male relatives amusing,' he corrected smoothly, though Ginny thought she detected an edge to the words.

'I wasn't fondled, as you so delicately put it. I tell a lie—one of your uncles tried to grope me, but he had had too much to drink.' She pooh-poohed the idea immediately.

'You should have slapped his face,' Roarke declared, and she stared at him in total surprise.

'He was just being friendly.'

'He was being familiar, and I didn't like it.'

Her jaw dropped. 'Then you slap his face,' she rejoined smartly. 'Roarke, you're being ridiculous,' she added irritably, yet inside she experienced a tiny glow of satisfaction at his reaction. Which then confused her because of course she didn't want him to be jealous. He was nothing to her, their recently discovered attraction to each other notwithstanding.

He was not impressed. 'May I remind you you're supposed to be here with me?'

She was beginning to get annoyed. 'I am with you, Roarke, but you're starting to make me regret it,' she told him bluntly.

'Lovers' tiff?' Jenna's catty question took them both by surprise. They had been so involved in their argument that they hadn't heard her arrive.

Ginny swung round on her chair. 'Do you make a habit of eavesdropping on private conversations?' she charged the other woman, eyes flashing angrily.

'Actually, darling, your conversation doesn't interest me in the slightest. I came to ask Roarke to dance with me,' Jenna responded disdainfully. She gave him her most alluring smile. 'One dance, Roarke, for duty's sake. What possible harm could there be in that?' she cajoled, leaving him very little choice.

He rose to his feet with a tight smile. 'Never let it be said I refused to do my duty,' he said, standing back so that Jenna could precede him on to the floor. The other woman left with a wave of her fingers and a smug smile.

Ginny decided she was coming to seriously dislike Jenna Adams. The woman was trouble and, judging from Roarke's past experiences with her, there were few lengths to which she wouldn't go to get her man. However, there was very little she could get up to on the dance floor with all the family around them, so Ginny took the opportunity to visit the ladies' cloakroom. She was sitting at one of the vanity units when the door opened again and Lucy came in.

'I thought I would never get the chance to talk to you,'

Lucy said after the sisters had greeted each other with a hug. 'This is the one place even Dad wouldn't dare to go!' she added with a laugh.

Ginny laughed too, but she realised they didn't have much time, and there was something she desperately wanted to know. 'So, what were you going to tell me this morning? Why had things turned bad?'

Lucy sighed heavily. 'I met someone, Ginny. His name is Peter McMillan, and he's a law student in his final year. He's wonderful, and…I love him, Ginny, so much it hurts,' she said fervently, holding on to Ginny's hands.

Ginny could see where this was heading, and her heart sank. 'The Brigadier has other plans for you,' she said flatly.

'How do you know?' Lucy asked in surprise, and Ginny winced sympathetically.

'He told me so last night.'

'You've seen him?'

'Oh, yes,' Ginny confirmed wryly.

Lucy looked dispirited. 'He gave me this list of people he wants me to pick a husband from! I couldn't believe it. It's positively medieval!'

'Have you told him about Peter?' Ginny queried, and Lucy shook her head forcefully.

'I didn't dare to. I was afraid of what he might do. Peter wanted to confront him, but I knew that wouldn't work. Now Dad's turning on the pressure and I don't know what to do.'

Ginny knew, but it depended on one answer. 'Does Peter love you?'

Lucy's face took on a glow that would have made words unnecessary. 'Oh, yes. But he's not a rich man, and he doesn't come from a prominent family. Dad would never agree. Never. I thought about running away, but Peter shares with two other students. I had nowhere to go.'

'You do now,' Ginny corrected firmly. 'You must come to me.' She reached into her purse for a pen and snapped a tissue from the nearby box. She wrote quickly and handed the paper to her sister. 'This is my address. Hide it somewhere safe. As soon as you can, you must leave home and come to me. The Brigadier can't stop you. You're eighteen now, and legally free to leave home.'

The relief on Lucy's face was countered by a swift frown. 'But, Ginny, are you sure? If Dad found out he would be furious.'

'He can't do anything to me, Lucy,' she reassured immediately. 'You can stay with me as long as you like.'

Lucy bit her lip. 'I couldn't pay you much until I get a job, but I'm willing to try my hand at anything. Peter and I want to get a place of our own as soon as we can, but he has a student's loan to pay off, so it won't be anything grand.'

Ginny gave a swift shake of her head. 'You don't have to pay me anything. I just want you out of that house.'

'Will Roarke mind if I move in with you?' Lucy surprised her with the next question.

'Why on earth should he?' she asked, quite forgetting the role she was playing.

Lucy coloured up. 'Well, I mean... You two are used to being alone, aren't you?'

The penny dropped with an almighty clang. 'Ah! Actually, Lucy, things aren't quite what they seem. I'm just doing Roarke a favour,' she explained uncomfortably.

'Are you trying to tell me there's nothing between you?' Lucy asked in surprise, and Ginny nodded. To which her sister gave an unladylike snort of disbelief. 'I don't believe it. When you two are together there's a positive zing in the air. There's something putting that buzz in the air, and it isn't bees!'

That was something Ginny didn't want to hear. 'Roarke and I have been at loggerheads since we met. That's what you're picking up.'

Lucy tutted disappointedly. 'I didn't come down in the last shower of rain, you know, but if you don't want to talk about it, that's fine with me,' she declared airily, getting to her feet. 'I'd better go before he sends Mum out in search of me.' Bending, Lucy kissed Ginny's cheek. 'Thanks Ginny, you're a lifesaver.'

'That's what big sisters are for,' she retorted with a smile.

At the door, Lucy glanced back over her shoulder. 'I'll come as soon as I can.'

'I'll be waiting,' Ginny promised, and sank back with a sigh as the door closed behind her sister. It was going to be all right. Lucy was smart. She would play the dutiful daughter until the moment she left, and after that their father couldn't touch her.

She had Roarke to thank in the long run. If he hadn't asked for her help, she would probably never have known about James, and would never have seen Lucy. A lot had happened in the last few days, and mostly for the good. Now, if only she could help Roarke out with his father, she would have gone some way to balancing the scales. As for her attraction to Roarke himself, she was going to do her best not to think about it at all, because it was frightening in its intensity, and she had no idea how to deal with it. She was unsettled by what she was experiencing. On the one hand she didn't want it, yet on the other she knew that she had never wanted anything as much.

If there was a funny side to this turn of events, she just couldn't see it.

CHAPTER EIGHT

WHEN Ginny returned to their table some time later she discovered it was still empty, and began searching the crowd of dancers for Roarke. She found him without too much trouble—and the blonde head resting on his shoulder.

Anger shot through her like a rapier at the sight, and she had to restrain herself from rushing on to the floor and pulling Jenna off him physically. She reminded herself that Roarke was not hers, but that did little to quell the anger. All she could think was that the woman had no right to be acting so possessively and that she, Ginny, was going to put a stop to it once and for all.

How, she didn't know, until her roving gaze fell on Lewis Adams and saw that he was watching the couple too. His expression was tight, and she didn't have to be a mind-reader to know that he wasn't happy with the situation. Ginny knew it wasn't Roarke's fault that Lewis's wife was behaving so brazenly, but she wasn't so sure that Lewis would see it that way. She knew Roarke was against telling his father what had really happened with Jenna, for fear of making the situation worse, but Ginny credited the older man with more wisdom now. Someone had to put him straight, and if Roarke wouldn't do it, it fell to her to do so.

She had got no further than that when the man himself appeared before her. He smiled as he stood looking down at her, then held out his hand.

'I think we ought to go and break that up, don't you?' he suggested, taking her by surprise.

'Well…er…I was thinking the same thing myself,' she admitted, getting to her feet and eyeing him warily. 'Only…the situation might not be quite what you think.'

'And just what would that be?' he queried, ushering her the few yards to the dance floor and swinging her into his arms with decided panache.

Ginny licked her lips nervously. 'Roarke isn't…I mean, he wouldn't…' The words tailed off lamely as she wasn't sure how to proceed.

As it happened, Lewis Adams smiled kindly. 'I'm fully aware of what my son isn't doing or wouldn't do, Ginny,' he told her confidentially, and she blinked at him.

'You are?' she asked doubtfully.

'Oh, undoubtedly. I'm grateful that my son has better instincts when it comes to women than I do. You, my dear young woman, are the real McCoy, whilst Jenna is merely fool's gold. Myself being the fool,' he added with wry humour.

Her lips twitched. 'It wouldn't be polite of me to agree with you.'

'But to disagree would be a lie?' Roarke's father finished for her. 'You're quite right, of course. I did my son an injustice some years ago, and I fully intend to put that right. Firstly, though, I think it's about time I put you and Roarke out of my misery.' With which he steered her over to where his wife and son danced and tapped Roarke on the shoulder. 'Ready to change partners, son? It's time I took care of my wife. Come along, darling.'

Ginny and Roarke watched as he danced a scowling Jenna away from them, then they were jostled by a couple and he guided Ginny out of the way.

'We're creating a minor log jam here,' Roarke declared humorously, and Ginny eyed the crush dubiously.

'Let's go back,' she suggested, but Roarke caught hold of her hand and used it to twirl her into his arms.

'And waste a perfectly good dance floor? I think not,' he countered, giving her no chance to refuse.

This wasn't at all what Ginny had had in mind, but she could hardly create a scene over a dance. And dancing was all it was, she told herself firmly. Slowly, they began to circle the room.

'What was all that about with Dad?' Roarke asked curiously, and Ginny pulled away enough to look him in the eye.

'That was your father's way of telling you he's not as blind as you think. At least, not any more,' she told him seriously, and saw the message strike home in his eyes. Roarke tried to find his father amongst the dancers, but he had vanished from sight. He turned back to Ginny.

'What did you do?' he challenged suspiciously, and she shook her head.

'Nothing, honestly. He came to me and suggested he break you and Jenna up—in the nicest possible way, of course. From what he said, he's no longer fooled by her, and he's sorry he misjudged you.'

Roarke's eyes shone with affection for his parent. 'The old fox. He said that, did he?'

Ginny smiled, pleased for him. 'Not in so many words, but I could read between the lines. I won't steal his thunder. Anything else you want to know, you'll have to take up with him.'

'I will, just as soon as the time is right,' he confirmed, then held her gaze, looking deeply into her eyes as if searching for something. 'You're something of a lucky charm, Ginny Harte,' he murmured softly, but she shook her head.

'There's nothing the least bit magical about me.'

His brows curved upwards. 'Then how come it feels as if you're casting a spell over me?'

Her nerves leapt, and her pulse started to beat just that little bit faster. 'That's indigestion from too much rich food,' she retorted, making him laugh.

'I can handle the food, it's you I'm worried about.'

Tiny tingles were being set off along her nerve-endings. 'I'm no threat,' she countered huskily, vitally aware that being this close to him was undermining her resolve to keep her cool. The warmth coming off him was heating her blood.

Still his eyes searched hers and she was unable to look away as he sighed. 'Maybe not to world peace, but my sanity is in real danger.'

Her throat closed over, for the banked fires in his eyes told her he was feeling just the same as she was. Together they were combustible, and it was happening so fast it took her breath away.

'Then let me go,' she suggested tightly, though her whole body was sending out the message that it wanted to be closer, not farther away.

'Something tells me that will be impossible unless you walk away,' he confessed, and her stomach tightened as desire flared inside her.

Her brain knew the right thing to do, the safe thing, but it reacted sluggishly, unlike her senses, which were going into overdrive. Walk away? When it came to doing that, she was in the same boat as Roarke. She didn't have the strength to do it right now. In a moment of perfect clarity, Ginny knew that there was only one thing she wanted to do. She would worry about the consequences later, but right now she made her choice and moved that fraction closer to rest her head on his shoulder, her arms rising to encircle his neck. Beside her she felt Roarke take in a deep lungful of air, and then his arms tightened round her. Her eyelids dropped, closing out the world.

They danced on as one slow song changed to another. Their bodies moved, touching just enough to tantalise. Ginny breathed in the aroma of his cologne, which made a heady potion blended with his own male scent. The brush of his hand tracing lazy patterns up and down her spine was totally alluring, and in response her hand sought his nape, her fingers caressing up into his lush dark hair in combing strokes.

And all the while they danced she could feel his body hardening, responding to the stimulus, whilst her own was going into meltdown. She hadn't wanted this, she told herself. Lord knew it was the very last thing she had wanted, and yet she couldn't seem to stop herself craving more. It felt so good, how could it be wrong?

A little while later the music changed to a faster tempo, and they were reluctantly forced to move apart. Ginny glanced into eyes as stormy as she knew hers must be. Tempestuous forces had been created, and were barely leashed. Neither had wanted the dance to end and that was why, when Roarke took her hand, she allowed him to lead her off the floor and out into the night without a word of protest.

There were extensive gardens surrounding the hotel and Roarke followed a meandering path, eventually stepping off it into the shadows round the bole of a tree. Leaning back against the trunk, he drew Ginny towards him. The freshness of the clear air brought with it a momentary return to sanity and she resisted, pressing her hands against his shoulders.

'We shouldn't be doing this,' she protested, though there was little force behind it.

Roarke continued to urge her closer. 'I know. This is the last thing I expected or wanted. I must be crazy, but what the hell...' He began to lower his head.

'No, Roarke,' Ginny commanded weakly as his lips hovered over hers. 'I don't...' The words were cut off as his mouth claimed hers with a devastating passion, and her resistance vanished like dust in the wind. A groan of satisfaction escaped her as her hands stopped pushing him away and clung on tightly instead.

The kiss was every bit as mind-blowing as the others they had shared, and it reinforced the strength of their attraction. Lost to the world, they were swept away by the passion they sparked in each other. One kiss was never going to be enough. They were caught in the grip of a fever, and the only cure was to allow it to run its course.

Finally, Roarke managed to drag his mouth from hers. Breathing heavily, he rested his forehead against hers and closed his eyes. 'If I don't stop now, I don't think I'll be able to,' he declared in a voice made thick by passion.

Ginny groaned, every bit as breathless herself. 'Why is this happening to us? What did we do to deserve it? I was happy disliking you!' She railed against the fate which had brought them together.

'You won't get an argument from me about that!' he agreed, planting a trail of kisses down her cheek to her jaw line.

Ginny's head tipped backwards, allowing him access to the tender skin of her throat. 'I didn't ask to want you this way!' she groaned achingly. It wasn't what she had planned. It wasn't fair.

Roarke's teeth nipped gently at her earlobe, making her

gasp and shiver. 'What have you done to me, you little witch? I can't seem to keep my hands to myself. You're like a drug, the more I have the more I want.'

Her hands had somehow found their way to his chest, delighting in the heat that scorched her fingers through his silk shirt. 'I know, but we have to stop,' she said vaguely, concentrating on freeing one of his shirt buttons so that her fingers could slip inside. His flesh was warm and firm, inviting her to explore further.

'God, that feels good,' Roarke groaned against her neck, his tongue darting out to taste her.

Ginny shivered, caught in the grip of an intense desire. She had never felt like this before. Not with Mark and definitely not Daniel. She froze. Daniel! His name was like a douche of cold water, cooling the fire in her blood. From somewhere she found the strength to wrench herself away.

'Oh, God! What am I doing?' she whispered in an agonised voice. She raised her head to look at Roarke, who stood watching her, breathing heavily. She shook her head slowly. 'This is wrong.'

Roarke dragged a hand through his hair. 'Not wrong, sweetheart, just damned unexpected,' he growled back. 'There's nothing wrong with a man and woman wanting each other.'

Ginny rubbed her forehead to ease the beginnings of a headache. 'But you're the wrong man, and I'm the wrong woman.'

That brought a twitch of humour to his lips. 'Obviously not. Nature seems to be telling us we're the right people, physically at least. Maybe we should listen to what we're being told.'

'And sleep with each other, you mean?'

'Sleeping comes later.'

She scowled at him 'You just couldn't resist that, could you?'

'Actually, it's you I'm finding impossible to resist. Experience tells me it isn't just going to go away, so ignoring it isn't going to work.'

Ginny had been reaching that conclusion herself. Words were easy to say, but they only had to look at each other to go up in flames! Her eyes met his, and even in the darkness she could see the intensity there. 'You seem to be taking this very calmly.'

His response to that was to take her hand and place it over his heart so that she could feel it racing. 'I'm not calm, Ginny, far from it. In fact, I'm as confused as I ever hope to be.'

'You're saying this has never happened to you before? I can't believe that,' she charged him mockingly and he grimaced.

'Laugh if you want to, but it's true. Finding myself wanting you this badly has knocked me for six. It isn't a feeling I'm familiar with. When I'm around you I can't seem to think straight. I only know I want to make love to you. You feel it too. We're caught in a fever, Ginny, and there's only one cure. We have to let it burn itself out.'

'It sounds so cold-blooded,' she said with a shiver that had nothing to do with coldness and everything to do with the idea of making love with him.

He laughed huskily. 'Believe me, sweetheart, our blood will be anything but cold. I'm not suggesting a long-term commitment. These things never last long. It will burn itself out quickly unless we try to ignore it. We wouldn't be hurting anyone.'

Ginny looked steadily into his eyes. 'And afterwards?'

'Normal service will be resumed. I have no doubts we'll be back to daggers drawn in no time.'

Ginny turned her back on him and took two paces away, needing the thinking room. She had to be crazy to even be thinking of doing it, but what he was suggesting made a strange kind of sense. It wouldn't be a love affair in the usual sense. All they needed was to drive the fever from their blood and turn things back to normal. No one need ever know.

'My choice?' she asked over her shoulder, and Roarke nodded.

'I leave the decision up to you.'

She chewed on her lip. 'You'd abide by my decision?'

He groaned audibly. 'I might want you with a certain amount of desperation, but I've never seduced a woman against her will, and I don't intend to start with you.'

Ginny shook her head in bewilderment. 'I've never met anyone like you. You've aggravated me constantly ever since we met, and yet...'

His teeth glittered as he grinned. 'You can't keep your hands off me?'

She sighed and winced. 'Something like that,' she agreed, then turned back to him. 'This has got to be the weirdest situation. I'm standing here actually considering sleeping with you, when only days ago I was having dinner with another man.' And planning to marry him—if he asked her.

That wasn't going to happen now. Not because Roarke figured in her future, but because her attraction to him was showing her that a marriage without love and desire was impossible. She was a woman with passion, and to contemplate ignoring those needs and settling for Daniel was wrong. She didn't love him, and certainly wasn't sexually attracted to him. Such a relationship would be a disaster. He deserved better—and so did she.

'Sweetheart, you can be damn sure we're no good to anyone else whilst we're wanting each other this way,' Roarke drawled with some of his old irony, uncannily echoing her own thoughts. 'Come on, let's head back before someone discovers we're missing and wants to know where we've been and what we've been doing. I'd hate to have to lie to my mother.'

Ginny laughed as he intended she should, and the tension which had been surrounding them eased considerably. 'She must know the kind of thing you get up to.'

They strolled back along the path. 'She imagines what I get up to; she doesn't know. I haven't talked to anyone about my relationships since I was in my teens. I once hurt a girl I liked very badly, by talking to someone who couldn't be trusted. She slapped my face in front of practically the whole school, and I deserved it.'

Ginny couldn't resist slipping her hand into his and squeezing it gently. 'You know, you really are a nice guy. Though it pains me to say it, I doubt I could go back to actively disliking you.'

Roarke glanced down at her quizzically. 'Your trouble is, you're not as frosty as you like to make out, which will make it impossible for me to see you as anything but warm-hearted. I used to enjoy taunting you in the office.'

She laughed softly. 'I know. What will we do now that we've started a mutual admiration society?'

He sent her a wolfish grin, the kind that curled her toes and set her heart tripping expectantly. 'Oh, we'll think of something to keep us amused. I have quite an imagination.'

It didn't sound to Ginny as if he was talking about verbal badinage, but she chose not to pursue it. For the moment the fires had been banked and it was easier to assume an appearance of calm.

Her thoughts were distracted not long afterwards by a sudden swell of noise from the front of the hotel, which separated itself into the sound of voices laughing and talking. As they rounded the side of the building, they could see the bride and groom were standing on the top of the entrance steps, clearly about to leave. As they joined the back of the group, Ginny could hear several voices urging Caroline to throw her bouquet. Laughing, she placed her hand over her eyes and launched the bouquet into the air with the other.

There were gasps and cries of 'Catch it!' but Ginny was so busy watching the arc it made that she didn't realise it was heading straight for her until almost the last second, when she raised her hands to protect her head—and caught the bouquet instead. Nobody could have been more surprised than she, but then she became aware of the pointed remarks about confetti and wedding bells which were being sent Roarke's way, and colour stormed into her cheeks. Instinctively, she looked around for someone more deserving to pass the flowers on to, but everyone was smiling at her and wishing her good fortune, so she could do nothing but hold on to it.

It really was a lovely bouquet, and smelled heavenly, she discovered when she buried her face in it to avoid having to look Roarke in the eye. Eventually, though, she had to look at him, to find him brushing off the comments with good humour. Sensing her watching him, he sent a questioning look her way.

'I'm sorry,' she apologised. 'I didn't mean to catch it. I thought it was going to hit me, so I put my hand up. I ought to have ducked.'

He grinned. 'If you'd done that, I would have caught

it instead. Something tells me Caroline knew what she was doing,' he added thoughtfully.

Ginny looked startled. 'You mean she threw it our way deliberately? Why?'

'Because people who are happy themselves want to see others find happiness the same way. She obviously thinks we should get married,' Roarke explained sardonically.

'That would be a sure-fire recipe for disaster. We're simply not compatible.' Ginny had the answer to that.

'We're not totally incompatible, either. In some areas we appear to be getting along like a house on fire,' he corrected wryly.

A chauffeur-driven car drew up outside the hotel, and that was the happy couple's cue to make their escape. They did so in a shower of confetti, and then they were in the car and being driven off to start their honeymoon. As ever, a faint sense of anticlimax settled over the party, and they slowly made their way back inside. However, it was not long before the younger family members were dancing, and the level of noise rose as the celebration got under way again. It showed every possibility of continuing long into the night.

By unspoken agreement Ginny and Roarke did not dance again, but spent the next few hours chatting with various members of his family. Though she had only met them briefly, Ginny knew she would miss them, for they had made her welcome with a kindness she was not familiar with. At least now she had had a glimpse of what a real family could be like, and that was what she wanted for herself.

Around midnight Ginny began to feel the effects of the long, eventful day, and when she stifled yet another yawn Roarke suggested they should leave. They made their farewells, and headed for the door. Ginny would have liked to have said a few words to her mother and sister, but the Brigadier had them under his watchful eye, and she decided it would probably be best not to rock the boat any more than she had already today.

It didn't take long to be driven back to the house. Lights were on, but most of the family and guests were still at the hotel. Roarke led the way into the drawing room, unfastening his tie as he went and slipping it into his jacket pocket before releasing the neck buttons on his shirt. His hair was mussed up from where he had combed his fingers through it, and there was the shadow of beard on his jaw. To Ginny he looked handsome and sexy as hell.

'Fancy a nightcap?' he asked, strolling to the sideboard where a stunning array of drinks were set out. He turned to her, holding a cut glass brandy snifter in one hand and a bottle of Napoleon brandy in the other.

I fancy you more. The thought just slipped into her consciousness, accompanied by the impulse to close the distance between them, pull his head down to hers and share a kiss that would do more for her than any alcohol ever could.

Something of what she was thinking must have reached him, for suddenly there was an intense look in his eyes.

'Are you going to carry through on that?' he asked in a tellingly husky voice, making her nerves jump at his perspicacity.

'Carry through on what?' she countered, equally gruffly.

He took a step towards her. 'What you were just thinking.'

She swallowed to moisten a dry mouth. 'How do you know what I was thinking?'

'You have very expressive eyes, and though I might

not know the exact words, the gist is sending my pulse-rate rocketing.'

Ginny licked her lips, an act that drew his gaze and made her breath hitch in her throat. 'I'm sorry about that, because I don't know what I'm going to do. I haven't made up my mind.'

'It's interesting to know you can be as typically female as the next woman, but you pick a hell of a time to do it,' Roarke responded wryly.

'Unintentionally. I'm not a tease.' She wouldn't want him to think that. He didn't, because he smiled ruefully.

'I know you're not, Ginny. It's not in your nature.'

His certainty confused her. How could he be so sure? 'I've been accused of it before.'

'Only by people who don't know you as well as I do.' He dismissed the statement easily.

'You've scarcely known me longer yourself,' she felt compelled to point out, but he merely shook his head.

'Time has nothing to do with it. You can know a person your whole life and not know them at all. Then you can know somebody for twenty-four hours, and know them better than you know yourself. I feel I've come to know you very well, Ginny Harte, in the last couple of days.'

As she had come to know him. He had turned into a man she couldn't help being attracted to. Not for his good looks, although there was no denying that, but for the man he was. He had awakened her dormant sensuality without even trying, and she was beginning to realise she had been denying a vital part of herself for too long. Wanting Roarke was making her feel alive in a way she hadn't been for years. And it felt good. Maybe something was telling her it was time to kick over the traces and start living again. Dared she?

'Have I grown another head?' Roarke asked, reminding her she was staring, and her lips twitched.

'No, the one you've got is quite handsome enough.'

His brows rose. 'Sounds interesting. Tell me more,' he urged, with a rakish glint in his eye that taunted her to do something that would surprise him.

She knew what she wanted to do, and why shouldn't she? There was nothing stopping her but herself. Once upon a time nothing would have stopped her following her instincts. She had liked that person, and she could be her again—if she had the courage.

Just do it, Ginny, a small but insistent voice urged her, and suddenly she found herself taking one step and then another. Several more and she was standing in front of him. Her hand went to his neck, and for a moment their eyes met, his showing mild surprise. Then, a smile curving her lips, her gaze dropped to his. Rising on to her toes at the same time as her hand exerted just enough pressure to urge his head down, she set her mouth on his. Her tongue traced a silken caress over his lips, and they parted, allowing her entrance. With his hands full, there was nothing Roarke could do save surrender, and it gave Ginny a heady sense of power to take the initiative this way. She explored his mouth at leisure, her tongue seeking his and joining in a duel that set her pulse hammering and caused Roarke to moan low in his throat.

That was her cue to move away, and she did so with a certain amount of reluctance, stepping back from him. She looked at him steadily, seeing an arrested look in his eyes.

'What was that for?'

'I wanted to surprise you,' she answered simply.

He shook his head and laughed huskily. 'Sweetheart, you did more than that. You've made it virtually impossible for me to sleep tonight.'

She was instantly contrite. 'I'm sorry.'

'Don't be.' He waved that away. 'I could do with a few more surprises like that. Right now, though, I need that nightcap. How about you?'

'I'm going to go up and shower,' she refused.

'Well, you don't have to worry about using all the hot water. I'll be taking a cold shower later,' Roarke returned drolly.

Laughing softly, Ginny left him there and went upstairs to their room. She wasn't sorry she had kissed Roarke like that. It had felt good to follow her instincts again and act on impulse. He had taken it well, but she had known he would. She was getting to know him very well.

In their room, she found the maid had already been in to turn down the bed. Collecting her nightdress, she kicked off her shoes and padded into the bathroom. Stripping off her clothes, she stepped under the shower and let the warm water send down its soothing spray over her. She did a lot of her thinking in the shower, and tonight was no different. She had a lot to think about.

Her eyes had been well and truly opened by her response to Roarke, showing her in no uncertain terms that it was time she stopped fooling herself and started being true to herself. She was not the cold-blooded type. She had cut herself off from feeling, for fear of being hurt. At eighteen, in her inexperience, she had allowed passion to cloud her judgement, because she had so wanted to be loved. She had been an easy mark but she was no longer that girl. She was a woman in control of her life, who shouldn't be afraid to go with her instincts. By ignoring them she had almost made a serious mistake again. She would break the news to Daniel as soon as she returned home.

That decision brought with it an amazing sense of freedom. She felt as if she could breathe again. Now she had to leave the past behind, look forward and see what came. There was nothing stopping her from doing anything she wanted to do. If getting involved with Roarke, even for a brief moment, was a mistake, then it was hers to make. As he said, they would be hurting nobody.

Taking a deep breath, she turned off the water and stepped out, reaching for a luxuriously fluffy towel and wrapping it around her. It was time to stop thinking and act. She dried herself, slipped into her nightdress and towelled her hair dry, finger-combing it into place.

When she stepped back into the bedroom, Roarke was coming out of his dressing room. He was barefoot, wearing only his trousers. He had already taken the pillow and cover from the bed and laid them out on the couch as he had last night. It pleased her that he had taken nothing for granted, but at the same time it piqued her that he had assumed the decision was made. As she had told him, she hadn't made up her mind.

'Feel better?' he asked casually, letting his eyes rove over the feminine curves scarcely hidden beneath the cream silk nightdress.

The way it sent a lick of fire over her skin made Ginny feel as if the material wasn't there at all. Goose-bumps chased their way over her flesh, and she felt her nipples harden to sensitive points that thrust against the silk covering. Roarke could scarcely miss her response, and she saw his chest rise as he took a deep breath, but although his eyes flashed, he made no move to approach her.

Ginny cleared her throat. 'I'm cleaner, I don't know about feeling better,' she told him openly, and amusement danced across his face.

'That makes two of us. Somehow I get the feeling the cold shower isn't going to count for very much. It's going to be one hell of a long night!' he added as he headed for the bathroom. The door closed with a soft click behind him.

Ginny stared after him, knowing that it would be a long night for her too, with him lying only a few yards away. Especially as they both wanted something else. Her gaze swept round to the makeshift bed on the couch. This was ridiculous. There was no reason why they shouldn't have what they wanted. It wasn't a first date, for heaven's sake! They had known each other for months. The passion was new, but the spark had been there. They'd just interpreted it as something else.

Before she even realised she was doing it, she had gone to the couch and retrieved the pillow and cover and returned them to the bed. Of course, as soon as she had done it, her stomach turned over at the decision she had made, but she knew she wouldn't change it. There was no way, however, that she could simply sit on the bed waiting for him, so she went to the French window that opened on to a tiny balcony and stepped into the cool night shadows.

Pretending to look at the view, her ears were straining to hear the sounds from the other room. She heard the water stop and imagined him towelling himself off, then fastening another towel around his waist. He would reach for the light switch, then... Another soft click alerted her to the fact that he had left the bathroom. She tensed, imagining him finding the changed sleeping arrangements. Her heart started to race.

'Ginny?' The soft question made her glance round.

Roarke was standing by the end of the couch, watching her. He looked pretty much as she expected. His broad, tanned chest with its mat of dark silky hair stood out in contrast against the white towel hitched on his hips. He looked good enough to eat, and she was hungry—very hungry.

'Are you sure about this?' he asked, inclining his head towards the empty couch.

'Oh, yes,' she replied huskily, and it was all he needed to hear. He came to her, reaching out to gently cup her face with his hands. Grey eyes searched hers for any sign of doubt and found none.

Nevertheless, he still gave her an out. 'You know you can change your mind at any time. All you have to do is tell me to stop, and I will.'

The words made her heart turn over. No matter what she might have accused him of in the past, she had discovered he was an honourable man. She set her hands on his chest and instantly felt the reverberations of his quickened heartbeats. Any nervousness she had been feeling drained away. She was suddenly very sure of what she wanted.

'That isn't going to happen. Just take me to bed, Roarke,' she suggested in little more than a whisper. It brought a glint to his eyes and a smile to his lips.

Releasing her, he swept her up into his arms with breathtaking ease. Automatically Ginny's arms slipped around his neck. 'Never let it be said I refused a lady anything,' he retorted in amusement, but as he carried her to the bed the laughter faded, driven away by a look of such intensity it hid a powerful need.

Despite that, he laid her on the bed with infinite gentleness, and when he joined her, seconds later, the hand that traced the line of her cheek and jaw, then carried on down to the tender cord of her neck and graceful curving shoulder, held the faintest tremor. He was holding himself in check by supreme self-control, and he touched her as if she was made of the finest glass.

It was amazingly arousing to watch him as he followed his hand's journey along the curves and planes of her body. His gaze was so intense as he enjoyed each new discovery, that Ginny felt as if she were being burned by a touch as light as a feather. She knew even then that she knew nothing about pleasure. That what she had experienced had been little more than fumbling in the dark. This was pleasure delivered by a man who knew there was more to making love than reaching the end as quickly as possible.

She quivered as his hand brushed across her thighs, and caught her breath when he approached the swollen mounds of her breasts. He had started fires everywhere he touched, and she was burning up, so needy she could scarcely hold back a groan. She ached for him to touch her breasts, and arched into his hand as he cupped her. For one moment his eyes met hers, and it was like being touched by flame.

'I know,' he murmured thickly, then his thumb flicked across her engorged nipple, sending pleasure shooting through her body and dragging a moan from her lips.

She closed her eyes, but that only heightened the sensations as she felt his mouth close on her breast, his tongue laving her through the silk of her nightdress. She could no longer lie still, and her hand rose to his hair, slipping into the damp strands and clinging on as he drew her into his mouth and suckled. Her other hand found the sleek planes of his back and delighted in the glide of flesh on flesh.

Then his mouth sought the twin peak, delivering to it the same sweet torture it had given its mate before abandoning her breasts and seeking the honeyed sweetness of her mouth. Now she could sense the leashed desire in him. His tongue was a silken ravishment, seeking hers and demanding a response that left the pulses racing and breathing ragged. Only the need for air had him drawing back to look down into her flushed face and fevered eyes.

'I wanted this to last, but you're so intoxicating I don't think I can hold out for much longer,' he told her in a voice made husky by passion.

Ginny felt the same, but words were beyond her. Her answer was to reach down for the towel he wore and tug at it until he shifted his weight enough for her to pull it free and toss it aside. Roarke's nostrils flared as he got the message loud and clear. In return he took the hem of her nightdress and slid it upwards until finally he eased it free of her arms and sent it to join the towel.

Roarke's groan was echoed by her sigh of pleasure as he moved over her, taking his weight on his elbows. One powerful thigh nudged her legs apart, and to their mutual satisfaction he settled himself between them. Deep inside herself Ginny could feel the coils of desire growing ever tighter, climbing towards the ultimate goal, and she began to move restlessly beneath him as he teased her with kisses that stoked the fire but always left her wanting more.

All she could do was explore him with her hands, allowing her fingers to trace their way across taut flesh. He felt wonderful, but it was not enough. She wanted him inside her. Needed to feel the power of him dispelling the emptiness she had felt for so long. As if he was connected to her psychically, Roarke moved, slipping a hand between their bodies and into the valley of her thighs, seeking the core of her. His touch made her gasp and arch into him, leaving him in no doubt of her readiness.

With a groan he thrust into her, and Ginny's gasp was due to discomfort, not pleasure. They both stilled. There hadn't been anyone since Mark, and her body had tightened. Foolishly, she hadn't been prepared for it, but already her muscles were relaxing to accommodate him. Roarke raised his head to look at her, confusion clouding his eyes, and she felt him tensing his muscles in order to move away. That wasn't what she wanted at all, and she quickly folded her legs around him, holding him where he was.

'No. Don't stop,' she urged in a voice thick with passion.

Roarke gritted his teeth with the effort it was taking to hold still. 'I hurt you,' he declared tautly, but Ginny shook her head in vehement denial.

'No, you didn't. It was nothing. Please, Roarke, I want you. Don't stop now.'

He searched her eyes and what he saw there must have convinced him, for he began to move again. She could feel him holding back, taking care, but there was no need, and she moved against him, matching his rhythm, urging him on until, with a groan, the magnificent control he had been using crumpled and his thrusts became faster and deeper, seeking release. Ginny held on, her nails digging into the flesh of his back as the coils of pleasure spiralled upwards and finally climaxed in a white-hot explosion of pleasure. She cried out, and her cry was echoed by Roarke's as he joined her. She clung to him as a depth of satisfaction she had never experienced before held her in its grip. She felt as if she had shattered into a million tiny pieces and was being put back together again better than before.

When she finally floated down to earth, her body was drained. She had no energy to move and her eyelids were weighted. She felt Roarke slide off her, and wanted to protest, but no words passed her lips. Then she was being moved, and the last thing she remembered before sleep claimed her was Roarke's arms slipping round her.

CHAPTER NINE

GINNY sighed and drifted into wakefulness. She stretched and winced slightly as seldom used muscles protested. However, recalling the cause of this morning's stiffness, a reminiscent smile slowly curved her lips. Last night had been—out of this world. Making love with Roarke had taken her to heights she hadn't realised it was possible to reach. It had been amazing, exciting, and...she wouldn't at all mind doing it again.

With which thought in mind she rolled over, only to discover the other side of the bed was empty. Frowning, she came up on her elbow and swept her hair out of her eyes so that she could search the room. Roarke was just coming out of his dressing room, pulling a lightweight argyle sweater over his head. Settling it over the denims he was already wearing, he finger-combed his hair back into place.

She had always thought he looked good in formal clothes, but he was just as gorgeous in casual wear. The jeans moulded his legs, emphasising the muscles, whilst the sweater outlined the chest she had come to know rather well. She experienced a stab of disappointment that he was already up and dressed.

'Why didn't you wake me?' she asked, with just the faintest of pouts.

Roarke glanced over at her and a smile curved his lips. He immediately came over to the bed and sat down on the edge. Lowering his head, he took her lips in a long lingering kiss, which went some way to appeasing her disappointment, drawing back with obvious reluctance, before the smouldering embers of their passion could be reignited.

'Good morning,' he greeted gruffly.

'Good morning,' Ginny returned equally gruffly.

Grey eyes quartered her face, and he brushed his knuckles gently over her cheek. 'How do you feel?'

'Pleasantly exhausted,' she responded, then grinned. 'But I have amazing recuperative powers,' she added suggestively, making him laugh softly.

'That's good to know, sweetheart, but that isn't exactly what I meant,' Roarke returned, holding her gaze. 'It had been a while for you, hadn't it?'

Faint colour washed into her cheeks at the unexpected remark. She had forgotten those brief moments of discomfort, and thought he had too. She instinctively distanced herself mentally. 'You were disappointed,' she declared flatly, feeling foolish, but Roarke was quick to correct her error.

'Nothing about you disappoints me, Ginny. Far from it. I only mentioned it because it was something I hadn't expected. It worried me that I could have been too rough, and hurt you.'

She relaxed again. 'Oh. I see. Well, let me tell you, Mr Adams, you didn't hurt me at all,' she told him honestly, and was faintly surprised to see relief flash across his face. His concern made her feel warm and bubbly inside. She wasn't used to being worried over.

'That's good, but I wish I'd known beforehand. I would have taken more care.'

More care? She couldn't help laughing. 'More care?

Roarke, you couldn't possibly have taken more care than you did.'

'So, what happened? Were all the men out there blind?' he teased, more like his usual self.

Ginny sighed. 'No. It was me. After Mark, I wasn't about to rush into anything,' she admitted, surprising him again.

'There's been no one since Mark?' he repeated in disbelief, and her shrug was just a little diffident. She didn't care to recall how stupid she had been.

'I made a fool of myself over him, confusing desire with love. The only way to make sure it didn't happen again was to keep all men at bay. When you've been burned, you learn to steer clear of the fire.' It was a philosophy which had worked well over the years, protecting her.

'OK, I can understand that. So why me? Why now?' Roarke asked curiously.

She could have said nothing, but she had already said so much, there was no point in hiding the truth. 'Because you're the only man who's ever made me want to change my mind.' She told the simple truth.

'Then I'm honoured,' he responded with an unexpected degree of sincerity, causing her heart to give a tiny lurch.

Feeling oddly emotional, Ginny had to make light of it or do something silly like burst into tears. 'You should be. The truth is, I'm under no illusion this time. You're here and I want you and, try as I might, I couldn't find a convincing reason not to have you.'

That brought a glint to his eye. 'You tried, though?'

Her laughter was openly flirtatious. 'Oh, yes. I didn't want sex rearing its ugly head and cluttering up my life, but if last night is anything to go by, I made the right choice.'

'I'm glad you were satisfied.'

Ginny reached out and trailed a finger along the V neck of his sweater. 'I was satisfied last night, but this morning... You should have woken me. Why didn't you?'

'Oh, I wanted to, believe me. You don't know how hard it was to keep my hands to myself and crawl out of this bed. All I wanted to do was kiss you awake and lose myself in you again. However, I thought you needed the sleep more, and the noble thing to do was leave you alone.'

'For future reference, I'm not that bothered about nobility,' Ginny told him wryly. 'So why don't you come back to bed?' she suggested with a winsome smile.

Roarke groaned but resisted temptation. 'I have to be crazy to pass up an offer like that, but I must. We don't have much time, and I want to speak to my father before he leaves this morning.'

She was disappointed, but she understood. 'Then what are you doing wasting time here? Go and find him. There will be other mornings.' Their desire for each other was not to be satisfied so quickly.

Grey eyes gleamed wickedly. 'You're right, and I shall be looking forward to every one of them. Last night was not the end, only the beginning. Now, I'd better go before my resolve weakens. I'll see you in a little while.'

He pressed a fleeting kiss on her lips then left the room. Ginny sighed wistfully. It was funny how things turned out. Nothing about this weekend had gone the way she expected, and yet it couldn't have turned out better. She had found her family again, and for that alone everything that had happened would have been worth it. Even running into her father.

And then there was Roarke. Neither of them would have bet on this happening, that they would end up in bed together. Yet she wasn't sorry. For the first time in a long time she felt as if she was truly herself again. The Ginny who knew what she wanted and went for it, unafraid.

She was older and wiser now. This time she wasn't going to mistake desire for love. It would be an affair, that was all. There was no love on either side, just a powerful desire. When it was over, she would walk away with her pride intact. There were no false promises, no impossible demands. They wanted each other, and they would enjoy every moment for as long as it lasted.

It was incredibly heady to feel free of the past, and Ginny lay there basking in the newness of it. But eventually her stomach started to rumble and she began to think of food instead of what she might be doing if Roarke was still here. Sitting up, she reached for the travel clock she had set on the bedside table and was startled to find it was getting on for eleven o'clock in the morning.

'Yipes!' she exclaimed, thinking of all the things she had to do before she could eat. Galvanised into action, Ginny flung back the covers, scrambled from the bed and hurried into the bathroom.

If either of them had thought that one week or even one month would see their passion for each other diminish, they would have been wrong. Six weeks after their return from the wedding, the attraction between them was as strong as it ever was. In fact, Ginny almost felt as if it was stronger.

As for herself and Roarke, they were virtually inseparable these days. At work they remained professional, but they no longer had the verbal battles everyone expected, which was causing even more talk amongst the staff. Ginny found herself being watched, and she knew they were being talked about, but it didn't bother her. She was happy, and breezed through even the most hectic of days because she knew that come the evening they would be together and the world would be shut out.

Roarke appeared happy too. At least the wastebasket in his office was spared the attentions of his foot these days. He had taken to spending most of his free time at her flat, only returning to his own apartment to pick up his mail. Sometimes they stayed in. More often they ate out or went to a show, but always when they came home they would make love.

Ginny was getting used to falling asleep in his arms, and waking to the gentle touch of his lips and hands in the morning. Like now. She had been awake for some time but she was pretending to be asleep for she loved the feel of his hands caressing her. He was so gentle, yet he could stir the embers inside her to life in no time at all. They lay moulded together spoon fashion, and she could feel his arousal pushing against her. It was becoming increasingly difficult to lie still, for as her body responded she wanted to move under his touch and purr like a cat.

'I know you're awake,' Roarke murmured in her ear before nibbling at her earlobe.

Released from the need for pretence, Ginny sighed ruefully and wriggled round to face him. 'Hi, do I know you?' she charged teasingly.

'Very well, if my memory serves me right,' he returned sardonically, running his hand over the curve of her hip and thigh. 'Um, this feels awfully familiar to me,' he added, grinning wolfishly.

Ginny shivered in response as a wave of tingles spread over her skin. 'And remind me just what it is you do,' she went on, tracing a finger down the line of his nose and round his lips.

'Oh, things like…this,' he told her with a wicked glint in his eye and trailed his hand to her breast, cupping it and circling her hardening nipple with his thumb.

Ginny sighed pleasurably. 'Ah, yes, now I remember you. We work together,' she declared, lowering her own hand to his chest and finding a flat male nipple nestling amongst the silky hairs.

'That's right.' Roarke nodded. 'It's always better when two people work together. It increases the pleasure.'

Her green eyes flirted with him. 'Is that so?'

'Want me to prove it to you?'

'I thought you'd never ask!' She laughed huskily. 'What do you want me to do?'

Laughing softly, Roarke eased her over on to her back and flung back the bedcovers. 'Nothing. All you have to do is lie there and take notes,' he told her against the tender skin of her neck. With infinite care he began to trace a wandering path over her body with lips and hands.

Biting her lip as a wave of pleasure washed over her, Ginny had to clear her throat to speak. 'Will you be asking questions later?' she asked, her laugh turning into a moan as he traversed the peaks of her breasts, leaving havoc in his wake.

Roarke paused in his roving somewhere around her navel and glanced up. 'The test will be a practical one. You have to repeat what you learn here. Points will be added for inventiveness,' he added as he returned to his ministrations.

She laughed, but when his hands parted her thighs and he sought the core of her with ravishing strokes of his tongue, amusement turned to gasping breaths and low moans of pleasure. With consummate ease he toppled her over the edge into a climax that appeased her immediate need, yet ultimately left her wanting more.

Roarke came up beside her, grinning wickedly. 'Do you understand what you have to do?' he asked teasingly, and Ginny sat up, eyes promising retribution.

'Let me see, we start here…' She trailed her fingers low across his stomach, and he jerked under her touch, taken by surprise. Smiling to herself, Ginny came up on her knees. 'No, no, that wasn't it.' She tutted. 'What about…?' Her hand closed around the velvety length of his manhood and squeezed gently.

'Hell's teeth!' Roarke exclaimed, coming up on his elbows, hot flags of colour staining his cheeks.

Instantly, Ginny was there, easing him back down. 'Take it easy. I'll get it right this time,' she promised, grinning devilishly, which made him groan and throw his arm over his eyes.

'You're nothing but a damned tease, Ginny Harte,' he told her tautly.

Ginny ran her hands over his chest, teasing the nipples into hardened nubs. 'I forgot to take notes—sorry. Something distracted me. Now, tell me how this feels.' Before he could guess what she was about, she was sitting astride his hips and had taken him inside her.

Roarke removed his arm and lay watching her, breathing raggedly. 'Feels good,' he murmured thickly.

'And this?' She moved, biting her lip as pleasure began to mount inside her.

'O—oh, yes,' he agreed through clenched teeth.

Her eyes met and held his as she continued to move seductively. It was incredibly arousing to entice him this way, but the need for satisfaction was growing inside her.

'Let go,' Roarke urged gruffly, and with a gasp she abandoned the fight for self-control and instead drove on towards the goal her body craved. Roarke's hands fastened on her hips as she flung her head back in an agony of pleasure, and he matched her rhythm. It was a wild, frantic ride, and minutes later they climaxed together with mingled cries.

Collapsing on top of him, Ginny closed her eyes and waited for her pulse to stop galloping. Finally she had enough breath to speak.

'It just keeps getting better and better, doesn't it?'

Roarke ran his hands caressingly up and down her back. 'Guess we must be doing something right.'

Sighing, she raised her hand and flicked her hair back out of her eyes. 'Was that inventive enough for you?'

'You can say that again. I don't know how I'm supposed to get up and go to work now.'

She knew how he felt, but the remark brought something else to mind. 'They're talking about us at the office, you know.'

'There's nothing new in that. They always talked about us,' Roarke was quick to point out.

'Yes, but now they're talking about us because we're not arguing. Do you think they suspect?'

'Probably.' Roarke used a finger to tease away hair that had stuck to her cheek. 'Do you mind them suspecting?'

'No,' she said with a shake of her head. It wasn't the

suspecting that bothered her, it was the knowledge that the staff would now be speculating on how long it would last, and how she would deal with the end of it. Something she didn't know herself and, frankly, didn't want to think about.

Sensing something was wrong, Roarke frowned. 'But?'

Easing herself away from him and sitting up, Ginny grimaced. 'It's nothing really. I simply realised that if they do suspect we're having an affair, they'll also be betting on how long it lasts. Your track record isn't good,' she reminded him dryly, making light of it though she wasn't that amused really. Whilst their attraction showed no signs of waning, she could not ignore the fact that the longer the affair lasted, the closer they came to the end. A prospect that was far from pleasant, though she wasn't ready to ask herself why.

Roarke sat up too. 'I'm sorry it's bothering you. Do you want me to put a stop to it?'

Ginny shook her head and slid off the bed, reaching for her robe and slipping it on. 'You can't stop them wondering. It's human nature.'

'Maybe not. But I don't like the idea of people gossiping about your private life.'

She laughed wryly. 'The only way to stop them is to end the affair. Is that what you want?'

'You know damn well it isn't,' Roarke growled, eyes gleaming wickedly. 'I don't know what makes you so different, but I can't get enough of you. There's no way I'm letting you go.'

It did her spirits a power of good to hear that, for she wasn't ready to end it, either. 'So we just let the gossips get on with it?'

'We're news now, but it will pass the minute something better comes along.'

He was right, of course, but as she showered a little while later she couldn't help remembering, and knowing that if they were news now one day she would be old news. It was a thought that tightened invisible fingers about her heart.

Ginny was busy working on a colour scheme for one of their small hotels, which was due to be redecorated in the off season, when Roarke let himself into her office via the connecting door. Glancing up, she smiled a welcome, then glanced at her watch.

'Hi. I thought you had a lunch appointment,' she reminded him, at the same time angling her head up to receive the kiss he deposited on her lips.

'I have,' he confirmed, perching himself on a corner of her desk. 'I just got off the phone from talking to Caroline.'

'They're back from their honeymoon at last? How are they?'

Roarke grinned. 'They're fine. They've been back a fortnight, apparently.'

Her brows rose. 'Two weeks? Where have they been hiding themselves?'

'In the house they've bought in Surrey. They've already entertained your parents, and my mother. Now it's our turn. We've been invited to dinner tonight,' Roarke informed her, and her smile faded to a wary look.

'Does James know?' Her last meeting with her brother had been less than comfortable.

'Um-hum. Apparently he's relaxed a lot. He even argued with your father during their visit.'

'James did?' Ginny couldn't have been more surprised. Her brother had had the stuffing knocked out of him by their father's strictness many years ago. That he would argue with him was tantamount to treason. 'I can't believe it. The Brigadier must have gone ballistic!'

Roarke rubbed the side of his nose judiciously. 'He wasn't too amused.'

Ginny started to laugh. 'Oh, I wish I could have seen that,' she said, wiping a tear from her eye. 'She didn't happen to say anything about Lucy?'

Ginny had been expecting her sister to turn up at her door ever since she had returned from Switzerland, but there had been no sign of her. Though she knew Lucy would come to no harm, she guessed that their father had been keeping an eagle eye on her, making it difficult for her to get away.

'No, she didn't. You'll have to ask her tonight. Are you worried about your sister?' Roarke asked in concern, and Ginny sighed, tapping her fingers on the desktop.

'No more than usual. I just wish she was here and not there.'

Roarke laid a reassuring hand on her shoulder. 'Lucy looked the resourceful type to me. She'll come when the time is right. Only she will know that.'

'You're right. It's the mother hen in me. I want her where I can look out for her,' Ginny replied wryly, then frowned as the rising sounds of a commotion in the outer office had them both turning and staring at the door.

'What on earth...?' Roarke muttered, but before he could make a move to go and investigate, the door was thrown open and Jenna stood in the doorway. 'Jenna?' he exclaimed in surprise, rising to his feet.

'Don't you Jenna me, you snake in the grass!' his stepmother declared in a loud voice. She took several not-quite-steady steps towards Ginny's desk, and it didn't take a genius to realise she had been drinking. It was by closing the distance between them that the woman finally recognised who Roarke was with. A sneer slid across her face. 'Well, well, well. If it isn't your little bedmate!' she exclaimed, and Ginny's heart sank as she saw the group of people huddled in the doorway. Judging from the looks on their faces, they had heard every damning word.

Roarke appreciated the situation too, and he waved the goggle-eyed group away. They went reluctantly, closing the door behind them. Only then did he turn his attention to the other woman.

'What are you doing here, Jenna?' he demanded to know in a voice that dripped ice.

'I came to tell you what I think of you, you rat! I suppose you're proud of yourselves, aren't you? You and this little tramp!' She waved a hand in Ginny's direction.

Frozen to her seat, Ginny was looking from one to the other like a spectator at a tennis match, but the thunderous expression on Roarke's face when he heard that made her catch her breath.

'Say what you like about me, Jenna, but don't even think of insulting Ginny in front of me. Believe me, you won't like what would happen next!' he told her in a voice so full of dislike the other woman must have felt it despite her condition.

'So that's the way the wind blows, is it? My, you must have got it bad to rush to her defence this way.' She laughed scornfully.

'My feelings for Ginny are none of your business.'

'What's she got that I haven't?' Jenna wanted to know. Roarke folded his arms and looked at her stonily. 'Integrity, for one thing. The ability to care about other people. And she doesn't see dollar signs when she looks at a man. Will that do?'

Jenna shot him a vicious look. 'All I wanted was a little fun, you sanctimonious hypocrite. What was so wrong with that?'

'You were married to my father, but I take it from your presence here that's about to change.'

'He's divorcing me, the rat! And it was her fault.' She stabbed a finger towards Ginny.

That brought Ginny to her feet. 'I did nothing, Mrs Adams,' she denied calmly. 'It was all your own work.'

Jenna glared at her. 'You said something to him. I know you did!'

Ginny shook her head. 'I said nothing. I admit I was going to, but as it turned out I didn't have to. Lewis had already seen through you.'

The other woman seethed with anger, and it took away any trace of her beauty. 'You think you're so smart, don't you? Well, Roarke may have the hots for you, darling, but he'll never marry you. He's all screwed up inside when it comes to love and marriage. So don't think you've got it made! You'll never keep him.'

Ginny looked at her coldly. 'I think you should go now, Mrs Adams.'

Jenna slayed them with a withering look. 'Don't worry, I'm leaving. The sooner I'm free of this lousy family, the better! There are other fish in the sea, and I'm going fishing!' she exclaimed, and flung herself out of the office with another crash of the door.

After a stunned moment when neither of them moved, Roarke crossed the room and shut the door after her. Letting out his breath in a silent whistle, he ran a hand through his hair. 'Jenna always did know how to make an entrance *and* an exit. Let's hope we've seen the last of her,' he declared feelingly. 'I'm sorry for the way she spoke to you.'

Ginny smiled faintly. 'That's OK. I have broad shoulders.'

Roarke grimaced. 'You're going to need them. If the staff didn't know about us before, they know now.'

She pulled a similarly wry face. 'So much for secrecy, then.' By now the office grapevine would have spread the news far and wide. 'What brought her here?'

'The desire to hurt me. She thinks if she can break us up, justice will have been done,' Roarke explained with a shake of his head.

Ginny frowned. 'But there's nothing to break up. We aren't in love with each other,' she added, when he looked a query. 'We're just...'

He eyed her with curiosity, amusement dancing in his eyes. 'Just?'

She narrowed her eyes at him. 'You know what I mean. We don't have that kind of relationship.'

Roarke pursed his lips as he considered that. 'No, we don't. It's just good old-fashioned sex,' he agreed at last.

She nodded, although the description didn't sit well. However, there was no denying the truth. Put plainly, it was just sex. 'Anyway, I'm not expecting a proposal.'

'That's comforting,' he rejoined sardonically, and she frowned at him.

'I just wanted you to know...'

'That ours is not a love affair. I got the message.'

Ginny blinked at his odd behaviour. 'Are you feeling all right?'

He laughed wryly. 'To tell you the truth, I'm not quite

sure. Look, I'm late for that meeting. Let's just forget about Jenna, OK?'

Blowing her a kiss, Roarke vanished back into his office and Ginny slumped into her seat, running over the last half-hour in her mind. Jenna's sudden appearance had certainly created a stir. The cat was out of the bag now, but she found she wasn't worried about that. What she did find uncomfortable was Roarke's description of their relationship.

True, they enjoyed great sex, but that wasn't all of it. She enjoyed being with him, and it was amazing how much they had in common. So it wasn't just sex. On the other hand, she didn't know what word to use to accurately describe it. It certainly wasn't love! She didn't love Roarke. She wanted him, but that wasn't love. So it had to be sex, and yet... It just didn't sit right, that was all.

With an irritable sigh, Ginny forced herself to forget about it. It was just words, after all. Semantics. It was what it was and that was that. There. Finished. She reached for the colour charts she had been studying before Jenna's arrival and gave them her total concentration. If her thoughts wandered from time to time, she dragged them back into line with grim determination.

Later that evening, Ginny sat beside Roarke in his car, her stomach churning with nerves. This dinner with Caroline and James was going to be very important and she hoped she didn't do or say anything to mess it up. She glanced across at Roarke, but he was concentrating on the road. He had been strangely quiet since he returned from his lunch appointment, almost introspective, and that added to her sense of disquiet. What was he thinking? It could be business, but generally he left that behind when they left the office. Tonight, however, his thoughts were elsewhere, and she couldn't help thinking it had something to do with Jenna's visit.

Having crossed the Thames, they were now driving through a leafy suburb, and Roarke turned into a road lined with large detached houses set back from the road. Eventually he steered the car through a pair of wrought-iron gates on to a driveway and parked the car before the house.

'Very nice,' he declared as he came round to open the door for her. 'At a guess, I would say it was a wedding present from our mother.'

'The Brigadier would have been impressed,' Ginny observed dryly. A sound behind them made them glance round, to see the gates gliding shut. She laughed. 'No uninvited guests. Good idea.' There could be a problem with crime here, but Ginny rather thought the gates would have been Caroline's idea.

Roarke smiled as they walked to the door. 'I told you Caroline was a determined woman.'

'Not only determined,' his sister declared from the door where she stood waiting, having anticipated them. 'But clever, too.' She stood back with a smile to allow them to step inside. 'I'm so happy to see you again, Ginny,' she said, giving Ginny a hug. 'Has Roarke been behaving himself?' she asked, kissing her brother fondly on the cheek.

'Mostly,' Ginny returned, handing her evening jacket to the waiting housekeeper.

'Good. I'm so glad the two of you are still together. Of course, I was pretty sure you would be,' she added, with a twinkle in her eye.

·Ginny exchanged an amused look with Roarke, who raised his shoulders in a helpless shrug.

'Where's James?' she asked. The fact that he wasn't at the door didn't bode well.

Caroline's response surprised her. 'He's in the drawing room mixing Martinis. He's nervous.'

'He is?' That was a first! James had always seemed so sure of himself.

Roarke's sister shepherded them towards a doorway. 'He thinks you might be angry with him. He wasn't very nice to you at the wedding,' she explained.

'He wasn't, but that made me sad, not angry,' Ginny replied wistfully.

The drawing room was large and designed for comfort. James was standing at a sideboard pouring liquid from a mixer into four glasses. He glanced round as they walked in, set the mixer aside and visibly braced himself with a deep breath before coming to join his wife.

'Hello, Roarke.' He shook his brother-in-law's hand, then looked at his sister warily. 'Ginny.'

Ginny searched his eyes, seeing some unease there, but the nervous tension that had always been with him when their father was around had vanished. As Caroline had said all those weeks ago, getting him away from his father would do him a world of good, and Ginny could see that it had. Consequently, she smiled at him and held out her hand.

'Hello, James,' she said huskily, then held her breath as he hesitated. However, it was only for a moment, and then he was squeezing her hand tightly.

'Good of you to come,' James added gruffly, clearing his throat. 'I wasn't sure you would.'

His uncertainty brought moisture to her eyes, and she

shook her head then laughed, overwhelmed by a mixture of emotions. 'You know me better than that. You're my brother and I love you.'

James's throat worked madly, and he shot a glance at his wife, who nodded encouragingly from the sidelines. 'I said some pretty rotten things to you.'

Ginny sighed, unable to deny it. 'Yes, you did. But I understood why, James. I've always understood. All I care about now is that I can see you and talk to you. You don't have to tell our father anything about it. Let's leave him and the past out of it and just be friends. Can you do that? Will you do that?'

'It's what I would like, if you can forgive me,' her brother responded stiffly, and without having to think about it Ginny slipped her arms about his neck and hugged him, feeling her heart swell as, after a short pause, he hugged her back.

'There's nothing to forgive. Nothing,' she told him, stepping back, and then Caroline stepped in and hugged them all, and the tears were replaced by laughter.

As she watched Caroline shoo James off to fetch the drinks, Ginny felt Roarke take her hand and squeeze it. She glanced up at him.

'OK?' he asked simply, and when she nodded he bent and pressed a swift kiss to her lips.

It seemed to Ginny, as she took the glass James handed her and they toasted each other, that life couldn't get any better.

From then on the evening buzzed with laughter. Ginny couldn't remember her brother ever being so relaxed, and she had quite forgotten that he had a wacky sense of humour. She couldn't have said what they ate for dinner, though it tasted wonderful. She was too busy watching and listening. The banter between Roarke and his sister showed them how family life should be, and Ginny was determined that that was how it would be once Lucy broke away.

She enjoyed watching James relax, and caught sight of the boy he had been, but mostly she watched Roarke. She sat back, fascinated by the play of emotions over his face as he said something serious or told a joke. Somehow, she just couldn't seem to take her eyes off him, and when he glanced her way and quirked a questioning eyebrow to check that she was all right, she smiled, feeling a warm sense of well-being swell up inside her. She was happy, and happiness had been in short supply all of her life. Which was why she hugged the feeling to her, for it was precious beyond words.

Eventually a lull fell as they exchanged the wine for coffee, and it was during the lull that Caroline set the cat among the pigeons.

'So,' she said, looking from her brother to Ginny. 'When are you two getting engaged?'

Ginny blinked and almost choked on her after-dinner mint. Roarke had gone still, his cup halfway to his lips.

'What?' they asked in unison, casting cautionary glances at each other, which Caroline found highly amusing.

'Oh, come on,' she chided. 'I can't recall ever seeing you so happy, Roarke. It must be love!'

Roarke set his cup down with a sharp tap of china on china. 'I'm not in love,' he said bluntly, and Ginny caught her breath sharply as she was struck by an unexpected shaft of pain. 'Neither of us are.' He looked to Ginny for confirmation, and she turned to his sister.

'We don't have that kind of relationship.' She repeated

the phrase she had used only hours before. It sounded lame now.

'Fiddlesticks!' Caroline exclaimed. 'Are you both ostriches? What kind of relationship do you think you have?'

James put his hand on his wife's arm. 'Er, Caro, I don't think this is the right time,' he warned awkwardly.

She frowned at him. 'But it's obvious!'

He smiled at Ginny and Roarke, then held his wife's gaze pointedly. 'Not to them, darling.'

Caroline looked confused. 'But...' She frowned at her brother. 'You're...not...in love?'

'No.'

Once again they spoke together.

The other woman's shoulders slumped and she shook her head. 'Well, OK, if you say you're not, you're not. Who am I to argue?'

'Surely we should know?' Ginny put in, trying to ease the uncomfortable moment, and Caroline smiled ruefully.

'Of course you should, Ginny. Forget I ever mentioned it,' she ordered, smiling at everyone. 'Now, who wants a brandy to go with their coffee?'

So the awkward moment was glossed over, and the remainder of the evening passed without anything else untoward happening. However, as they drove home, Ginny couldn't help thinking about it.

'It's funny that your sister should think we're in love,' she remarked. 'What made her think that?'

'Being in the happy state herself, no doubt,' Roarke returned sardonically, then spared her a glance. 'You don't love me, do you?'

Ginny turned startled eyes his way. 'I think I'd know. You don't?'

'You know my feelings on the subject. Love is for the birds.'

'So it's still sex, then?' She sought confirmation.

'Just sex,' he agreed, and they fell silent.

Ginny stared out into the darkness and saw her own reflection. It seemed to be asking a question. If this was just sex, why did she suddenly feel so empty inside? Neither she nor her reflection had an answer.

CHAPTER TEN

ABOUT ten days later Ginny stirred in the night, and knew instantly that she was alone in the bed. Running a hand over the sheets, she found they were cool, and knew that Roarke had been gone some time. Sliding from the bed, she slipped on her robe and went in search of him. He had been acting a little strangely ever since they had had dinner with Caroline and James, and now finding him out of bed like this gave her a vague feeling of disquiet.

She almost didn't see him. Roarke was sitting on the sofa in the dark, his feet propped up on the coffee table. She stood and watched him in silence, unable to dispel the feeling that he was a million miles away instead of just a few feet.

'What are you doing here in the dark?' she asked quietly, and his head turned towards her.

'Just sitting and thinking. I thought you were asleep.'

She padded into the room. 'Something woke me, and I discovered you were gone. Can't you sleep? Is something bothering you?'

Roarke held out a hand to her, and Ginny took it, allowing herself to be pulled down on to the sofa beside him. She tucked her feet under her and rested herself against him. The closeness should have helped but, contrarily, it didn't quite. She still had the feeling something was wrong, but couldn't put a finger on it.

'I'm going to New York tomorrow morning,' he said into the darkness.

Ginny frowned, for there was nothing scheduled or she

would have known about it. 'You are? Has something happened?' she asked in all seriousness, and was surprised to hear Roarke laugh wryly.

'You could say that. There are some…people I have to see,' he added, and she didn't miss the faint hesitation.

People? That was an odd way of putting it. 'You're making it sound very mysterious.'

'Am I? Well, it isn't. It's just something I have to do. For Grandfather,' he explained, and Ginny felt a sense of relief totally out of proportion to the situation, which showed how uneasy she had been feeling lately.

'Oh, I see. Family business. Ah, well, if he needs you, he needs you, but I'll miss you,' she declared, touching a hand to his chest.

'I'll miss you, too,' he responded, dropping a kiss on her head.

A lump lodged itself in her throat as she started to miss him already. 'How long will you be gone?'

Roarke ran his hand gently up and down her arm. 'I really have no idea, but not too long, I hope.'

'Do you want me to pack for you?' she offered helpfully, but he shook his head.

'No. I'll pop into my apartment on the way to the airport and collect some fresh things from there.'

Ginny sighed heavily. 'I don't suppose you can pack me in your suitcase and take me with you?' she joked, though if he had asked she would have gone with him in a trice.

He laughed huskily. 'Much as I would like to have you with me, this is something I have to do alone.'

'There's nothing I can do to change your mind?' she asked, running her hand over his chest and slipping it inside the towelling robe he was wearing.

Roarke's free hand came up and stopped her roving one

in its tracks. 'There's plenty you could do, but it won't make me change my mind, sweetheart.'

She hadn't supposed it would, but it was worth a try. 'Will you ring me? Let me know how things are going on?'

Roarke raised the hand he held captive to his lips and pressed a kiss to her palm. 'Every day, and that's a promise.'

As satisfied as she could be with the situation, Ginny eased herself away from him and stood up. 'Come back to bed, then, and let me give you something to remember whilst you're away,' she suggested huskily, and she saw his teeth flash in the darkness as he grinned and stood up.

'There might be some men who could ignore an offer like that, but I'm not one of them, thank God,' he declared, sweeping her up into his arms and striding back to the bedroom.

Maybe it was knowing that they would be apart for some time that gave their lovemaking a degree of urgency which made it impossible for either of them to hold back. From the first touch they wanted each other with a hunger and need that would not be denied, and the result was white-hot passion. Limbs tangled, bodies grew slick with sweat, and their moans of almost unbearable pleasure led on to a climax that left them so satiated they fell asleep in each other's arms.

Roarke had showered and was already eating breakfast when she woke next morning. Memories of the night before brought a smile to her lips as she showered and dressed, then joined him in her tiny kitchen.

Their eyes met and a silent message passed, though neither mentioned the passion they had shared. They remembered, and that was enough.

'What time's your flight?' she asked, nibbling at a piece

of toast whilst watching him wash his breakfast things and set them on the drainer.

'Eleven. I'll have time to run you to work, then go on to my apartment,' Roarke informed her after glancing at his watch.

'You'll be exhausted. You didn't get a lot of sleep last night,' she commiserated with him, though her eyes twinkled flirtatiously.

He grinned ruefully. 'Never mind. I can catch up on lost sleep during the flight.'

Ginny pulled a face. 'I wish you weren't going.'

Rounding the table, he tipped her chin up and kissed her deeply. 'It's important I do this. I'll tell you all about it when I get back. Now, get a move on or we'll both be late.'

She rose, finishing off her toast and taking a last sip of coffee before following him. 'I'll have to complain to my boss about you.'

Roarke laughed. 'Think it will do you any good?' Collecting his briefcase, he waited by the door.

'We—ell, I do have some influence with him. I have a trick or two up my sleeve,' she teased, slipping on the jacket of her suit and gathering up her bag.

He held the door for her to precede him out. 'Save them till I get back, then we'll try them out and see how effective they'll be,' he suggested, and Ginny floated down the stairs with a sigh of contentment.

Roarke was as good as his word and telephoned her each evening, just when he knew she would be in bed. The sound of his voice kept her spirits up, but she missed him terribly. More than she thought she could possibly miss anyone. The days dragged by, but the nights were the worst. She missed his presence in the bed beside her.

Roarke had become a vital part of her life without her even realising it was happening. She felt as if a part of herself was missing, and couldn't wait for him to come back.

Working helped, and she buried herself in it so as not to daydream about what Roarke might be doing. A few days into his trip, she was busily working out a timetable for some renovation work when Roarke's grandfather called.

'Where's that grandson of mine got to?' Stephen Adams's voice demanded down the telephone line. 'His secretary tells me he's abroad.'

Naturally, Ginny blinked, surprised by the question. He had to know where Roarke was. He had sent him there. She couldn't help wondering if his memory was getting a little rusty with age. 'He's in New York, Mr Adams,' she reminded him politely, aiming to jog his memory. His response startled her.

'What's he doing there?' the elderly gentleman asked in astonishment.

She frowned at the receiver, more than a little alarmed by this depth of forgetfulness. 'He's doing whatever it was you sent him to do, Mr Adams,' she enlarged, unable to help more because she was in the dark too.

'My dear Ginny, I may be old but I am not yet senile. I never sent Roarke to New York. Why would I do that? He's supposed to be playing golf with me tomorrow,' Stephen Adams challenged, sounding amused, but Ginny froze, her stomach knotting.

What was going on here? She wasn't mistaken about what Roarke had said, and yet his grandfather was saying he knew nothing about it. Licking her lips, she sought confirmation. 'Roarke told me he had something to do for you. Are you saying that's not the case?'

'I most certainly am, young Ginny,' Roarke's grandfather confirmed, and she closed her eyes as she realised he had lied to her.

Ginny pressed her fingers to where an ache had started up between her eyes. 'I'm sorry, I must have misunderstood what he said,' she apologised. 'Roarke is in New York, though.' At least she thought he was ringing from America. For all she knew, he could be in Timbuktu. It gave her a queasy feeling to realise she had no real idea where he was.

'When's he coming back?'

'I don't know when he's due back. He couldn't say.' Couldn't or wouldn't?

Stephen Adams harrumphed down the line, not best pleased. 'I'll have something to say to that young man when he gets back. This is our Saturday grudge match. We haven't missed one in ages.'

Ginny sympathised and they exchanged a few more words, then Stephen Adams rang off and Ginny sank back into her chair, feeling chilled to the bone.

What was going on? She knew full well what Roarke had said, and she would have gone on believing it if his grandfather hadn't called. Why had Roarke found it necessary to lie to her? It hurt incredibly to know that he had. The only answer she could come up with was that he didn't want her to know what he was doing. That made her angry as well. He could have just told her it was private. He hadn't had to lie like that. Anger fuelled by hurt seethed in her for the rest of the day. By the time she headed home she had made up her mind that he was going to have some explaining to do that night.

That evening she was a bundle of nervous energy as she waited for the telephone to ring. Unable to sit still, she prowled around her flat like a big cat in a cage. When the call finally came, she took a deep breath and lifted the receiver.

'Hello?'

'Ginny?' Roarke queried in some surprise. 'Are you all right?' Obviously, though she had tried to sound normal, he must have picked something up. In which case, she wasn't going to put on a pretence of being happy when she was far from it.

Folding her arm across her waist, Ginny paced away as far as the flex would allow. 'Do I sound OK?' she challenged, that seething mix of anger and hurt growing inside her.

There was a brief pause before Roarke answered. 'You sound...odd.'

Her eyes narrowed. 'That's funny. I thought I sounded angry,' she retorted, pacing back to the sofa.

'What's wrong, Ginny?' Roarke asked shortly, and she smiled to herself, choosing to ignore the question.

'How's New York?' she asked instead, with false brightness.

'New York is fine. What's wrong?' His tone was more abrupt, and she could sense his growing unease.

'You are *in* New York, aren't you?' she queried next, and felt the tension coming down the line to her.

Roarke took a steadying breath. 'I told you I was. Ginny...' he began patiently but she interrupted him.

'Your grandfather called today,' she informed him tersely, and the silence which followed the words was palpably fraught. 'He was just checking that your golf match was still on for tomorrow. It was careless of you to forget about that when you lied to me.'

'I didn't lie to you, Ginny,' Roarke said carefully, and she could sense his frustration that this conversation was taking place over the phone and not where he could see her.

Ginny laughed harshly. 'Of course you didn't lie, you were just being economical with the truth! That's what they say these days, isn't it?'

'This is impossible!' he declared in exasperation. 'I can't explain to you over the phone.'

'Just tell me why you had to lie,' she commanded, feeling the sting of angry tears behind her eyes.

'I lied because I couldn't tell you the truth.'

'Gee whizz, Roarke, I never would have worked that out for myself!' she shot back scathingly. What kind of an answer was that to give an angry woman?

'Sweetheart, I can't explain over the phone, it's too complicated. Will you please stop getting upset?' he urged down the line.

A single tear trailed hotly down her cheek and she brushed it away. 'I'm not upset. I'm furious!' she corrected, and again there was a pregnant silence.

'You feel that strongly about it, do you?' Roarke asked searchingly.

'I want to murder you!' she added.

'Why?' he asked simply.

'Why what?' Ginny launched back, prowling to the window.

'Why are you furious, Ginny?' Roarke spelt it out for her. There was an expectant edge to his voice, as if the answer was really important to him.

She held the receiver away from her ear for a moment and glared at it. 'Why am I furious? You lied to me, that's why!'

'Have you any idea what you sound like?' Roarke asked in the wake of her explosion, and to Ginny he almost sounded amused. It had the effect of stoking the angry fire inside her.

'I don't care what I sound like!' she snapped, and he laughed. He actually had the gall to laugh.

'Well, I do care, and to me you sound like a woman who feels she's been betrayed,' Roarke told her with a certain amount of satisfaction.

Adding that to everything else, it was no wonder Ginny's temper hit the roof. 'You're darn right I feel betrayed! I thought I could trust you. You had no right to lie to me for whatever reason! There are no good reasons for doing what you did! It hurt, damn it!'

'Why?' he asked softly.

'Because I love you, you horrible man!' she exclaimed wrathfully, then went into total shock when she realised what she had said. Her hand went to her mouth as she stared at the receiver as if it were a snake. 'Oh, God!' she whispered, then slammed the receiver back down.

Almost immediately, it rang again but, knowing who it must be, Ginny jiggled the receiver to cut off the call and then set it down beside the phone. She sank slowly on to the sofa, pressing her hands to scalding cheeks. What had she done? How on earth could she have just told Roarke she loved him?

The answer was simple. She had said it because it was the truth. She had fallen in love with him. Only being in love with him would explain why she felt betrayed by his lying to her. Having finally admitted it, she now realised she had loved him for a long time. Maybe even from the beginning.

As she sat there, the shock began to subside and she fully appreciated the discovery she had made. She loved Roarke Adams with a depth and breadth she hadn't thought possible. He was everything she wanted, she told herself, then her shoulders slumped as she grimaced. He was also the one person she couldn't have. Because Roarke didn't want to love or be loved. He had been more than clear about it.

And, just minutes ago, she had told him what he least wanted to hear. She hadn't meant to. He had made her so angry, the words had just slipped out. She groaned helplessly. If only she hadn't said it. They could have gone on the way they were, with her being the only one who knew, but now... He wouldn't like it.

What was she going to do if he wanted to end the relationship? What *could* she do? She uttered another heartfelt groan. Lord, what a fool she was. Trust her to deal a knockout blow to the one thing that really mattered in her life! It was over. It had to be. They wanted different things from life.

Ginny went from the heights of elation in realising how much she loved him, to plumb the depths of defeat. She called herself all the names she could think of for being so stupid, but in the end it changed nothing. She loved him, he wouldn't love her... and no doubt when he came back he would tell her it was all over. Well, she wasn't going to weep all over him. She had her pride. It wasn't his fault she had fallen in love with him. She'd managed to make that mistake all on her own.

Sighing, she reached out and replaced the receiver back on its rest. If he rang she would speak to him. After all, she had already made a big enough fool of herself. What else could she do?

Roarke didn't ring, but half an hour later the front doorbell startled her. It was getting late, close to midnight, and Ginny took care to look through the peephole before considering opening the door. The figure she saw standing in the fisheye had her fumbling with the locks and throwing the door wide.

'Lucy!' she exclaimed in delight. 'I'd almost given up on you!' she added, picking up the case sitting by the door, and pulling her sister inside.

'I had to wait until Dad dropped his guard,' Lucy explained as the sisters hugged each other. 'I'm sorry I arrived so late, but it took longer than I expected.'

'You didn't walk here at this time of night, did you?' Ginny gasped, shuddering at the idea. No street was really safe these days.

Lucy shook her head. 'No. Peter borrowed a friend's car and dropped me off. I thought you might have been in bed, but then we saw the light on.'

Ginny wasn't about to go into why she was still up. It was bad enough knowing the reason herself, let alone spreading it around. 'Have you eaten? Can I make you something? A sandwich? How about a cup of tea or coffee?'

'I'm fine, really,' Lucy refused with a laugh. 'We had something a little while ago. Are you sure it's OK for me to be here?'

'Of course it is. I already made up the spare bed. Come and see.' Ginny led the way to the box-like room that passed as the second bedroom. It was small but cosy, with a view over some gardens. 'You can stay here as long as you like.'

Lucy retrieved her case from the hallway and laid it on the bed before looking at her sister with serious eyes. 'You're sure this is OK with Roarke? Where is he?'

Ginny felt faint colour wash into her cheeks at the question. 'Er, he's in New York at the moment, but I know he'll be glad you're here.'

'I'd hate to be a gooseberry,' her sister teased, then

tried to stifle a big yawn. 'I'm sorry. I really wanted to sit and have a long chat with you, but now I'm here I can barely keep my eyes open.'

'Don't worry. We'll talk in the morning. We've got plenty of time now. The bathroom's across the hall, and my room is the next door along. Make yourself at home,' Ginny told her as she walked to the door. 'Help yourself to anything in the kitchen, and you know where I am if you need me.' She turned to leave, but hesitated and glanced back over her shoulder. 'It's wonderful to have you here at last, Lucy.'

'I'm glad to be here,' Lucy responded thickly and Ginny closed the door before her sister could see the tears in her eyes.

Life was strange. If something had gone badly wrong today, then something else had gone wonderfully right to balance it out. Feeling happier than she had been an hour ago, Ginny headed for her bed.

She was jolted awake the next morning by someone thundering on her front door. Squinting at the clock, she saw it was after nine but, as she had slept only fitfully, Ginny was not best pleased. Scrambling from her bed, she grabbed up her robe and tied the belt around her waist as the ruckus continued.

'All right, all right!' she muttered as she stomped to the door.

Lucy appeared in the doorway of the other bedroom, looking mussed from sleep. 'Who is it?'

'Haven't a clue,' Ginny returned grouchily. 'Whoever they are, they're going to get the rough edge of my tongue!'

The banging continued. 'Open up!' a familiar voice ordered and Ginny stiffened, glancing at Lucy, who had frozen on the spot. They both knew who was on the other side of the door. 'Go in the bathroom and lock the door,' she ordered, and didn't move to unfasten the locks until her sister had scuttled across the hall and she had heard the key turn.

The second Ginny turned the latch, the door was thrust backwards, crashing against the wall and rebounding towards the man who strode into the flat, allowing nothing and no one to stand in his way.

'Where is she?' Sir Martin demanded to know, rounding on Ginny, who had followed in his wake.

Ginny folded her arms and prepared to do battle. 'Do you make a habit of bursting into other people's homes like this?'

Her father ignored the question. 'I'm here to take your sister home with me. Where is she?'

'How did you know where to find me?' Ginny wanted to know first. Her telephone number was ex-directory, so she wasn't in the book.

'I had someone do a background check on you. It was fascinating to discover you work for Adams. What did you do, sleep your way to the top?' Sir Martin looked down his nose at her, and Ginny gritted her teeth.

'I think you had better leave before I call the police,' she said coldly.

'I'm not leaving without Lucy.'

'You're certainly not leaving with her. She's eighteen and she's not answerable to anyone but herself,' Ginny countered.

'Hah! So she is here! I knew you would be responsible for poisoning her mind against me.'

'On the contrary, Sir Martin, you managed to alienate your family all by yourself,' Roarke's frosty voice declared from behind, and they both turned.

Ginny felt her cheeks turn pink as she faced him. The last words she had spoken to him had been stunners. 'Roarke!' She managed to croak out his name.

Smiling faintly, he strolled to her side and draped an arm around her shoulders. 'Hi,' he greeted her softly, and dropped a swift kiss on her surprised lips. Then he turned his attention back to her father. 'Lucy is staying here with us. You can leave as soon as you like. The door is open.'

'How dare you order me about?' Sir Martin spluttered.

'I dare because I won't let you hurt any of the people I care about,' Roarke told him bluntly.

'Lucy is my daughter...' Sir Martin started to bluster, but Roarke took a step towards him and he faltered to a stop.

'Ginny is your daughter, too, and look what you did to her. My God, you disgust me. You had something precious and you threw it away. Well, I found it and I intend to keep it, for I value Ginny far above anything you could possibly name,' he told the older man in a voice that shook with suppressed emotion.

'You're welcome to her. And if Lucy chooses to stay here, you're welcome to her, too,' Sir Martin snarled. Turning to go, he came face to face with his youngest daughter, who had come out of the bathroom at the sound of Roarke's voice. 'Well, are you coming?' he demanded, and Lucy stepped out of his way.

'I'm staying.'

'Then I wash my hands of the lot of you!' he declared scornfully. 'You're no children of mine!' He walked out without a backward glance and seconds later they heard the front door slam shut.

Lucy hurried across the room and hugged first Ginny and then Roarke. 'Thank you. Thank you both so much. You were marvellous,' she said huskily. Then, because she was young, her spirits lifted and she grinned at them. 'I can't believe it's over and he's gone. I think I'll go and ring Peter and tell him the good news.'

'You can use the phone in my room,' Ginny offered, smiling at her happy face.

'Thanks, I will,' her sister chirped, almost dancing across the room. However, she halted in the doorway and looked back. 'Did you mean what you said about Ginny?' she asked Roarke.

He smiled back at her. 'Every word.'

Lucy laughed. 'Then I'll stay out of the way for a while, shall I?'

'We'd be grateful,' he told her dryly, and she waved her fingers at them before disappearing.

The second she was gone Ginny, who had been stunned to hear him utter those words to her father, squared up to him.

'You shouldn't lie to Lucy. You couldn't possibly mean what you said,' she said sternly, and Roarke quirked an eyebrow at her.

'Why not?'

Ginny really wasn't in the mood for games. She just wanted him to get the bad news over with. 'Because we both know you don't...care about me.'

He smiled faintly. 'We do? I don't?'

Already agitated, she didn't care for him pushing her buttons one by one. 'Don't mess with me. You know I'm just the woman you...'

'Have great sex with?' he offered helpfully, and his grey eyes glittered with amusement and something else she couldn't put a name to.

Hot colour stained her cheeks at the blunt words, and she turned her back on him because emotional tears were stinging her eyes, making them sparkle like diamonds.

'OK, have your fun. I know I deserve it. I've ruined everything with what I said last night. If you hadn't made me so mad, it never would have popped out and surprised us both!'

'I'm glad it did. It was what I was aiming for, after all,' Roarke informed her matter-of-factly, and she spun round, her mouth dropping open.

'What?'

'I do love you, you know,' Roarke told her simply. 'I tried to tell you as much last night, but you hung up on me.'

Ginny searched his eyes, her heart lurching madly in her chest. She saw an earnestness there that seemed to suggest he meant it, but... 'You can't love me. You told me you don't intend to love anyone!' she exclaimed breathlessly.

'I know I did, and up until a few days ago I fully believed I meant it. Then something happened to change my mind,' he told her gently. 'I had to get away to check it out. *That* was why I went to New York. I couldn't tell you until I was certain, so I lied about the trip. My mind was so mixed up I forgot about Grandfather, though.'

Having spent a night of sheer misery, cursing her own foolishness, Ginny only slowly began to accept that the sky hadn't fallen in after all. On the contrary, a miracle had happened.

Her heart began to swell with unexpected joy. 'You really love me?' she asked in a voice thick with emotion.

The laughter faded from his eyes, and he looked down at her intently. 'I really do.'

Tears overflowed, but they were happy ones. It only took a step to bring her to him, and then she threw her arms about his neck and hugged him painfully close. 'Oh, God, I thought I'd ruined everything!' she exclaimed, and

Roarke framed her head with his hands and looked down at her.

'Instead your anger gave me hope. I nudged you into saying what I wanted to hear, but when I wanted to tell you how I felt, you cut me off. So I caught the first plane out in order to get to you and make it right. Have I made it right? Do you forgive me for deceiving you?'

Her smile was watery. 'It couldn't be righter. And of course I forgive you. How could I not, when I love you so much?'

'Then come and kiss me. I need it like a thirsty man needs water,' he growled.

It was a kiss like no other they had shared for, whilst passion hovered in the background, this kiss was a promise. A sealing of what they had just said in words. It transcended the physical, and yet left them with a sense of profound fulfilment.

'So, what made you change your mind about love?' Ginny asked some time later when Roarke had carried her to the sofa and stretched out on it with her in his arms.

'Caroline,' he replied, rubbing his cheek gently over her hair. 'She thought we were in love. She thought it was obvious. So I asked myself the question. Did I love you? The reply stunned me. I did.'

Ginny settled her hand over his heart, feeling it beating strongly. 'So why did you go to New York?'

'Because I had to be sure. I went to the place where I was bound to run into any number of attractive available women. Do you know what I found out? I wasn't interested in a single one of them. The highlight of my day was talking to you at night. It didn't take more than forty-eight hours to make me certain I didn't want anyone else.'

'It only took me ten minutes,' Ginny countered smugly. 'After I'd winkled the truth out of you!'

'That was a dastardly trick. Do you know how miserable I was, thinking I'd scored an own goal?' she charged aggrievedly.

Roarke laughed. 'I'll make it up to you.'

'The list is growing. You already said I could have anything I want for agreeing to help you out,' she reminded him.

'I did say that, didn't I? Have you decided what it's to be?'

Ginny smiled to herself as her finger traced lazy patterns over his shirt. 'I think what I would really like is a baby. Two, actually, to keep each other company. Then we could add to them as time goes by.'

Roarke laughed huskily. 'Don't you think we should get married first?'

She lifted herself enough to meet his eyes. 'Are you asking me?'

'Sounds like it,' he confirmed lazily.

'Then the answer is yes. However, it doesn't stop us working on the baby, does it?' she flirted with him, eyes gleaming suggestively.

Roarke groaned and settled her back down. 'You're shameless, do you know that? You only said it because Lucy's in your bedroom.'

Ginny laughed happily. 'She won't be long. Besides, we have time. All the time in the world.'

Which was just as well, for when Lucy came out of the bedroom some time later she found them wrapped in each other's arms, fast asleep.

0207/24/MB072

Flowers make great gifts...until they wilt.
Chocolates are always popular...calories are not.
Baby daughters are just adorable...but they grow up!

Carly and Cici have both tried Plan A – being
perfect wives and mothers. Now they're about to
start over...with their darling daughters.

This collection of brand-new stories is the
perfect gift for Mum – or yourself!

Available 2nd February 2007

Available at WHSmith, Tesco, ASDA,
and all good bookshops

M&B™

www.millsandboon.co.uk

Romantic reads to
Need, Want

International affairs, seduction and passion guaranteed
8 brand-new books every month

Pure romance, pure emotion...
4 brand-new books every month

Pulse-raising romance, – heart-racing medical drama
6 brand-new books every month

From Regency England to Ancient Rome, rich, vivid and passionate romance...
3 brand-new books every month

Scorching hot sexy reads
4 brand-new books every month

*Mills & Boon® books are available on the **first Friday of every month** from WHSmith, ASDA, Tesco and all good bookshops.*

MILLS & BOON®

M&B/SIL/GENERIC a

satisfy your every
and Desire...

Two passionate, dramatic love stories in every book
3 brand-new books every month

Life, love and family
6 brand-new books every month

Breathtaking romantic suspense
4 brand-new books every month

Passionate and thrilling romantic adventures
6 brand-new books every month

Enjoy the drama, explore the emotions, experience the relationship
4 brand-new books every month

*Silhouette® books are available on the **third Friday of every month** from WHSmith, ASDA, Tesco and all good bookshops.*

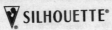 **SILHOUETTE®**

M&B/SIL/GENERIC b

0107/05a

MILLS & BOON®

Live the emotion

In February 2007 Mills & Boon present
two classic collections, each featuring three
wonderful romances by three of our
bestselling authors...

Italian
Proposals

Featuring
The Venetian's Proposal by Lee Wilkinson
The Italian Doctor's Wife by Sarah Morgan
The Italian Doctor's Proposal by Kate Hardy

On sale 2nd February 2007

*Available at WHSmith, Tesco, ASDA,
and all good bookshops*
www.millsandboon.co.uk

MILLS & BOON®

0107/05b

Live the emotion

Sinful Secrets

Featuring
A Secret Vengeance by Miranda Lee
Sarah's Secret by Catherine George
Morgan's Secret Son by Sara Wood

**Make sure you buy these
irresistible stories!**

On sale 2nd February 2007

*Available at WHSmith, Tesco, ASDA,
and all good bookshops*

www.millsandboon.co.uk

0107/01a

MILLS & BOON®

Live the emotion

Modern
romance™

TAKEN BY THE SHEIKH *by Penny Jordan*

Prince al Drac'ar al Karim, Sheikh of Dhurahn, must find a bride for his brother – and who better than virginal Englishwoman Sadie Murray? But Drax has to make sure that Sadie is as innocent as she seems. While she's in his power, he'll test her wife-worthiness at every opportunity…

THE GREEK'S VIRGIN *by Trish Morey*

When Alexander Koutoufides set out to seduce Saskia Prentice it was for revenge! But now that she is back and in need of his help, Alex decides to finish what he started…for pleasure! Saskia cannot forgive or forget the sexy Greek who nearly stole her innocence, but how long can she resist him?

THE FORCED BRIDE *by Sara Craven*

Emily would be the wife of formidable Italian count, Rafael Di Salis, until her trust fund was released – on the day she reached twenty-one. Count Rafael has bided his time – he has kept his passions under iron control for two years… But now Emily has come of age – she will be his!

BEDDED AND WEDDED FOR REVENGE
by Melanie Milburne

Billionaire Andreas Trigliani is set on revenge. Spoilt heiress Gemma Landerstalle, who wrecked his past, needs a husband – *fast!* And Andreas is more than happy to help. Women may throw themselves at his feet every day, but it's this stunning socialite who he wants to see begging…

On sale 2nd February 2007

*Available at WHSmith, Tesco, ASDA,
and all good bookshops*

www.millsandboon.co.uk

MILLS & BOON®

Live the emotion

Modern
romance™

THE ITALIAN BOSS'S SECRETARY MISTRESS
by Cathy Williams

Rose is in love with her gorgeous boss Gabriel Gessi – but her resolve to forget him crumbles when he demands they work closely together…on a Caribbean island! She knows the sexy Italian is the master of persuasion, and it won't be long before he's added her to his agenda…

THE KOUVARIS MARRIAGE *by Diana Hamilton*

Madeleine is devastated to learn that her gorgeous Greek billionaire husband, Dimitri Kouvaris, only married her to conceive a child! She begs for divorce, but Dimitri is determined to keep Maddie at his side – and in his bed – until she bears the Kouvaris heir…

THE SANTORINI BRIDE *by Anne McAllister*

Heiress Martha Antonides is stunned when she arrives at her Greek family home – billionaire Theo Savas has taken it over! Forced together, they indulge in a hot affair. But Theo will *never* marry. Although Martha knows she must leave, her heart and body won't obey her mind…

PREGNANT BY THE MILLIONAIRE
by Carole Mortimer

Hebe Johnson has always secretly admired her wealthy boss, but she never believed she'd end up sharing his bed! After one intense and passionate night, Hebe is in love. But Nick doesn't do commitment… And then Hebe discovers she's having his baby…

On sale 2nd February 2007

*Available at WHSmith, Tesco, ASDA,
and all good bookshops*

www.millsandboon.co.uk

0107/01b

0107/02

MILLS & BOON®

Live the emotion

Romance

RANCHER AND PROTECTOR *by Judy Christenberry*

Cowboy Jason Barton is all business, and he wants
Rosemary's ranch! But she's a fighter, and means business
too. When Rosie and Jason get stranded under the starlit
Western sky, there's only one place Rosie wants to be: in the
arms of her cowboy, who has vowed to protect her...

THE VALENTINE BRIDE *by Liz Fielding*
The Brides of Bella Lucia

Since discovering she is adopted, Louise is not feeling
charitable towards the Valentines, and when Max Valentine
asks her to help save the family business sparks begin to fly.
Soon they are both falling hard and fast – but will the past
stand in the way of a special Valentine wedding...?

ONE SUMMER IN ITALY... *by Lucy Gordon*

When on holiday, Holly became enchanted by the pleading
eyes of a motherless little girl and entranced by the girl's
enigmatic father, Matteo. Before she knew it, Holly had
been swept away to their luxurious villa. But then Holly
discovered Matteo was hiding some dark secrets...

CROWNED: AN ORDINARY GIRL *by Natasha Oakley*
By Royal Appointment

The untimely death of Prince Sebastian's father meant
he had to leave behind his normal life. But accepting the
crown meant giving up his most precious gift – the love of
an ordinary girl... Now, years later, Marianne Chambers is
back. Can Seb claim her as his very own princess?

On sale 2nd February 2007

*Available at WHSmith, Tesco, ASDA,
and all good bookshops*

www.millsandboon.co.uk

1206/10/MB069

wicked or *innocent*?

Introducing a 2-volume collection that's
sinful and saintly all at once!

Be deliciously wicked this holiday season!

Three scorching hot stories of seductive women, strong men and steamy, spine-tingling sex…

Available
15th December 2006

Start the New Year on a clean slate!

Three passionate tales about three innocents who just can't resist temptation…

Available
5th January 2007

Available at WHSmith, Tesco, ASDA and all
good paperback bookshops

www.millsandboon.co.uk

0207/10/MB070

PASSIONATE ARABIAN NIGHTS...

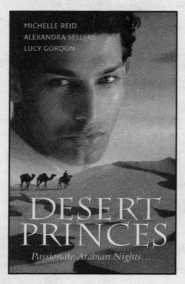

Three stories of seduction by sensual Sheikhs!

Featuring

THE ARABIAN LOVE-CHILD *by Michelle Reid*

BELOVED SHEIKH *by Alexandra Sellers*

THE SHEIKH'S REWARD *by Lucy Gordon*

On sale 19th January 2007

*Available at WHSmith, Tesco, ASDA,
and all good bookshops*

M&B™

www.millsandboon.co.uk

0107/25/MB068

NEW from M&B™ by *New York Times* bestselling author DIANA PALMER

A dazzling novel that will leave you breathless...

At the tender age of twenty-four, Rebecca Cullen already has her hands full with a full-time job, raising two teenage brothers, supporting her elderly grandfather and tending to the family farm. When her troubled brother Clay is arrested, Rebecca's complicated world falls apart and the last thing she needs is arrogant, but devastatingly attractive, lawyer Rourke Kilpatrick prosecuting her brother...

On sale 5th January 2007

Available at WHSmith, Tesco, ASDA, Borders, Eason, Sainsbury's and all good paperback bookshops

www.millsandboon.co.uk

M&B™

0207/25/MB071

From No. 1 *New York Times* bestselling author Nora Roberts

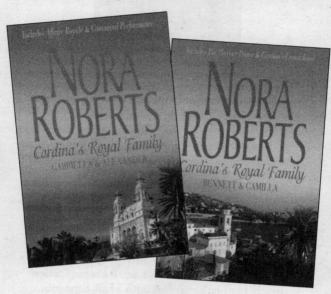

Romance and intrigue are woven together in these classic stories about Cordina's royal family

Gabriella & Alexander
Available 2nd February 2007

Bennett & Camilla
Available 4th May 2007

www.silhouette.co.uk